The Camel

The Camel

R.T. WILSON

Longman
London and New York

Longman Group UK Limited
Longman House, Burnt Mill, Harlow,
Essex CM20 2JE, England
and Associated Companies throughout the world

First published 1984
Second impression 1988

ISBN 0 582 77512 4

British Library Cataloguing in Publication Data

Wilson, R. T.
  The camel
  1. Camels
  I. Title
  599.73'6 QL737.U54

ISBN 0-582-77512-4

**Library of Congress Cataloging in Publication
Data**

Wilson, R. T.
  The camel.

  Includes bibliographies and index.
  1. Camels.   I. Title.
  SF401.C2W54   1983   636.2'95   82-7808
  ISBN 0-582-77512-4

Produced by Longman Singapore Publishers Pte Ltd
Printed in Singapore

For Mary, who never thought her part of it
   was to stand and wait,
and Andrew, who, on occasions, can also serve.

Contents

Acknowledgements

This book, as no doubt the majority of books, owes much to many. Although a truism, it is nonetheless true to say that it would not be possible to thank them all individually.

To the very large number of owners of camels with whom it has been my pleasure to associate over the last 10 years I owe a debt which few people will understand. Their good humour and patience faced with what must have seemed to them very childish questions; their generally complete incomprehension when I insisted on sticking my head into their camels' mouths; their astonishment (and mine) when eventually my estimates of age from this method more or less agreed with what they knew the age to be with reference to their own age class system: I can never forget these moments nor the people who made them possible and shared in them.

Had I not learned French this book would have been very much poorer. My initial penetration into this language was made almost completely painless by J. Arnault. The Director and staff of the *Institut d'Elevage et de Médecine Vétérinaire des Pays Tropicaux* on the outskirts of Paris then made available to me their very wide-ranging literature on the camel. My researches into the English language literature were facilitated by an English base of operations close to the British Lending Library at Boston Spa in Yorkshire: my very odd requests for references literally miles apart on their shelves (I was doing research on barn owls at the same time) were always accepted – and only occasionally unfulfilled – with good humour and I could not have achieved as much without them. Access to Italian and German sources, fortunately much less voluminous, was more difficult for me but I hope I have not done them too much injustice.

During much of my time in some of the world's less accessible places in the course of my career I have worked for Hunting Technical Services and the International Livestock Centre for Africa. Both of these organisations had sufficient vision to recognise that not everyone is at his best in Head Offices and both gave me ample opportunity to be away from them. In particular I thank Harry Piper of HTS for recognising my needs and for the opportunities he made available to me. Perhaps above all I thank him for my introduction to Bill Payne, who understood these needs, and who more than anyone else has made this book possible.

Most of the actual writing was done during 1980 while I was employed by ILCA although this particular book forms no part of their research activities. Had they not posted me during this period as near to Timbuctoo as most people ever get I would not have had sufficient off-duty time free of administrative duties and social obligations to devote to writing and the book would have been much longer in its evolutionary process.

My wife was there at conception, throughout most of gestation and at parturition. Her presence with me during almost 20 years and her consequent liberation from Coffee in the morning and Cocktails in the evening has enabled her also to achieve an understanding of traditional livestock production (to say nothing of the breeding cycles of owls and hamerkops) to which few aspire and even fewer achieve. Her typing of this manuscript has, as always, been the last, but far from the least of her contributions.

The publishers are grateful to the following for permission to reproduce the photographs in the text:

Animal Breeding Library, Edinburgh, fig. nos. 3.6, 3.7, 3.8, 3.10, 4.3; Barnaby's Picture Library, fig. nos. 2.7, 2.8, 7.1; Anne Cloudsley, fig. no. 3.3; Bruce Coleman, fig. nos. 7.3, 7.4; Mark Haywood, fig. no. 1.6(a); Nicola Ingram, fig. no. 1.17; M. Kassas, fig. no. 9.6; Picturepoint, fig. nos. 1.6(c), 3.4; Royal Geographical Society, fig. nos. 1.7, 1.15, 2.5, 2.6, 10.4, 10.11; Dr S. Schwartz, fig. no. 4.6; Jeremy Wight, fig. no. 3.12; R. T. Wilson, fig. nos. 4.2, 8.4, 10.2, 10.3, 10.6, 10.7, 10.8(c), 10.8(d), 10.9, 10.12; E. Melville, frontispiece.

The publishers are grateful to Hutchinson Publishing Group for permission to reproduce the illustrations in fig. nos. 1.4, 1.8, 1.11 and 1.16.

The publishers would like to thank Mark Haywood for permission to reproduce the cover photograph.

Though every effort has been made, we are unable to trace the copyright holder of extracts from *Le Chameau* by Cauvet and would appreciate any information which would enable us to do so.

Preface

*'The dromedary is an
important domesticated
animal of the tropics and its
wider distribution and larger
total population demands that
it should receive.....
attention...... Unfortunately
this demand is seldom met,
possibly because of the dearth
of scientific literature on the
subject.....'*

Webster and Wilson 1980

While it is true to state that the numerical importance of the dromedary makes it worthy of considerable attention, there is scarcely a dearth of scientific literature about it. This book is based on research into more than 1 200 references on the one-humped camel, references which may be compared to the tip of an iceberg with regard to the whole of the literature on the camel.

The literature is widely scattered and often not readily available. Some aspects have been more thoroughly researched than others. As research has gone on changes in emphasis have occurred. Thus, much of our knowledge on palaeontology and the evolution of the camel dates from 100 to 70 years ago; that on diseases from 70 to 40 years ago (although research on this still continues); while that on physiology is confined almost entirely to the last 30 years and continues to increase. There still remains, however, much to be done, especially in the field of nutrition, if the camel is to fulfil a role as a provider of human food.

This book attempts to fill a gap which has not just recently developed but which has always existed. It synthesises existing knowledge and aims to present it within the general framework of a series of books on tropical agriculture. This has not been done before and it is true to say that no general book of this nature has ever been written on the camel. Where reference to a specific piece of research or field work is possible this has been in-dicated in the text without, it is hoped, interfering too much with the flow. Such references are listed at the end of each chapter and a comprehensive bibliography containing over 2000 references is given at the end of the text.

None of the foregoing means that books about the camel have not been written before and it might be useful to mention the principal ones. With one exception they were all written more than 35 years ago by either veterinarians or military transport officers. Perhaps it is not without coincidence that one book of each type was written in three different languages – Italian, French and English (although, in fact, there are two veterinary books in English). In the first, or veterinary, category are the works of Droandi (1936), Curasson (1947), Leese (1927) and Cross (1917). In the second, military, category the relevant books are by Vitale (1928), Cauvet (1925) and Leonard (1894). The exception referred to above, by Bulliet (1975), is not only more recent but of a different type, being a historical and socio-economic account of the camel and its relations with man. Very little scientific work appears to have been published in Arabic or in the Indian languages, in the areas where the camel is indigenous or naturalised.

Today there is a large body of opinion that considers the camel an anachronism, an animal of the past, an animal without a future. This opinion, it goes without saying, is mainly held by people who do not own camels but who, nonetheless, are often surrounded by them. In a world rapidly running out of food and of energy sources the camel must provide at least a partial answer to some of the problems. As a provider of milk, meat and fibre, and as a source of transport and power, especially in some of the more extreme environments inhabited by humans, it is well worthy of further study and improvement. It is hoped that this book will help to form a basis for such studies.

This particular book is concerned almost entirely with the Arabian or one-humped camel (*Camelus dromedarius*) often called the dromedary. However, the name dromedary, derived from the Greek word for run, has strictly only been applied to fast, riding camels. In addition to the Tropics, the book deals with the camel in tropical-type climates where aridity and heat are two of the principal factors. The other extant species, the Bactrian or two-humped camel (*Camelus bactrianus*) is confined to cold, dry, rather than hot, dry, regions and is dealt with only incidentally in this book. References to the camel should therefore be taken to refer to *C. dromedarius* unless the context makes it clear that this is not the case.

Further reading

Bulliet, R. W. (1975). *The camel and the wheel*. Harvard University Press: Cambridge, Massachusetts, USA.

Cauvet, G. (1925). *Le chameau*. Baillière: Paris, France.

Cross, H. E. (1917). *The camel and its diseases: being notes for veterinary surgeons and commandants of camel corps*. Baillière, Tindall & Cox: London.

Curasson, G. (1947). *Le chameau et ses maladies*. Vigot Frères: Paris, France.

Droandi, I. (1936). *Il cammello: storia naturale, anatomia, fisiologia, zootecnica, patalogia*. Istituto Agricolo Coloniale Italiano: Florence, Italy.

Leese, A. S. (1927). *A treatise on the one-humped camel in health and disease*. Haynes & Son: Stamford, Lincs, UK.

Leonard, A. G. (1894). *The camel: its uses and management*. Longmans Green: London.

Vitale, M. A. (1928). *Il camello ed I reparti cammellati*. Sindicato Italiano Arti Grafiche: Rome, Italy.

Webster, C. C. and Wilson, P. N. (1980). *Agriculture in the Tropics*, 2nd ed. Longman: London.

Part 1   Origin and distribution

1   Origins and domestication

'The camel appears late in the register of man's domestic animals'

Bibby (1970)

Systematics and taxonomy

The extant Camelidae are classed in two genera. The Old World genus of *Camelus* is generally accepted to comprise two species: *C. dromedarius*, the dromedary, one-humped or Arabian camel; and *C. bactrianus*, the Bactrian or two-humped camel. The habitat of the dromedary is Northern Africa (the Mediterranean littoral, the Sahelian states of West Africa, Sudan, Ethiopia, Somalia and northern Kenya), the Near East and west-central Asia. The Bactrian camel occupies the colder areas of southern Russia, Mongolia, east-central Asia and China. The species are sympatric in parts of their respective ranges. The separation of the genus *Camelus* into two species was based on morphological differences – the one hump of the dromedary and the two humps of the Bactrian camel – and on the belief that hybrids between the two species were not possible. In fact, embryonically the two species are indistinguishable and there is ample living proof that fertile hybrids of the two camels are possible (see Chapter 3). There might, therefore, be some justification for considering *C. dromedarius* and *C. bactrianus* as sub-species of a single species. Where distinctions need to be made, this book will follow the general practice of treating them as two separate species.

In the New world there also exists a single genus of the Camelidae, comprising four species. Two, *Lama guanacoe*, the guanaco and *L. vicugña*, the vicuña, are wild and two, *L. glama*, the llama and *L. pacos*, the alpaca, are domesticated. The vicuña is occasionally considered as a separate genus but most authorities (Simpson, 1945) now consider it to be part of the single South American genus.

Both genera belong to the sub-family Camelinae of the family Camelidae and are generally referred to as ruminants. While it is true that camels do ruminate, in that they chew their cud, it is wrong to class them as Ruminantia in the strict taxonomic sense. The Ruminantia are one sub-order of the order Artiodactyla which have four-chambered stomachs; the other sub-orders are the Tylopoda, camel-like forms with three-chambered stomachs, and the Suiformes, pig-like animals with simple stomachs. A complete classification of the camels, including the higher taxa, is shown in Fig. 1.1. It

Kingdom	Animalia
Subkingdom	Metazoa
Superphylum	
Phylum	Chordata
Subphylum	Vertebrata
Superclass	Tetrapoda
Class	Mammalia
Subclass	Theria
Infraclass	Eutheria
Cohort	Ferungulata
Superorder	Paraxonia
Order	Artiodactyla
Suborder	Tylopoda
Infraorder	
Superfamily	
Family	Camelidae
Subfamily	Camelinae
Supertribe	
Tribe	
Subtribe	
Genus	*Camelus*
Subgenus	
Species	*dromedarius* *bactrianus*

fig. 1.1 The taxonomy of the camel (*Source*: **Simpson, G. G.** (1954). The principles of classification and a classification of mammals. *Bull. Amer. Mus. Nat. Hist.*, **85**, 1–350.)

has also been suggested that in addition to differences between ruminants and tylopods in the form of the stomach, the capacity to ruminate has been acquired independently by the two sub-orders (Bohlken, 1960) and that the apparent similarities may be due to convergent evolution. Additional anatomical differences which would support a taxonomic grouping for the Tylopoda separate from that of the Ruminantia are the dental pattern, the lack of horns and the lack of fusion between the bones of the tarsus and carpus. Some of these differences are discussed more fully in Chapter 4.

Origins of the Camelidae

Like the horse, the camel has its origins in North America. There are only two extant species which gives little indication of the richness of genera which have arisen and become extinct in geological time. The Tylopoda were recognisable in the Middle Eocene (50 million years ago) and were well developed by the Upper Eocene, approximately 40 million years ago (Simpson, 1945). As Fig. 1.2 shows they became differentiated from the primitive artiodactyl stock very early on and

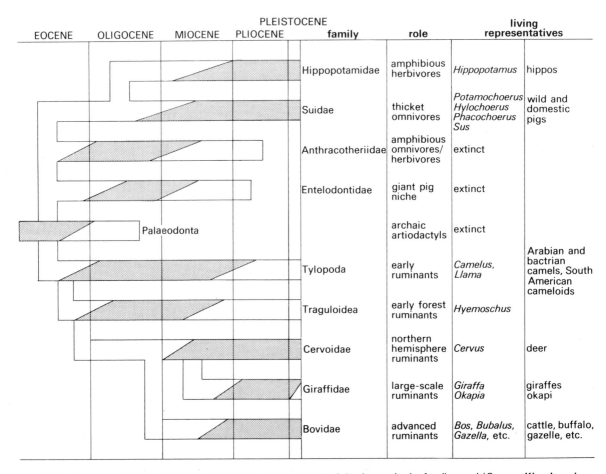

fig. 1.2 Development of the artiodactyla: dark shading shows period of dominance in the fossil record (*Source*: **Kingdon, J.** (1979). *East African mammals*. Volume III Part B. *Large mammals*. Academic Press: London.)

remained an important part of the fauna – if the fossil record is representative of the numbers of species present at any one time in history – through to the Lower Pleistocene, about 2 million years ago.

The Tylopoda contains two families. One of these, the Xiphodontidae, is very primitive and all its representatives have been extinct since the Lower Oligocene, about 35 million years ago. The second family is much richer in the fossil record with five sub-families. All the representatives of four of these sub-families are extinct although some persisted through to the Lower Pliocene,

about 7 million years ago. The fifth sub-family, the Camelinae, contains the direct ancestors (some genera of which persisted into the Pleistocene) of the extant camels *Camelus* spp. and lamoids *Lama* spp. A schematic family tree of the Tylopoda, reconstructed from the palaeontological record and based on Simpson (1945) is shown in Fig. 1.3.

The earliest true members of the Camelidae belonged to the sub-family Poëbrotheriinae, appeared in the Upper Eocene and had become extinct by the Middle Oligocene. The first to appear, *Protylopus*, were very small, about the size of a

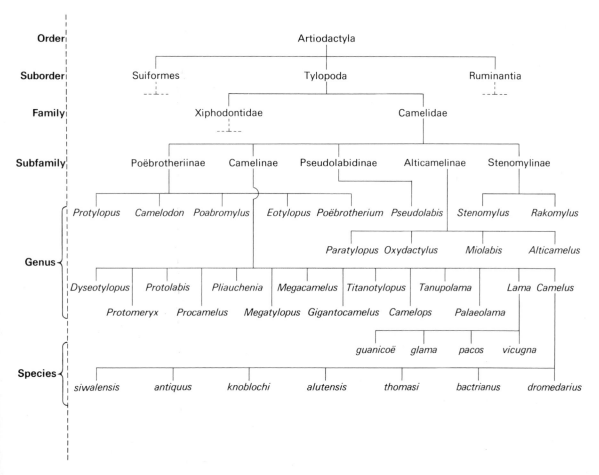

fig. 1.3 A genealogy of the artiodactyla with special reference to the camel (*Source*: as for Fig. 1.1.)

3

large rabbit. This was followed in the Middle Oligocene by *Poëbrotherium* which was about the size of a sheep. These two, and all other poëbrotheriinids were confined to North America.

No representatives of the other four sub-families appeared until the Upper Oligocene, some 30 million years ago, with the exception of *Paratylopus* in the Middle Oligocene of about 35 milion years ago. Indeed, the three minor sub-families of Pseudolabidinae, Alticamelinae and Stenomylinae were all apparently confined to relatively few genera and persisted for a geologically short period. The principal sub-family has been the Camelinae and, as we have seen, it is only members of this taxon which are extant. The first genus which can be considered to lead directly into the recent line of *Camelus* was *Protomeryx*, known from the Upper Oligocene of North America, probably followed successively by *Protolabis*, *Procamelus* and *Pliauchenia*, in the middle and late Miocene and the Pliocene. All these are North American camels. Some of these, but particularly the slightly later genera of the Camelinae, as can be seen from their names in Fig. 1.3, on p. 3, were of large size (Simpson, 1945; Zeuner, 1963).

No early forms of tylopod other than the Camelinae have succeeded in breaking out of North America. This probably occurred in the Pliocene or early Pleistocene, 4–3 million years ago. The earliest fossils outside North America date from the Pliocene. They were found in northern India and relate to *Camelus siwalensis* and *C. antiquus*, neither of which appears to be very closely related to either *C. dromedarius* or *C. bactrianus*.

Apart from these records the genus *Camelus* first appeared in the Pleistocene of North America from whence it presumably migrated (across the land bridge which is now the Bering Straits) in the late Pleistocene, a migration which could have continued into early glaciation times. The subsequent dispersal of these true camels was fairly rapid along the dry zone of the northern hemisphere although some animals certainly penetrated south of the equator. Pleistocene representatives include *C. knoblochi* in southern Russia and *C. alutensis* in Rumania as well as *C. thomasi* over much of Europe and Asia. *Camelus dromedarius*, or its ancestors, separated from the northern branch in western Asia and spread across Arabia (Clutton-Brock, 1962) and into North Africa. Some camels, probably differing little from the present day dromedary, penetrated as far south as Olduvai Gorge in Tanzania during the Pleistocene (3 million years ago) while other fossils have been found at Marsabit in northern Kenya and in southern Ethiopia (Howell, Fichter and Wolff, 1969; Gentry and Gentry, 1970).

During the late Pleistocene, then, *Camelus dromedarius*, or something very close to it, ranged from the Atlantic to northern India. By the dawn of history, it had probably become extinct throughout the western part of its range, that is in North Africa. It was reintroduced into this area after being domesticated although a certain body of opinion asserts that a truly wild stock of dromedaries persisted in north-western Africa and that domestication there was independent of the process elsewhere.

Domestication

General considerations
It has been suggested that animals have become domesticated for widely differing reasons. Zeuner (1963) provides six groups or types which are:

1   Mammals domesticated in the pre-agricultural phase: dog; reindeer; goat; sheep.
2   Mammals domesticated in the early agricultural phase – the crop robbers: cattle, buffalo, yak and banteng; pig.
3   Mammals domesticated primarily for transport and labour:
    (a)   domesticated by agriculturalists in the forest zone: elephant.
    (b)   domesticated by secondary nomads: horse; camel.
    (c)   domesticated by river-valley civilisations: onager; ass.
4   Pest destroyers: cat, ferret, mongoose.
5   Various other mammals: rabbit; experimental domestication including cheetah, gazelle, etc.; New World species.
6   Birds, fishes and insects: fowls, ducks, geese; goldfish, carp; honey bees and silk moths.

It is probable that with very few exceptions the process of domestication has come to an end, although it is perhaps also necessary to mention the present attempts being made in Africa to domesticate certain large antelope (Lewis, 1978). The process of domestication for an individual species has probably followed a number of more or less clearly defined stages which might have been as follows.

1 Early association with humans, a few individuals being tamed, but interbreeding with wild animals remaining common.
2 Subjugation of large numbers of a species and making them wholly dependent on humans. Some morphological changes would occur over a long period in this phase.
3 Intentional development of economic traits in the now fully domesticated animals, e.g. size, milking ability, hair and wool production.
4 Elimination of the wild ancestor.

While the six groups of animals are distinct in origin and to some extent in the purpose of domestication, it does not necessarily follow that the chronological sequence was exact. The time of domestication would depend very much on the state of advancement of the human group involved and their needs for animals to provide clothing, food or transport. This is especially true for animals with a wide geographical range. Table 1.1 gives some details of the approximate time and area of domestication of the major domestic animals.

It appears that the camel was among the most recent of animals to be domesticated although the evidence is not particularly clear. For most species the indications of domestication can be related not only to the number of bones, artefacts or pictorial representations of the animal in the archaeological record but to morphological changes in the animal itself. These changes are related largely to the economic considerations outlined in 3 in the second list above. In the case of the camel the archaeological record is rather sparse and often discontinuous. In addition, few morphological changes are apparent in the domestic camel and there has been little differentiation into breeds. This may be due partly to the lateness of the

Table 1.1 Approximate time of domestication (years before present) and area of first domestication of main species of domestic animals

Species	Domesticated (year BP)	Area
Reindeer	14 000	Northern Europe/Germany
Dog	11 500 (8 900)	Northern Iran
Goat	9 000(10 000)	Middle East/Jordan
Sheep	8 000 (9 200)	Northern Iran/Jordan
Cattle	7 000 (9 000)	Europe
Donkey	5 500 (5 500)	Nile Valley
Buffalo	5 000	? India
Pig	5 000 (9 000)	Mesopotamia
Horse	5 000 (6 350)	Turkestan
Cat	5 000	Nile Valley
Silkworm	5 000	China
Bee	5 000	Nile Valley
Fowl	4 500	Indus Valley/East Asia
Elephant	4 500	Indus Valley
Onager	4 000 (9 000)	Mesopotamia
Camel	4 000	South Arabia

Figures in brackets are from radio-carbon datings from **Protsch, R. and Berger, R.** (1973). Earliest radio-carbon dates for domesticated animals. *Science, USA* 179, 235–239.

camel's domestication and the reasons for it – its use primarily as a pack animal rather than as a producer of meat, milk or clothing. It is thus often difficult to say with any certitude whether the archaeological evidence refers to wild or domestic animals. Further problems arise from the uncertainty regarding the exact geographical distribution of the wild ancestors and whether in fact these can be identified with *Camelus dromedarius*, with *C. bactrianus*, or with some other very closely-related but extinct camel.

The cradle of domestication
Taking into account the survival of wild camels in Arabia into historic times, and possibly even into the early Christian era about 2000–1800 BP, it

5

seems probable that the process of domestication began somewhere in the Arabian peninsula. This locus is by no means universally accepted and there is a particular body of opinion, although poorly supported by the evidence, that some camels survived in the wild state in the central-west Sahara and were separately domesticated there (Cauvet, 1929; Lhote, 1953). The argument suffers from several faults. Firstly, there is no real evidence that the wild camel in northern Africa was, in fact, *C. dromedarius* and, secondly, the record from rock paintings shows no camels for very long periods of time, thus throwing considerable doubt on their continuous presence in the area.

The general theory that the domestication of the camel first occurred in southern Arabia can be supported in several ways. The Hadhramaut in the south of Arabia, with its remote valleys and its arid climate, would provide a refuge for any remaining wild camels. In addition the area was cut off by the great central Arabian desert from the civilisations of the north. Both Mikesell (1955) and Bulliet (1975) are in agreement on southern Arabia while Zeuner (1963) suggests that domestication may have first occurred further to the north in central Arabia. The acceptance of the Hadhramaut area is based not on the historical or archaeological record, which is scanty before about the sixth century BC (2600 BP), but on the classical literature. Two of the few engravings or artefacts of this period, from the Temple of Hureidha and from Seiyun (both in the Hadhramaut) are shown in Fig. 1.4. However, there are many literature reference before this period. The camel was used by the Midianites when they invaded Palestine about 3100 BP and the Arabian origin of domestication is further supported by the reports of the Queen of Sheba bringing her luggage on camels when she visited King Solomon, in about 955 BC (2935 BP). The dromedary, on the other hand, appears to have been domesticated in connection with the trade in spices, incense and possibly salt, and this was certainly its principal use around 3000 BP, although it may have been used earlier as a sacrificial and religious animal. Use in the spice trade at this time does, however, suggest considerably earlier domestication – Ripinsky (1975) puts the date as about 5500 to 5000 BP – as the

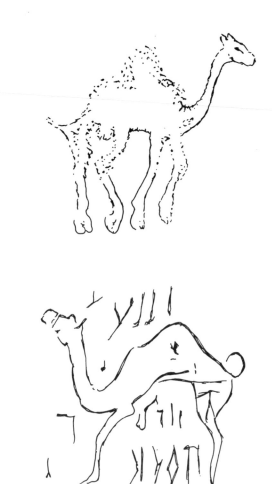

fig. 1.4 Two camel engravings from the Hadhramaut, Southern Arabia (Hureidha and Wadi Djethma, Seiyun) (*Source*: **Zeuner, F. E.** (1963). *A history of domesticated animals*. Hutchinson, London.)

'caravan' instinct of the camel (i.e. its tendency to walk in single file rather than in a herd group) would certainly take several generations to develop. Domestication could have taken place at some time prior to the development of the caravan trade when, perhaps, small numbers of camels were used to provide milk in this area where few alternative domestic animals were available.

There appears no reason for the camel to have been domesticated at this early stage in other areas. Most societies already had animals for meat and milk and most transport requirements could be fulfilled by the donkey. The late domestication of the camel can only be accounted for by its isolation. The need for a fast, powerful transport animal in an area whose economy was dependent on the caravan trade accounted for the large numbers that were eventually domesticated. Mesopotamia, Egypt, the western seaboard of Arabia and the Persian Gulf were all relatively well-known areas to the ancients and all rather well supplied with other species of animals. The Hadhramaut and the deep valleys of the Yemen best fulfil the theoretical conditions that lead to camel domestication and it can be concluded with some certainty that domestication did occur there.

The spread of the camel after domestication

The subsequent spread of the camel from its focus of domestication in southern Arabia is shown in Fig. 1.5.

In all the areas where the camel is found today, with one exception, it fulfils an economic role as a riding or transport animal in addition to its other functions which now are generally more important. The exception is Somalia in the Horn of Africa where the principal use of the camel is as a provider of milk; here it serves in a subsidiary capacity as a pack animal for moving camp but it is used as a riding animal hardly at all.

This feature has been used by Bulliet (1975) in his argument for southern Arabia as the cradle of domestication: he is of the opinion that even in southern Arabia the principal reason for camel domestication was for its milk. He postulates that

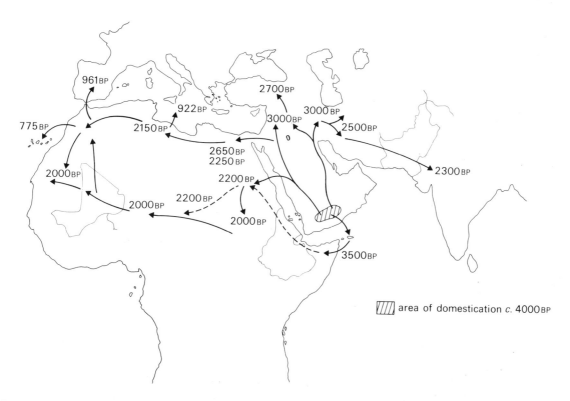

fig. 1.5 The centre of domestication and subsequent spread of the camel

7

the early Semites of the Hadhramaut learned of Somalia from sailors who plied across the Gulf of Aden and who were perhaps already shipping incense to Egypt by way of the Red Sea. He thus introduces a case for the transfer of the camel, by sea, via the small island of Socotra, to Somalia at a very early date within the range 4500–3500 BP. His theory is supported by Epstein (1971) although Zeuner (1963) does not even mention Somalia.

As supporting evidence for his thesis Bulliet uses the primitive design of the Somali camel saddle which in fact is described by Leese (1927) as less of a saddle than a collection of mats thrown on to the back and secured by a long rope. One or two pairs of sticks are then used to complete the assemblage to which the pack is attached. The Socotra saddle is similar to the Somali one but no cross sticks are used and the load is slung in baskets as in the Hadhramaut.

Somali and Socotra saddles are shown in Fig. 1.6. These are all primitive saddles which have been superceded elsewhere. Their disadvantages are that they are heavy and thus reduce the payload (the Somalis do not use their camels for economic transport); they are difficult to fit and usually press on the withers; they are difficult to load and require time and skill; the load is too far forward for efficient transport, and galls caused by the attaching rope can be a problem.

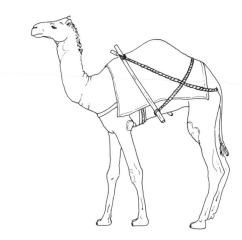

(b)

(c)

fig. 1.6 Camel saddles a) Somali b) Somali c) Socotran (*Source*: **Monod, Th.** (1967). *Notes sur le harnachement chamelier*. Bull. IFAN **29B**, 234 - 306).

(a)

8

The earliest written references to the camel in the Christian bible occur in Genesis Chapter 24 and Chapter 25, and relate to Abraham. The most likely date for Abraham's time is around 1800–1700 BC (3800–3700 BP) which would put the camel outside Arabia and in Palestine at a very early date. Much reliance has been placed on this evidence (Free, 1944) but one eminent authority (Albright, 1942; 1961) rejects outright such an early date and goes so far as to suggest that the original chronicles were altered at a later date by priests who had come to know the camel and could not conceive of its not being used by their forefathers. Albright firmly puts the first entry of camels into Palestine at about 3000 BP when the Midianite camel troops attacked the Israelites under Gideon. It is fairly certain' that the camel would have become relatively well known in southern Mesopotamia, across Palestine and in northern Arabia by this time as a pack animal used in the incense or salt trade. But by the time of the Midianite invasion, it had made an important transition from pack to riding animal.

According to Bulliet (1975), the camel was used as a pack animal by north Arabian tribes prior to 3000 BP. They would have taken over the camel from the south Arabian tribes who used it as a source of milk. It was at this early date that the

fig. 1.7 Position of South Arabian riding saddle

south Arabian saddle was developed. This saddle was positioned behind the hump (Fig. 1.7) which suggests that the Somali and Socotran saddles were derived from this one. The south Arabian saddle thus would predate all other forms of saddlery and its subsequent development could be used to attempt a reconstruction of the spread of the camel historically and geographically.

The introduction of the camel into Egypt is a constant source of conjecture and discussion. There appear to be three main theories.

1　The camel was rare or unknown in Egypt prior to the Assyrian and Persian invasions of the seventh and sixth centuries BC (2700–2600 BP).
2　Camels were known from prehistoric times.
3　Wild camels survived on the frontiers of Egypt in prehistoric times, then disappeared or became extinct and were reintroduced later.

These theories are not incompatible with each other. There is sufficient evidence of the occasional presence, or at least a knowledge of, the camel before the Assyrian invasion. The oldest evidence of the camel relates to a cord made of camel hair found in a tomb of the III or IV Dynasty (4700 BP). There are figurines and other artefacts relating to the XII–XVIII Dynasties (4000–3300 BP) and the New Kingdom (3500–3000 BP) as well as a pottery jar in the form of a camel carrying water vessels in a tomb dated about 3000 BP. With the exception of the last, none of these is evidence either of common use or of domestication. It is this last find, also, which brings us nearest to the first certain knowledge of the camel in Lower (northern) Egypt. Camels, probably belonging to Arabs, were used to carry water for the Assyrian army under Asarhaddon about 670 BC (2650 BP) and 50 or so years later they were used by the Persians (Mikesell, 1955; Zeuner, 1963; Epstein, 1971). But it was not until the Ptolemaic period (2250 BP), and as a result of increased trade with the east, that camels really entered the commercial life of Egypt. The majority of these camels could make the land crossing across the Sinai peninsula but a number may have crossed to the desert east of the Nile by way of the Red Sea, probably about 2200–2100 BP, in connection with the by now well-established incense trade with Upper (southern) Egypt (Zeuner, 1963; Bulliet, 1975).

It is also possible that the camel reached Upper Egypt from the south, either along the Red Sea coast through the Danakil Desert or south round the Ethiopian Highlands and north through what is now the Sudan (Walz, 1951; 1956). Their entry into eastern Upper Egypt and use by the Beja tribes of that area marks the first adoption of the camel by non-Arabs. During the Roman period (from 2200 BP) the camel had assumed in Egypt the role it fulfils today (Fig. 1.8). From Upper Egypt the camel moved southwards along the Nile into what is now the Sudan, perhaps as early as 2200 BP (Robinson, 1936) although the first remains to have been dated, from Meroë, relate to about 2000 BP. In this instance the camel's southward movement would be facilitated by the difficulty of river transport on the Nile due to the numerous cataracts.

In what today are Iraq and Syria the camel was used for military operations and was certainly known by 2900 BP (Fig. 1.9). Fighting between the Arabs and the Assyrians continued until the latter,

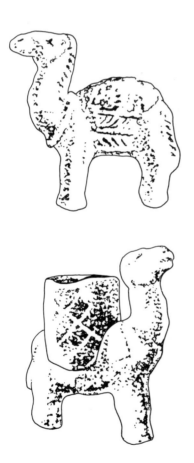

fig. 1.8 Two figurines of working camels of the Roman period, Egypt (*Source*: as for Fig. 1.4.)

fig. 1.9 Rider on a saddled camel, from Syria, showing structure called 'furniture' in the Bible; one of the orthostats found at Tell Halaf (c.900 BC)

under Ashurbanipal, attained dominion over the former about 2700 BP (Fig. 1.10). Final conquest of the Arabs was achieved by the Assyrians themselves adopting the camel as a military beast but it was not until the Persians, under Cyrus, conquered Mesopotamia that camels were generally used in warfare against, rather than by, the Arabs. By the time the camel reached northern Mesopotamia, as Fig. 1.9 shows, some advance in

fig. 1.10 Tribute of dromedaries being brought to Tiglathpileser III of Assyria (745-727 BC); relief from the palace of Nimrod (*Source*: as for Fig. 1.4.)

saddle design towards what Bulliet (1975) describes as the north Arabian saddle had been made, giving greater control of the animal and thus making its use as a military animal more feasible. By about 2100-2000 BP Palmyra, in the middle of the Syrian desert, had become very important in the general caravan trade traversing the desert from the Euphrates to the Mediterranean. The camel had assumed such a dominant position in this trade that the Palmyrans maintained a camel crops, which used the north Arabian saddle (Fig. 1.11), and also imposed differential taxes in favour of camels as against wheeled vehicles. Bulliet (1975) bases many of his arguments for the introduction of the camel to various areas on the relation between the camel, the wheel and the disappearance of the latter. Fig. 1.12 summarises, the possible sequence of events and some of the factors involved, with particular reference to the Syrian desert areas.

Not surprisingly perhaps, the camel spread from Syria and Iraq to Asia Minor (present day Turkey), probably between 2700 and 2500 BP, and played an important role at the Battle of Sardis in 546 BC (2526 BP) in which Cyrus defeated Croesus of Lydia. The sight and smell of the camels was used

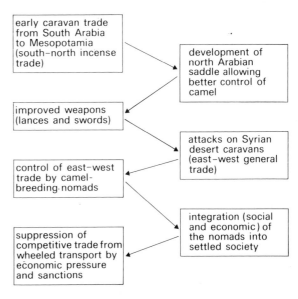

fig. 1.11 Relief from Palmyra showing equipment of Palmyrene camel corps

fig. 1.12 Integration of camels and camel owners into the Syrian economy of about 2100 BP

11

to frighten the horses of Croesus' army. In Australia 2500 years later it was again found impossible to work horses alongside camels because, it was alleged, of the smell.

The time of introduction of the dromedary into Iran is particularly difficult to determine on account of the pre-existence there of the Bactrian camel. Much can be made of the linguistic differentiation employed for the two animals but this is not always clear cut, just as today one tends to use the word 'camel' for both species. Thus in the Avesta, the holy book of Zoroaster written in the main between 2570 and 2530 BP, references to the 'camel' are common but it is not clear to which species reference is being made. It is reasonable to assume, nonetheless, that the dromedary entered Iran concurrent with the Persian conquests in the west. This assumption is borne out by carvings on the walls at Persepolis, constructed some time during the sixth or fifth century BC. One-humped camels are shown being led as tribute by Arabs (Fig. 1.13) while five delegations are shown leading two-humped camels (Fig. 1.14). It is apparent that

fig. 1.13 Arab leading one-humped camel in procession of tribute bearers at Persepolis, note halter

fig. 1.14 Two-humped camels for tribute at Persepolis

the Bactrian camel was widespread in west-central Asia at this time (2500 BP) but its use appears to have declined as the dromedary increased. The Bactrian camel was certainly gradually replaced on the Silk Route by the dromedary. The use of the dromedary as a general purpose, fast transport/milk and meat animal led to the gradual withdrawal of the Bactrian to the north until climatic and other conditions became too severe for the dromedary. One result of this inter-specific overlap has been the Turkman or Turkestan camel (see Chapter 3). While this account represents a general consensus (Zeuner, 1963; Bulliet, 1975) it is possible that the dromedary did not establish a strong foothold in Iran until the Sassanian period lasting from AD 211 to 651 (1760–1330 BP) (Mikesell, 1955).

In India, the dromedary was probably not known to the Aryan invaders of about 3000 BP (Zeuner, 1963; Epstein, 1971) although this is not certain and Mikesell (1955) is of the opinion that it could have been introduced by them. It is more likely that the domedary was brought into India in small numbers by the invasion of Alexander the Great at about 2300 BP. But in India, as in Iran, it was to some extent in competition with the Bactrian and, away from the main trade routes, probably made little initial impact. Bulliet (1975) has suggested that the dromedary did not assume significance in the Indo-Pakistan area until about 1000–800 BP when the Baluchis, who are still important camel breeders, first occupied their present territories in south-eastern Iran and Pakistan. The north Arabian saddle was used in India to enable the dromedary to be harnessed to carts; the saddle is still employed there for this purpose but scarely anywhere else except Tunisia, neighbouring Morocco and south-western Arabia. This form of use is thought to have been part of the transfer of technology from the Bactrian camel, as is the use of the nose ring for control (as opposed to the more simple headstall normally used for the dromedary).

With regard to the presence of the camel in north Africa west of the Nile there are three possibilities.

1 The camel has always been present and the extant domestic camel is a direct descendant of wild camels which roamed the Sahara in the Pleistocene. This is the view, for example, of Charnot (1953) and Cauvet (1925). The latter occasionally goes even further and has claimed that this camel is a separate species (Cauvet, 1929).

2 The camel was introduced to western North Africa before the Romans arrived either by way of the Mediterranean littoral or by way of a southern route across the chain of highland massifs from Darfur, through Ennedi, Tibesti, Air and Tamanrasset. These routes could have been used separately or at the same time. This view is held by Demougeot (1960).

3 The camel was introduced to North Africa by the Romans from Egypt or possibly from Syria, a view strongly supported by Gautier (1927).

The first specific mention of camels in North Africa relates to 46 BC (2026 BP) when Caesar records that he captured 22 of them from the Numidian army. This does not exclude the possibility that it was known in the interior of the Sahara somewhat earlier. There are rock paintings at 'Uweinat on the present Libyan–Sudanian–Egyptian border dated 2500–2000 BP. The polyglot nature of the camel's appearance in the west is supported by the variety of saddles which can be found, a subject which has been best studied by Monod (1967). Thus, in the south along the edge of the Sahara, an area which was probably isolated from Roman influences (and so from north Arabia) for a long time, a variety of saddles only distantly related to the north or south Arabian saddle has been developed. All these are positioned in front of the hump (Fig. 1.15) and this is one of the reasons advanced by Cauvet for independent domestication. However, there is ample evidence from rock paintings (Lhote, 1953; 1959) that the various designs have coexisted and the indigenous theory of domestication must be discounted. So it is likely that the camel was present in western North Africa at least in small numbers before the Romans arrived. As the Romans were already aware of the uses of the camel from their experience of it elsewhere, they very quickly adopted it into their economic life. By the middle of the fourth century (1630 BP) the camel in North Africa formed an important part of the economic system

fig. 1.15 Typical posture of rider on Saharan shoulder saddle; note use of feet on neck to control animal

fig. 1.16 Ploughing illustrated on a Roman tomb from Ghirza, Tripolitania, third to fifth centuries AD (*Source*: as for Fig. 1.4.)

shown in Fig. 2.1 on p. 16. A final impetus was given to its consolidation by the rise and spread of Islam approximately 1350 BP in North Africa, perhaps 100 years later in India and again about 930 BP when Muslims were encouraged to settle the North African littoral by being given a camel and a piece of gold as incentives (Epstein, 1971). The spread of Islam also took the camel to Spain in AD 1020 and to Sicily 39 years later in AD 1059. Camels were even seen on the Rhine in the year AD 1136.

But the excursions outside Asia and mainland Africa were of little importance. Subsequently the camel was taken to the Canary Islands in AD 1405 by a French landowner from Normandy. This was the first move in its modern extension of range and was the base for its subsequent re-exportation to many of the new lands, as we shall see in Chapter 2.

fig. 1.17 Harness of Tunisian camel cart

and was used not only for pack and riding but also to draw ploughs (Fig. 1.16) and wheeled transport (Fig. 1.17). It is still used for both purposes.

Thus, by the beginning of the Christian era (2000 BP) the camel was at least known, if not common, throughout its present-day natural range

Further reading

Albright, W. F. (1942). *Archaeology and the religion of Israel*. Johns Hopkins Press: Baltimore, USA.

Albright, W. F. (1961), *The archaeology of Palestine*. Penguin Books: Harmondsworth, Middlesex, UK.

Bibby, G. (1970). *Looking for Dilmun*. Collins: London.

Bohlken, H. (1960). Remarks on the stomach and the systematic position of the Tylopoda. *Proc. Zool. Soc. Lond.* **134**, 207-215.

Bulliet, R. W. (1975). *The camel and the wheel*. Harvard University Press: Cambridge, Massachusetts, USA.

Cauvet, G. (1925). *Le chameau*. Bailliere: Paris, France.

Cauvet, G. (1929). *Dromedaires à 34 dents et dromedaires à 36 dents*. *Bull. Soc. Hist. Nat. Afrique Nord*, **20**(9), 247-256.

Charnot, Y. (1953). *De l'évolution des camlidés; apparition du dromadaire au Maroc*. *Bull. Soc. Sci. Nat. Phys.* Maroc. **33**, 207-230.

Clutton-Brock, J. (1962). An analysis of the mammalian remains from three prehistoric sites in India and Western Asia. Thesis, University of London: London.

Demougeot, E. (1960). *Le chameau et l'Afrique du nord romaine*. *Annales: Economies, Societés, Civilisations*, **15**, 209-247.

Epstein, H. (1971). *The origin of the domestic animals of Africa*. Africana Publishing Corporation: New York, USA.

Free, J. P. (1944). Abraham's camels. *J. Near East Stud*, **3**, 187-193.

Gautier, E. F. (1927). *Les siecles obscurs du Maghreb*. Payot: Paris, France.

Gentry, A. W. and Gentry, A. (1970). Fossil camels in Kenya and Tanzania. *Nature, Lond.*, **222**, 898.

Howell, F. C., Fichter, R. and Wolff, R. (1969). Fossil camels in the Omo beds, Southern Ethiopia. *Nature, Lond.*, **221**, 15.

Leese, A. S. (1927). *A treatise on the one-humped camel in health and disease*. Haynes & Son: Stamford, Lincs, UK.

Lewis, J. G. (1978). Game domestication for animal production in Kenya: shade behaviour and factors affecting herding of eland, oryx, buffalo and zebu cattle. *J. Agric. Sci., Camb.*, **90**, 587-595.

Lhote, H. (1953). *Le cheval et le chameau dans les peintures et gravures rupestres du Sahara*. *Bull. IFAN*, **15**, 1138-1228.

Lhote, H. (1959). *Nouvelle contribution à l'étude des gravures et peintures rupestres du Sahara central; la station de Tit (Ahaggar)*. *J. Soc. Africanistes*, **29**, 147-192.

Mikesell, M. K. (1955). Notes on the dispersal of the dromedary. *Southwestern J. Anthropol.*, **11**, 231-245.

Monod, Th. (1967). *Notes sur le harnachement chamelier, Bull. IFAN* **29B**, 234-306.

Ripinsky, M. M. (1975). The camel in ancient Arabia. *Antiquity*, **49**(196), 295-298.

Robinson, A. E. (1936). The camel in antiquity. *Sudan Notes Rec.*, **19**, 47-69.

Simpson, G. G. (1945). The principles of classification and a classification of mammals. *Bull. Amer. Mus. Nat. Hist.*, **85**, 1-350.

Walz, R. (1951). *Zum problem der Zeitpunkts der Domestikation der altweltlichen Cameliden. Zeit Deutsch. Morgenländ Ges.*, n.s. **26**, 29-51.

Walz, R. (1956). *Beitrage zur ältesten Geschichte der altweltlichen Cameliden unter besonderer Berücksichtijung des Problems des Domestikationazeitpuntes. Act VIe Congr. Inter Sci. Anthropol. Ethnol.*, Vienne 1952, **3**, 190-204.

Zeuner, F. E. (1963). *A history of domesticated animals*. Hutchinson: London.

2   Distribution, numbers and importance

"Lambs are enclosed where
it's never exposed,
Coops are constructed for
hens;
Kittens are treated to houses
well heated,
And pigs are protected by
pens.
But a camel comes handy
Wherever it's sandy –
Anywhere does for me"

The Camel's Complaint by Charles E. Carryl

Distribution

In general terms the camel is considered as an animal of the Tropics but, as Fig. 2.1 shows, much of its present-day normal range is extra-tropical.

Of the 18 African countries in which it forms an important part of the domestic livestock population, four are wholly outside the Tropics and a further six have at least part of their land area north of the Tropic of Cancer. In Asia only two countries

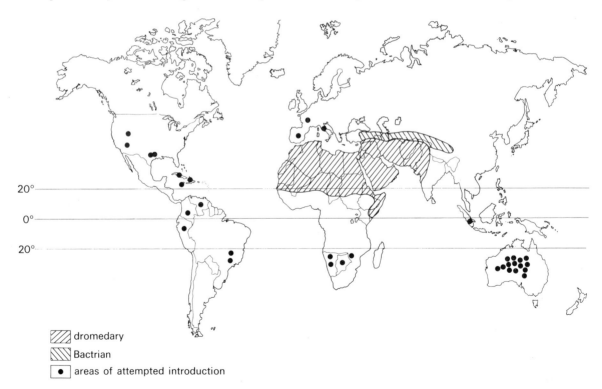

dromedary

Bactrian

● areas of attempted introduction

fig. 2.1 The normal distribution of the camel and areas of attempted introduction

16

are wholly within the Tropics while four are partially within and twelve completely outside. The fourteen countries north of the Tropic contain 1·84 million camels and it is probable that the ten which are astride the Tropic have a total of 1·2 million in the parts of the countries to the north of it. Thus, of the 1978 world total of 15 million camels, about 20 per cent, spread rather thinly over a vast area, are not found within the Tropics.

Environmental factors governing camel distribution.

The camel cannot be considered as a wholly tropical animal within the strict geographic sense of the term. It would be correct, however, to consider it as being 'tropical' in general climatic terms. With very few exceptions it is found in areas where low rainfall occurs in a relatively short period. This is followed by a long dry season which is often hot for most of the time and lasts for over 8 months of the year. These are the prevailing conditions in the palaearctic deserts of northern Africa and western and central Asia. The few areas outside this region where the camel has been introduced or has penetrated are climatically similar.

At the northern and eastern edges of its range in Asia it is replaced in the mountainous regions of southern Russia and in the cold deserts of China by its close relation, the Bactrian camel. (In South America the llamoids are a close parallel to the Bactrian in the Old World). Its southern boundary in Asia is delimited by the Sea of Oman (except in India) and the Gulf of Aden. In Africa the northern and western edges of its range are delimited by the Mediterranean Sea and the Atlantic Ocean while its southern edge is controlled not only by physical but also by biotic factors.

The success of the camel in climates hotter and drier than other domestic animals (with the partial exception of the donkey) can tolerate is due to its peculiar physiology (Chapter 5). Its ability to withstand torrid heat and extreme desiccation are thus of paramount importance in determining its distribution. In addition, however, to its physiological adaptations the camel also is anatomically adapted to a desert life (Chapters 4 and 5). The camel's gait enables it to cover long distances with much less effort than the walk of other animals and

its feet form cushions which spread its weight on sand. The padded feet are in some cases a disadvantage; it is less at home in stony than in sandy deserts and is generally incapable of surviving in swampy or permanently wet areas. There are well-known exceptions to the camel's inability to live in areas which are wet underfoot, for example, in the Nile delta of lower Egypt, the delta camels of India and the camels of the Marsh Arabs in southern Iraq. Normally, however, the buffalo replaces the camel in these situations as it is much better adapted to delta conditions and can perform most of the camel's functions including provision of meat and milk, agricultural power and some transport, while other forms of transport are assured by the donkey.

Increasing humidity, whether from higher rainfall or from more or less permanent bodies of surface water, is unfavourable to the camel. In Africa the southern limit of the physical environment favouring the camel over the other domestic species can be found at about 15°N in West Africa from the Atlantic coast of Senegal, through central Mali and the south of Niger. In Chad and the Sudan the southern limit has been put at 13°N although in recent years the normal range has gradually been pushed southwards. In rainfall terms it corresponds to about 400 mm annually. South of these limits the physical environment favours other domestic animals – donkeys and cattle (to a limited exent) for transport, and cattle, sheep and goats for meat and milk. An additional biotic factor limiting the distribution of the camel in the south is the presence of the tsetse and other biting flies.

In eastern Africa the arid conditions prevailing on the Red Sea coast, in the Gulf of Aden and in the hinterland of the Indian Ocean coast as far south as 2°S are favourable to the camel. This region is entirely to the south of the extreme southern limit of the camel's normal range yet it supports about 35 per cent of all the world's camels. In certain limited areas rainfall may even be as high as 550 mm per year.

Social factors involved in the distribution of the camel

The camel is essentially a nomadic animal and a domestic animal of nomads. It is unusual to find camels in areas where permanent cultivation is practised, except where this is based on desert oases. Thus the environmental barriers to the extension of the camel's range are reinforced by cultural ones. By contrast with owners of the Bactrain camel, who probably already owned other domestic animals and, therefore, had alternative sources of transport, meat and milk, the nomadic owners of the dromedary were obliged to take their camels with them to assure these basic services. In eastern Africa the gradual spread of the camel to tribes not owning it in ancient times has resulted from a pre-existing nomadic or semi-nomadic way of life: examples are the Rendille and Samburu, the Suk, who first adopted camels as herd animals in the 1870s, and the Turkana.

It cannot be doubted that the greatest social impact on the recent distribution of the camel came after the advent of Islam. While camels were undoubtedly present in small numbers in many areas in which they are found today it was not until after the seventh century AD (1300 BP) that they were present in quantity. As the Arabs poured from their heartland to conduct their Holy Wars they took their camels with them, consolidating their range northwards and eastwards in Asia and westwards along the Mediterranean littoral of North Africa.

Recent economic factors affecting the camel's distribution.

Although the introduction of the wheel had some impact on camel distribution and numbers it was on the whole relatively minor, and until the advent of motorised transport and the monetarisation of certain nomadic economies the camel remained almost the only beast of burden and personal transport animal in the areas to which it was adapted.

In many areas in the twentieth century the motor vehicle with balloon tyres has taken over many of the transport functions previously performed by the camel. This has not, in most cases, been economic in real terms as it simply means that the cost of transport has risen. It is perhaps an unfortunate coincidence of circumstances that it is in precisely those areas where camels have been replaced by motor transport that oil is found. The cost of modernisation (if not efficiency), therefore,

has been very largely offset by oil production. Although these developments have affected to a very great extent the transport role of the camel they have had much less effect on its cultural importance. So far, there has been very little reduction of the camel's range due to economic factors although current numerical trends in the areas affected would lead one to expect such a reduction in the future.

The increasing cost of motor transport and the increased world demand for meat and milk will have the opposite effect. It is most probable then that these factors will lead to the continued existence and perhaps an increase in numbers of the camel, in those areas where the camel is still the most efficient domestic animal for transforming vegetable matter into work, meat and milk.

Numbers and densities

The camel is distributed, often sparsely, over large areas; this and the nature of the management system make accurate enumeration difficult. To these problems are added the prejudices and ignorance of the authorities responsible for livestock census work who often, at best, regard the camel as an anachronism and, at worst, ignore its existence completely.

Present numbers

The data available on present numbers are shown in Tables 2.1 and 2.2. The principal source is the FAO Production Yearbook for 1978. In many cases the figures should be regarded as indicative only and some are little more than rough estimates. While some countries furnish regular returns others do so only irregularly and these may be occasions when it appears politically expedient to do so – for example, if it is wished to emphasise a drought or other natural castastrophe.

The dromedary is numerically far superior to the Bactrian camel, and totals almost 90 per cent of the genus *Camelus* in the world today. More than 80 per cent of Arabian camels occur in Africa.

Somalia and Sudan contain about 50 per cent of all Old World Camelidae and 55 per cent of all dromedaries. In Africa these two countries account for 70 per cent of camels while three of their neighbours – Ethiopia, Chad and Kenya – contain a further 12·5 per cent. Apart from these countries Mauritania, Niger and Mali have important populations as do the Maghreb countries of Algeria, Morocco and Tunisia.

In Asia the greatest number of camels is found in India with 40 per cent of the continent's dromedaries (7·8 per cent of the world total) while Pakistan has 28 per cent. Apart from these two countries only Afghanistan and Iraq, and to a lesser extent Saudi Arabia and the Yemen Arab Republic, have important numbers of camels.

Density in relation to land and human population. Two other measures of importance, density and the ratio of camels to the human population, show higher figures in the African than in the Asian range. In terms of density, at 0·7 camels per square kilometre, Africa has a population three times as important as Asia while there are almost 17 times more camels per human being in Africa than in Asia. Somalia has by far the highest density and the highest camel to human ratio. Mauritania is also important in this respect, while Djibouti, Ethiopia, Kenya, Sudan and Tunisia are important in terms of density but relatively less so in camel to human ratios. In Asia, if the small island of

Table 2.1 Land areas, human population, camel population and importance of camels in African countries (*Source*: **FAO** (1978). *Production yearbook*, Vol. 32. FAO: Rome.

Country	Land area km²	Human population ('000)	Camel population ('000)	Camel density (number per square kilometre)	Camels per person	Camels as per cent of DHB[1]
Algeria	2 381 741	17 530	147	0·06	0·01	5·87
Chad	1 259 200	4 157	405	0·32	0·10	11·04
Djibouti	21 980	114	26	1·18	0·23	30·86
Egypt	995 450	37 977	95	0·09	0·003	2·29
Ethiopia	1 101 000	30 350	960	0·87	0·03	3·69
Kenya	569 250	14 658	574	1·01	0·04	7·76
Libya	1 759 540	2 625	75	0·04	0·03	9·07
Mali	1 220 000	6 146	198	0·16	0·03	4·65
Mauritania	1 030 400	1 527	718	0·70	0·47	28·92
Morocco	446 300	19 168	200[2]	0·45	0·01	3·82
Niger	1 266 700	5 006	350	0·28	0·07	10·46
Nigeria	910 770	68 724	18	0·02	0·0003	0·17
Senegal	192 000	5 364	6	0·03	0·001	0·26
Somalia	627 340	3 446	5 400	8·61	1·57	53·83
Sudan	2 376 000	16 693	2 904	1·22	0·17	17·59
Tunisia	155 360	6 213	205	1·32	0·03	15·25
Upper Volta	273 800	5 986	5	0·02	0·0008	0·28
Western Sahara	266 000		86	0·32		88·69
Africa	16 852 830	245 684	12 192	0·72	0·05	12·07

1 domestic herbivore biomass, calculated from mean population weights of: cattle 206 kg; sheep 30 kg; goats 18 kg; horses 250 kg; mules 160 kg; donkeys 107 kg; buffaloes 250 kg; camels 307 kg; pigs excluded
2 FAO Production Yearbook gives 20×10^3 head which I assume is a printing error.

Table 2.2 Land areas, human population, camel population and importance of camels in Near and Middle East countries. (*Source*: **FAO** (1978). *Production yearbook*, Vol. 32. FAO: Rome.)

Country	Land area km^2	Human population ('000)	Camel population ('000)	Camel density (number per square kilometre)	Camels per person	Camels as per cent of DHB[1]
Afghanistan	647 500	20 882	290[2]	0·45	0·01	4·77
Bahrein	620	276	1	1·61	0·004	18·48
India	2 973 190	660 976	1 174	0·39	0·002	0·65
Iran	1 636 000	33 945	27	0·02	0·0008	0·26
Iraq	433 970	12 269	232	0·53	0·02	6·22
Israel	20 330	3 712	11	0·54	0·003	3·93
Jordan	97 180	2 156	19	0·20	0·01	10·65
Kuwait	17 820	1 200	5	0·28	0·004	15·66
Lebanon	10 230	3 152	1	0·10	0·0003	0·87
Oman	212 460	843	6	0·03	0·007	4·79
Pakistan	778 720	77 732	819	1·05	0·01	3·31
Qatar	11 000	101	9	0·82	0·09	44·99
Saudi Arabia	2 149 690	7 860	108	0·05	0·01	15·19
Syria	184 120	7 990	8	0·04	0·001	0·58
Turkey	770 760	43 063	15[2]	0·02	0·0003	0·09
U.A. Emirates	83 600	690	45	0·54	0·07	57·74
Yemen Arab Republic	195 000	5 800	105	0·54	0·02	5·81
Yemen Democratic Republic	332 970	1 815	40	0·12	0·02	13·70
Asia	10 555 160	884 462	2 915	0·28	0·003	1·17

1 domestic herbivore biomass, calculated from mean population weights of: cattle 206 kg; sheep 30 kg; goats 18 kg; horses 250 kg; mules 160 kg; donkeys 107 kg; buffaloes 250 kg; camels 307 kg; pigs excluded
2 includes some Bactrian camels.

Bahrein is excluded, only Pakistan has any important density of camels while in all Asian countries there are very few camels compared with the number of people.

Importance of the camel in the livestock economy.

Perhaps the most important figures in Tables 2.1 (on p. 19) and 2.2 (above) are the percentages of the domestic herbivore biomass (DHB) which camels constitute. These figures give an indication of the relative importance of camels in the national and individual livestock economies of the countries in which camels are found. In terms of percentage

DHB, the countries have been grouped into four categories, shown graphically in Fig. 2.2.

Category 1 This comprises those countries in which camels, while present even in considerable numbers contribute less than 1 per cent total DHB. For example, India has almost 1·2 million camels, which is only 7·8 per cent of the world total. In Africa, Nigeria, Senegal and Upper Volta are peripheral to the camel's distribution and they do not contain large populations of any ethnic groups to which the camel is important socially or culturally. Nigeria imports many camels to supply meat to reduce the protein deficit but in all these countries

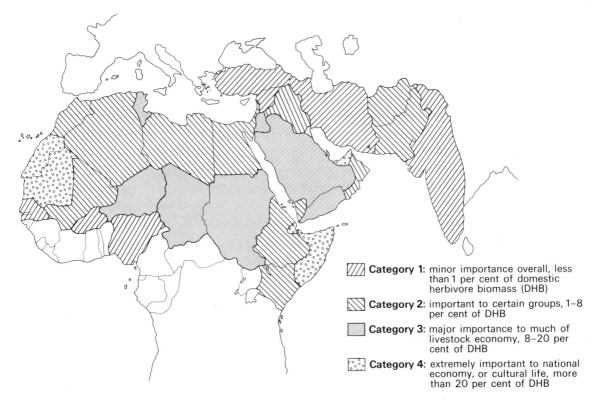

Category 1: minor importance overall, less than 1 per cent of domestic herbivore biomass (DHB)

Category 2: important to certain groups, 1–8 per cent of DHB

Category 3: major importance to much of livestock economy, 8–20 per cent of DHB

Category 4: extremely important to national economy, or cultural life, more than 20 per cent of DHB

fig. 2.2 Importance of the camel in the livestock economy of countries of its normal distribution

cattle are equivalent to 75 per cent of DHB and provide most of the meat and milk. In Asia five countries - Turkey, Iran, Syria, India and the Lebanon - fall into this category. These countries are again peripheral to the camel's distribution and three of them grade into the domain of the Bactrian. With the exception of India, which in this regard is a special case, cattle are generally less important than in the African countries and their place as meat and milk producers is to some extent taken over by sheep which account for between 20 and 50 per cent of DHB. In India, the buffalo is important as a milk and meat producer and as a source of power.

Category 2 Here camels contribute between 1 and 8 per cent of DHB. The category is composed of seven countries in Africa and six in Asia. In

Africa the countries are Egypt, Ethiopia, Morocco, Mali, Algeria, Kenya and Libya; in Asia they are Pakistan, Israel, Afghanistan, Oman, Yemen Arab Republic and Iraq. To a certain extent these countries are also peripheral to the generalised area of the camel but they contain at least one group of people to whom the camel is the most important animal. Thus in Mali it is the Tuareg, in Egypt the Bedu, in Ethiopia the Afar and the Oromo, and the Somali in Kenya. Egypt represents a special case with its agricultural-livestock economy based on the delta and the Nile. Here the buffalo is the principal source of power and milk, but like Nigeria, Egypt imports many camels for meat. The other African countries have a considerable part of their area which is suitable for permanent cultivation: the highlands of Kenya and Ethiopia; the littoral of Algeria, Morocco and

21

Libya; and the south of Mali. In all the African countries, with the exception of the relatively well developed Kenyan economy, the donkey plays a more important and widespread role as a transport animal. In Asia, Israel is the economic exception. The donkey is the general beast of burden in all other countries and the buffalo provides agricultural power, meat and milk in Pakistan.

Category 3 This comprises those countries in which camels account for 8-20 per cent of DHB. In Africa four countries - Niger, Chad, Tunisia and Sudan - are in this category and there are five in Asia - Jordan, Yemen Democratic Republic, Saudi Arabia, Kuwait and Bahrein. Category 3 is rather mixed and is evidently transitional between Categories 2 and 4. In all the countries considerable sections of the population have cultural affinities with the camel and the animal assumes real importance economically as a provider of meat and transport and some milk. Cattle remain important in these countries. In Africa the countries merge into savanna and forest in the south and in Asia the wealth from oil deposits has helped to diversify the livestock economy to a considerable extent. Sudan has the second largest camel population of the world and the camel is all important in the north. Bahrein has a very small total number of animals. However, both countries merge into Category 4.

Category 4 This comprises the countries in which camels are of overwhelming importance culturally, economically and ecologically, and constitute more than 20 per cent of DHB. In Africa four countries are in this category. They are Mauritania, Djibouti, Somalia and Western Sahara. Together they form a large area and contain about 40 per cent of the world's camels. In Asia the two countries involved are Qatar and the United Arab Emirates, both small but in which camels retain much of their former importance for cultural reasons.

Variation of numbers, distribution and importance within countries.

The data in Tables 2.1 and 2.2 on pp. 19 and 20

refer to those countries as a whole. It is evident, however, that within most countries the camel's distribution will be very uneven and its importance variable. This is particularly the case both in countries bordering the natural limits of the camel's range and in very large countries in which the camel is the dominant animal in certain areas and is totally absent from others. This is true even when these countries remain pastoral in economy.

Camels, rainfall and humans in Senegal.

Based on administration calculations, Senegal at present falls in Category 1 in terms of DHB; it also has a very low total number of camels and a low camel to human ratio of 0·001. The camel population figures have decreased by about one-fifth over the last 50 years while the human population has probably doubled. Nonetheless some administration figures of 50 years ago (based on Rousseau, 1943) are enlightening. Fig. 2.3 shows the distribution of the camel in Senegal in relation to rainfall, the number of months in which rain falls and the human population. The camel is confined to the north-west of the country but even in that region there are important differences in its density and in the camel to human ratio. The maximum density is 0·84 per square kilometre and 0·6 camels per person, i.e. figures similar to those for Mauritania, the northern neighbour of Senegal. However, figures refer only to resident camels censused by the Administration of Senegal. For long periods during the dry season, and particularly after the harvest of groundnuts, numbers and density are considerably augmented by Mauritanian camels on seasonal transhumance. These are used to transport the groundnut crop and to some extent are fed on the by-products.

Regional and seasonal variations in Sudan and Kenya.

Recent developments in low-level aerial surveys have contributed very greatly to our knowledge of regional (spatial) and seasonal (temporal) distribution of livestock.

Variation in regional distribution in the Sudan and Kenya arise due to factors such as climatic variations and cultural preferences. Some data are shown in Table 2.3 and show that a high camel

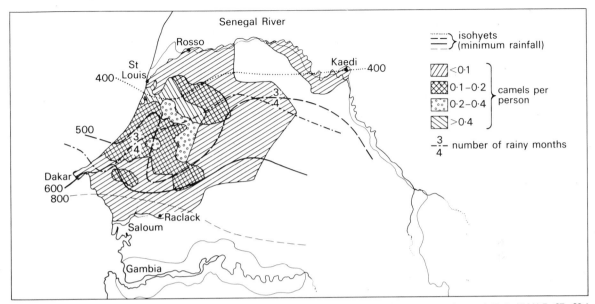

fig. 2.3 The distribution of the camel in Senegal (*Source*: **Rousseau, R**. (1943). *Le chameau au Senegal*. Bull. IFAN **5**, 67 - 69.)

Table 2.3 National and regional camel numbers and density in the Sudan and Kenya. (*Source*: FAO (1978). Production Yearbook Vol. 32. FAO: Rome; **Watson, R. M.** (1972). *Results of aerial livestock Surveys of Kaputei Division, Samburu District and North-eastern Province*. Statistics Division, Ministry of Finance and Planning: Nairobi, Kenya. **Watson, R. M., Tippett, C. I., Rizk, F., Jolly, F., Beckett, J. J., Scholes, V. and Casbon, F.** (1977). *Sudan Livestock Census and Resource Inventory, (Jebel Marra)*, Vol. 31. Range Management and Research Ltd: Nairobi, Kenya.)

Country and region	Land area km[2]	Human population ('000)	Camel population ('000)	Camel density (number per square kilometre)	Camels per person	Camels as per cent of DHB
Sudan[1]	2 494 291	20 511	2 361	0·95	0·12	15·46
Kassala	124 795	1 774	568	4·55	0·32	46·02
Gezira	23 684	1 875	146	6·16	0·08	20·55
North Kordofan	241 351	2 406	842	3·53	0·35	45·73
Five Southern[2] areas	637 098	5 675	71	0·11	0·01	1·59
Kenya[3]	569 250	14 658	574	1·01	0·04	7·76
North-eastern Province	122 911	253	176	1·43	0·70	30·38
Samburu District	20 478		12	0·59		3·48
Kaputei Division	2 862		0	0·00		0·00

1 data from Watson *et al*. (1977), i.e. the same data base as used for the regions
2 Upper Nile, Blue Nile, Jonglei, Equatoria and Bahr el Ghazal
3 data from FAO, 1978, i.e. not the same data base as used for the regions which is Watson (1972).

density is not always correlated either with a high camel to human ratio or with a high percentage of total DHB.

Seasonal variations can also be important, as already mentioned with regard to Senegal. Climatic factors are usually the greatest influence, either primarily, e.g. when rain creates unsuitable soil conditions or secondarily as in the following example. Camels may be forced to move from a particular area because the land is required for crop growing but they may also be drawn into a crop-growing area to fulfil a transport function or because of the availability of supplementary food. Temporal importance expressed as a percentage of DHB depends very much on the movements of other animals, for example, whether these are directly or inversely correlated to camel movements. Table 2.4 gives some data for Darfur province in Sudan for late dry season (April) and late rainy season (September) distribution of camels in relation to some of the factors discussed in this section.

Recent changes in numbers of the world camel population

Some data on changes in camel numbers over the last 30 years or more are given in Table 2.5. In general there has been a steady increase in numbers over the period, which perhaps bodes well for the camel's future. Where numbers have decreased this has been largely for two unrelated reasons. In countries in which oil is now the principal commodity and where the nomadic way of life is no longer the major one there has been a steady decrease in the numbers of camels over recent years; the countries mainly concerned are those of the Persian Gulf, with Libya in Africa showing a similar trend for the same reasons. The second reason for reduction in numbers is the Sahel drought of the 1960s and early 1970s; for example, Mali in Table 2.5. Niger and Mauritania have shown similar trends.

Two rather anomalous countries are Spain and Cyprus. In Spain as recently as 1925 there were an estimated 4 000 camels which probably disappeared during the Civil War while in 1938 Cyprus had 3 000 camels of which none remain.

It would not be correct in every case to interpret reductions in certain countries as net losses to the world's camel populations. Thus from the oil-producing states of the Gulf there has apparently been some movement of camels into the Yemen Arab Republic. The states on the southern edge of the Sahel, especially Upper Volta, but probably also Nigeria and perhaps the Cameroons have received some camels from Mali, Niger and Chad.

Table 2.4 Seasonal variations in the importance of camels and other domestic animals in a part of Darfur province, Sudan. *Source*: **Watson, R. M., Tippett, C. I., Rizk, F., Jolly, F., Beckett, J. J., Scholes, V. and Casbon, F.** (1977). *Sudan Livestock Census and Resource Inventory (Jebel Marra)* Vol. 31. Range Management and Research Ltd: Nairobi, Kenya.)

Class of Stock	Dry season (April)			Wet season (September)		
	Number per square kilometre	Number per person	Per cent of DHB	Number per square kilometre	Number per person	Per cent of DHB
Camels	10·3	0·9	30·5	0·7	0·1	5·3
Cattle	31·5	2·6	62·5	18·4	2·0	89·9
Sheep	13·0	1·1	3·8	0·8	0·1	0·6
Goats	6·7	0·6	1·2	7·0	0·7	3·0
Donkeys	1·5	0·1	1·5	0·2		0·6
Horses	0·2		0·5	0·1		0·6

Table 2.5 Numbers of camels ('000 head) in selected countries for varying periods to 1978 (*Source*: 1 FAO (1970). Production yearbook, Vol. 24. FAO: Rome; 2 **FAO** (1975). Production yearbook, Vol. 29. FAO: Rome: 3 **FAO** (1978). Production yearbook, Vol. 32. FAO: Rome.)

Country or area	Year							
	1932	1940	1950[1]	1960[1]	1965[1]	1970[1]	1975[2]	1978[3]
Africa			7 070	8 051	8 273	8 972	9 624	12 192
Egypt			165	174	176	190		95
Kenya		179	152	173	178	184	530	574
Libya	·		324	252	275	163	120	75
Mali		34	79	172	217	250	160	178
Somalia	800	1 000	2 730	2 560	2 400	2 200	3 089	5 400
Upper Volta			1	3	4	6		86
Asia			2 678	3 054	2 942	3 485	3 545	2 915
Iran			450	247	220	243		27
Saudi Arabia			265	460	490	550	606	108
Yemen Arab Republic			48	54	56	58	120	105
World			9 757	11 105	11 113	12 457	13 169	15 107

The camel in new lands

In the last few centuries, human beings and their domestic animals have expanded into newly discovered lands some of which have been inhospitable to conventional stock. In the extremely harsh environments of parts of southern Africa, the south-western USA and central Australia, the camel has offered possibilities for exploitation unsuited to other domestic animals. Other attempts to introduce the camel have been made or considered in South America, the Caribbean and even in Europe (Fig. 2.1 on p. 16)

Australia

Australia has the second largest expanse of continuous arid land in the world and the potential utility of the camel was appreciated early in the history of the country. Some 50 years after the first European settlement and only 25 years after the crossing of the Blue Mountains into the interior the first suggestions for importation of camels were mooted. This was about 1835 but it was not until October 1849 that the first camel – apparently the only survivor of six shipped from the Canary Islands – arrived at Port Adelaide in South Australia. Two more arrived at Hobart in Tasmania in December of the same year and were later shipped to Melbourne. In spite of considerable public enthusiasm and the offer of a prize of £100 by the Government of Western Australia for the first pregnant camel to be landed, no further animals were imported until 1860. These notes and all that follow in this section are based on McKnight (1969).

In January 1860, 24 camels and three Afghan handlers arrived at Melbourne, Victoria from Karachi. A further six camels of unknown origin also arrived and 26 of the total accompanied the ill-fated attempt by Burke and Wills to make the first south – north crossing of the continent; camels were used afterwards in a number of explorations (Fig. 2.4). The first large-scale importation was made by an eminent pastoralist, Sir Thomas Elder;

fig. 2.4 An Australian stamp paying tribute to the camel in the exploration of the country

breeding stock. Over the next 70 years there were numerous other importations but the Elder stock continued to be preferred.

By 1895 there were probably some 6 000 camels (including a very small number of Bactrians) in Australia. While actual figures are difficult to find, Table 2.6 gives some data on the Australian camel population for the 70-year period from 1890 to 1960. After 1960 very few camels remained under domestic conditions. In 1966 there were probably about 400 camels owned by Aborigines in the Northern Territory, Western Australia and Southern Australia in addition to just under 100 working on stations in the same areas and another 70 or so pet and retired camels.

But these were not, and are still not, the only remaining Australian camels. The first feral camels in Australia were two abandoned by the Burke and Wills expedition. Feral camels probably reached their peak in numbers in the late 1930s and early 1940s, some time after the peak of domestic camels. By the 1960s feral camels, perhaps 15 000 – 20 000 of them (possibly even up to 90 000 head) were thinly spread over an area of more than

the animals (a mixed bunch of 121 camels, 28 donkeys, 80 sheep, 3 cattle and 1 quagga) were landed at Port Augusta, from Karachi, in 1866. The shipment was accompanied by 31 Afghan handlers. The camels were of mixed types – riding, light and heavy pack animals – and although 59 of the camels died of mange in a short time the remaining animals formed the basis of the Australian

Table 2.6 Camel numbers reported for Australia 1890–1960. (*Source*: **McKnight, T. L.** (1969). *The camel in Australia.* Melbourne University Press: Melbourne, Australia.)

Year	State					Total Australia
	South Australia	West Australia	Queensland	New South Wales	Northern Territory	
1890		45				
1895		3 456				
1900		3 246				
1905		2 413				
1910	2 870	3 443	656	1 013		8 426
1915	4 300	4 938	855	1 698		12 389
1920	4 217	5 995	740	1 172		12 649
1925	2 994	5 594	480	368	452	9 904
1930	1 360	3 623	215	554	562	6 187
1935	737	2 182	453	340	298	4 179
1940	516	1 063		245	220	2 267
1945					298	
1950					94	
1955					59	
1960					40	

1·5 million km^2 in the arid heart of Australia. Because of their liking for the extreme arid and remote areas they were rarely seen. In normal times they did not compete with other domestic stock; they browsed at higher levels and ate food not usually eaten by other animals, including eucalyptus and mulga (*Acacia aneura*). In addition they could survive for months on end in the cool season, without access to water, by browsing a succulent shrub called paraheelya (*Calandrinia balonensis*). This is similar to the situation of *gizu* grazing in Sudan (see Chapter 9). There were times, nonetheless, when they came into conflict with established stock: they used common grazing around townships, they destroyed fences and, in time of extreme drought, they competed for precious water supplies. A Camels Destruction Act was passed in 1925 to allow for the removal of unclaimed and unmarked camels and many thousands of camels were shot as a result of this legislation. In the drought of 1961–2 more than 1 150 camels were shot at only three water holes.

Despite the relatively small numbers involved, the camel has played an important role in the development of Australia. In this respect its contribution to the development of a modern economy (as opposed to sustaining a traditional one) is perhaps unique. It is strange that it has hardly ever been used to provide meat or milk nor as an agricultural beast for ploughing, but it has been used for almost everything else. From its initial role as a life support adjunct for exploration – in which role it was used as late as the 1960s and even more recently, as a press gimmick in the 1970s – it developed into a general transport animal. As a pack animal it carried sleepers for the Transcontinental Railway, wire and poles for the telegraph, and netting and posts for rabbit-proof and state boundary fences. For some 30 years, the camel also carried almost all Australia's wool from remote sheep stations to railheads. The railway also provided the camel with a further role, perhaps its most important in Australia. As a draft animal, yoked sometimes 20 animals to a cart, the camel was able to move heavy machinery as well as general supplies to the mineral deposits, and to move ore back to the railway (Fig. 2.5). It also supplied remote townships with many basic necessities

fig. 2.5 Camel being loaded up to carry a heavy load in Australia

fig. 2.6 Camels in Australia being used to transport supplies along an unmetalled road

more surely under the difficult conditions prevailing, and at more competitive rates, than horse or donkey-drawn wagons (Fig. 2.6). With the post-war development of Australia in the 1960s, and later, new roads and closer settlement, the camel has been on the decline for a relatively long period. Policemen and postmen, among the last users in the late 1950s and 1960s, and using a *pakra* (Fig. 2.7), are now motorised although there are stories, perhaps not entirely apocryphal, of camels still being used to rescue bogged-down vehicles.

fig. 2.7 A riding camel with a *pakra* saddle

The camel may continue to play some role in the Australian economy. Other feral, as well as wild, animals are being managed in the remote areas for meat, usually to provide petfood. A rational exploitation of the camel might well be possible for this purpose in addition to its current roles as an Aboriginal mount and a pleasure beach joy-ride.

While Australia represents the most successful attempt to introduce camels to areas outside the palaearctic deserts it is far from being the only one and it is certainly worthwhile to consider a few others.

The USA
The first camels were imported to North America as curiosities as early as 1701 when two were brought to Virginia by a slave trader and two others were taken to Salem about the same time (Dareste, 1857). However, serious consideration was not given to the economic importation of the camel until 1836, (Lesley, 1929). In the early days, the intended use of the camel was for exploration, similar to the role it played in Australia, and indeed its first importation was at about the same time. The possibilities of using the camel as a military animal were quickly recognised and in 1848 it was suggested for the first time that the camel might be used for the pacification of the West. After some discussion in Congress an appropriation of US$30 000 was made, little of which was actually used. The military officer entrusted with the mission then set off in search of camels – stopping off in London and Paris to learn all he could about them!

A total of 34 camels (2 Bactrian, 1 hybrid and 31 dromedaries) was landed in Texas in 1856 and a further 44 in the following year. Some camels were imported privately in 1858 but the military importations remained the most important ones and a herd of camels belonging to the army was established at Camp Verde, some 97 kilometres north-west of San Antonio on the Mexico–United States border. Perhaps unfortunately from the camel's point of view the Civil War intervened and in 1866 the remaining 66 of the Camp Verde herd were sold at $31 per head. Little is known of their subsequent fate although between 20 and 30 were caught in 1877 near Tucson, Arizona, and used as pack animals; two more were seen in 1907 in Nevada; and there were unconfirmed reports of sightings as late as 1929 (Legge, 1936). The reason for the failure of camels in the USA can perhaps, at least in part, be related to the fact that no-one familiar with the animals was taken to America to handle them – a factor which undoubtedly contributed to their successful use in Australia.

South and Central America and the Caribbean
Several minor attempts were made to introduce the camel into Latin America, the earliest (to Peru from the Canary Islands) in the middle of the sixteenth century. This attempt was frustrated by complaints from slave traders about the possible effects of competition for transport. The first camels imported to Brazil arrived in 1793 and although this was the most important attempt several others were made, notably one in 1859 when 4 males and 10 females were landed after a passage of 14 days from Algiers. This latter importation failed because the Arab handlers brought over to care for the animals were apparently incapable of doing so, disease broke out and the animals died (Legge, 1936).

Two other South American attempts are worthy of note. An introduction to Venezuela from the

Canary Islands with the intention that they should be used for carrying cane failed because a number of the camels died from snake bite (Dareste, 1857). Bolivia imported 30 head in 1845 which had multiplied to about 100 by 1864, although what subsequently became of them is not clear (Legge, 1936).

In the Caribbean camels were imported to Barbados as early as 1675 and to Jamaica before 1774 where they survived at least 50 years eventually succumbing to the effects of the jigger flea (Legge, 1936). In Cuba there were 70 camels in 1841 which at that time were used for carrying copper ore but were subsequently used for carrying cane (Dareste, 1857).

Southern Africa

Both Germany and Britain attempted introductions into southern Africa towards the very end of the nineteenth century. Britain's attempts to introduce 14 riding and 44 baggage camels from India into Zimbabwe (Rhodesia) were less energetic and less successful than the German attempts in South-West Africa and in present-day Botswana (Fig. 2.8). The first introductions to South-West Africa were from the Canaries in 1898. A further 500 were later brought from there and 2 000 from Somalia (Legge, 1936). About 60 camels are still used for police work in Botswana (Simpson, 1979) and two bulls were imported from northern Cape Province in 1977 in order to change the blood lines (Simpson, personal communication). Camels in this area probably failed because the introduction was attempted too late: motor transport became available soon after their arrival and before they became established.

Europe

Apart from the early Muslim importations into Spain a royal stud was in existence at Aranjuez at least as early as 1786 and this herd was still in existence up to the Spanish Civil War. Various other importations are known to have been made including 30 to Barcelona in 1831 (Graells, 1854). In France a number of camels were used in the salt mines of the Midi in the middle of the nineteenth

fig. 2.8 Camels in the Kalahari desert

century and some attempts to introduce them to Germany were also made.

The most prolonged European enterprise other than in Spain took place, however, in Italy. Camels were imported from Tunis or possibly (according to another authority), from India about 1622, by Ferdinand II of Medici (Cochi, 1858). The Italian camels were subject to varying fortunes and in the early eighteenth century their numbers had fallen to six. Further importations enabled their numbers to increase to 196 head by the end of the eighteenth century. A further setback occurred in the very cold winter of 1811–2 but the Tuscany camels survived right through until World War II.

Finally it might be worth mentioning that a serious proposal to introduce Bactrian camels to Britain was made as late as 1861 (Swinhoe, 1861), and that an attempted introduction of the dromedary to Java failed when the animals all succumbed to a liver disease (Saint-Hilaire, 1861).

Further reading

Cochi, I. (1858). *Sur la naturalisation du dromadaire en Toscane. Bull. Soc. Imp. Zool. Acclimatation*, **5**, 479–483.

Dareste, A. (1857). *Rapport sur l'introduction projetée du dromadaire au Brésil. Bull. Soc. Imp. Zool. Acclimatation*, **4**, 190–215.

Graells, M. P. (1854). *Sur l'acclimatation des animaux en Espagne. Bull. Soc. Imp. Zool. Acclimatation*, **2**, 109–116.

Legge, C. M. (1936). The Arabian and the Bactrian camel. *J. Manchester Geogr. Soc.*, **46**, 21–48.

Lesley, L. B. (1929). *Uncle Sam's camels*. Harvard University Press: Cambridge, Massachusetts, USA.

McKnight, T. L. (1969). *The camel in Australia*. Melbourne University Press: Melbourne, Australia.

Rousseau, R. (1943). *Le chameau au Sénégal. Bull. IFAN*, **5**. 67–79.

Saint-Hilaire, I. G. (1861). *Acclimatation et domestication des animaux utiles*. Librairie Agricole de la Maison Rustique: Paris, France.

Simpson, V. R. (1979). Bluetongue antibody in Botswana's domestic and game animals. *Trop. Anim. Hlth Prod.*, **11**, 43–49.

Swinhoe, R. (1861). *Narrative of the North China Campaign of 1860*. Smith, Elder: London.

3 Types and breeds

"There is undoubtedly something about the camel which is at first repulsive, not merely in its odour, but in its peculiarly reptilian appearance. He has been very aptly described as resembling a cross between a snake and a folding camp-bedstead."

Hira, 1947.

A general classification

In almost all species of domestic animals differentiation into types or breeds started soon after domestication was achieved. Animals were selected for specific economic traits resulting in morphological changes, particularly size, shape and colour. These changes have often been used to establish more or less precise dates and places of initial domestication.

In the camel no, or very few, such changes took place when it was first domesticated (see Chapter 1). Even in modern times there has been very little selection into what can truly be considered as breeds, and virtually no specialisation into separate functions for meat or milk production. Exceptions to this generalisation can, of course, be found but such lack of specialised functions undoubtedly reflects the uniformly difficult conditions in which camels have to find their existence.

The argument of Bulliet (1975) that camels were first domesticated in southern Arabia, by a people who had no other domestic animals for milk production, may well have some substance. It is, however, in the transport role that specialisation has occurred to the greatest extent and the simplest classification of camels is into heavy transport and riding types, with possible further subdivisions of the heavy type into hill and plains types.

The concept of upland and lowland types introduces the possibility of a different classification based primarily on habitat and only secondarily on function, as opposed to primary functional classification with a secondary habitat division. The two systems are shown in Fig. 3.1; the basic

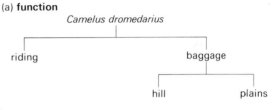

(a) **function**

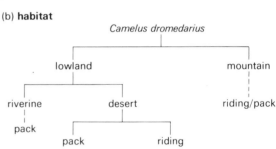

(b) **habitat**

fig. 3.1 Two possible general classifications of camels based on a) function, and b) habitat

concepts for this figure are derived from Leese (1927).

It needs to be noted that there is no geographical differentiation in either of the classifications. Some distinctions of geography can be implied, however. The mountain type is virtually confined to India, Pakistan and the northern limits of the camel in Asia. The lowland, on the other hand, is widely distributed and covers a wide range of habitats (ecological zones) and functions. The riverine camels of the Pakistan Sind and the Egyptian delta, for example, have much more in common with each other than either of them has with

31

Table 3.1 Principal physical characters of lowland and mountain camels

Character	Camel type	
	Lowland	Mountain
Overall size	large	small
Height at withers(m)	1·93 – 2·13 +	1·82 – 1·96
Conformation	rangy	compact
Neck and legs	long	short
Hindquarters	light, sloping	well developed
Feet	oval, usually soft	round, hard
Coat	short, fine	long, coarse

Table 3.2 Conformation and performance differences between riverine and desert camels

Trait	Camel type	
	Riverine	Desert
Head	coarse, Roman nose	small, fine muzzle
Bone and muscle	heavy, solid	finer, less muscular
Carrying capacity	very heavy loads	lighter loads, people
Speed	slow	faster

their nearest desert neighbours (Williamson and Payne, 1978). Some of the main physical traits of the mountain and lowland camels are shown in Table 3.1. Further distinctions between riverine and desert types are made in Table 3.2. While it might be more correct to discuss camels in terms of ecotypes, associated perhaps to particular ethnic groups, it will be more convenient to use breed as a term which is more easily understood. It should be remembered nonetheless that, apart from exceptional cases, few breed characteristics that would be understood in other branches of animal husbandry actually exist. Mason (1951) makes no attempt to list camel breeds and in a later collaborative work says that no true breeds are recognised but that camels are named after the tribes that breed them (Mason and Maule, 1960). As a final indication of the difficulty even very experienced camel men have in distinguishing breed types let us give

the last word to Leese: '*Wasms* or tribal brands are of particular importance in Arabia, Egypt and the Sudan; types can often be identified with the help of these marks'.

Conformation of riding and pack types

Riding types

Leese (1927) gives the following description.

Head: small with fine muzzle, small lips, ears small set close together, eyes alert, lower jaw deep below the eye. The head should be carried so that the bridge of the nose is on a level with the poll.

Neck: fine and supple, joined to trunk low down.

Shoulder: long and fine.

Chest: very deep, ribs well sprung right to the back and terminating not far from the pelvic bone.

Forelegs: fairly close together, straight, must not 'brush' at the knees and must not have turned out feet.

Hindlegs: straight with no tendency to cow hocks [i.e. the hocks must be well spaced apart].

Quarters: well muscled, the tail set high.

Feet: neither too small nor too large.

Skin: fine and supple.

Pace: easy and tireless, should not have to be driven.

Pack or baggage types

Baggage camels should not have any of the faults which would be inadmissible in riding camels, such as brushing knees or sickle hocks. In general they are much coarser animals than riding types with a heavier head and neck, better formed quarters and less narrow in the gut. Legs may be shorter, bone heavier and feet larger than in riding camels. The pace is shorter and slower than that of the riding camel but should be equally tireless.

A representative cross-section of some of the world's camel types giving size and weight where known is given in Table. 3.3.

Camels of the Indian sub-continent

If it is true that Leese (1927) has been made

Table 3.3 Physical data of some of the main camel types and breeds

Country	Habitat type	Function	Breed name	Height (m)		Weight (kg)		Notes
				shoulder	hump	male	female	
Afghanistan	mountain	pack	Northern	2·01		500		very big for mountain type
India	lowland/riverine	pack		2·13				
India	mountain/lowland	pack	(Dera Ismael Khan)	1·90		660		
Sudan	lowland/desert	pack	Arab				450	may weigh considerably more
Sudan/Eritrea	lowland/desert	riding	Bishari	1·92/2·00				
India	lowland/desert	riding/pack	Bikaneri	1·98/2·07	2·10/2·30			females smaller
Sudan/Eritrea	lowland/desert	riding/pack	Beni Amer	1·83/2·00				
Eritrea	lowland/desert	pack/riding	Grain	1·80				
Somalia	lowland/desert	(milk)			2·06	350–400		
Somalia	lowland/desert	riding	Mudugh	1·70/1·95				
Somalia	lowland/desert	(milk)	Benadir			554	514	
Libya	lowland/desert	riding	Arab			500		large, heavy riding camel
Mauritania	lowland/desert	riding	Mehari Reguibi	2·00				

generally very much out of date by more reccent work, the same cannot be said of his classification of breeds and types. A number of more recent papers do him the honour of providing long verbatim quotations, unfortunately without any acknowledgement. If it is also true that camels became little differentiated in the first 4 000 years of their domestication there should be no surprise if there is nothing new to be said about breeds.

Leese himself, in effect, remarked on an evolution in the opposite direction. He attributed the decline in the number of breeds to irrigation development (thus making former good camel country unavailable to desert types) and to forest conservation (thus closing areas to hill or mountain breeds). If these trends have continued, and indeed for a long period they undoubtedly accelerated, then it is probable that there are now even fewer breeds than in Leese's time. Additional factors which have contributed to the further blurring of distinctive breed types (and this applies not only in India but almost wherever camels are bred) are the greater ease of communication between camel-owning groups and the decline of importance in general of the camel and more especially as a fast carrier of people.

In India and Pakistan baggage camels are generally known as Ladhu while riding camels are known as Sawari or Mhara. The word *mehara* in various guises is used throughout much of the world's camel areas to distinguish the fast riding camel from all others. A derivative of this word is used in present day Pakistan to describe the easiest pace of the camel at about 12·8 km per hour (Yasin and Abdul Wahid, 1957), a faster pace of 16–24 km per hour being known as *kharwak*. Table 3.4 is an attempt, based mainly on Leese with some very minor additions from other sources, to classify the principal types and breeds of camels in the areas in which they are found (or from which they originate). As a corollary to this table the main distribution areas of the types in India, Pakistan and Afghanistan are shown in Fig. 3.2.

The most celebrated camel in the Indian sub-continent is the Bikaneri, bred in the vicinity of that town in Rajasthan and also in the Punjab. Its homeland is classic desert with 100–200 mm rainfall and temperature variations from 0–50 °C. Leese describes it as the typical desert breed but tending to be heavier than desert types of other countries. It has a fine coat very variable in colour from sandy to almost black. There is a distinct 'step' on the forehead, a slightly upturned nose with a fine muzzle, small ears and a generally small head (Fig. 3.3). It is said to have an intelligent and noble look and the male is said to be capable of passing on his aristocratic conformation to his crossbred progeny. Height at withers in males

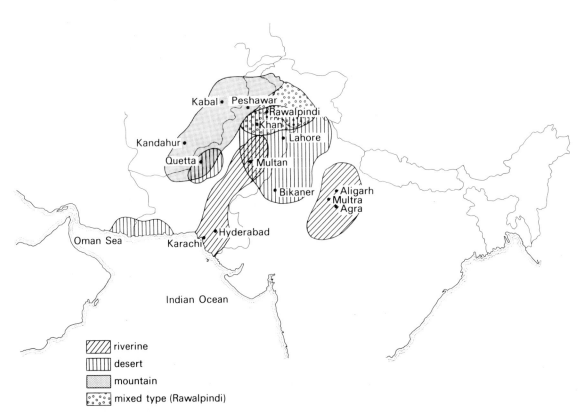

fig. 3.2 Distribution of principal types of camel in the Indian sub-continent

Table 3.4 A classification of types and breeds of camels in the Indian sub-continent (*Source*: **Leese, A. S.** (1927). *A treatise on the one-humped camel in health and disease*. Haynes and Son: Stamford, Lincs, UK.)

Area	Lowland — Riverine	Lowland — Desert Pack	Lowland — Desert Riding	Mountain
India/Pakistan		(Bikaneri)		
Rajputana				
Alwar		(Alwar ———————————————)		
Bahawalpur		(Bahawalpur)		
Agra, Mutra, Aliyarh	(Riverine)			
Chaj, Rachna, Ban, Doabs	(Riverine)			
Dera, Ghazi Khan	Rojani			
Atock, Rawalpindi, Jhelum, Dera Ismael Khan	(Sohama, Bagri, Bari ———————————)			
Peshawar				Frontier
Fatteh Jhang				Kala Chitta
Thall Desert		Thall Mianwali		
Multan	(Multan)			
S.E. Punjab		(Bagri)		
Sind (Hydarabad)	(Riverine)		Thari	
Baluchistan (Quetta)	(Kachee, Mekrani, Brohi, Peshin ———————)			
Aghanistan				Powindah
Kandahar				Kandahar
North Afghanistan				Northern

averages 2·07 m and in females 1·98 m, the height to the top of the hump being generally 0·20 m more. The Bikaneri is not as fast as some Arabian or African riding camels, but has a good steady pace and is capable of carrying considerable weight when compared with other riding types. It is expected to carry two people and often some baggage as well, weights of up to 200 kg being normal for it. It is noted for being phlegmatic, taciturn and indifferent to its surroundings; it has great stamina and considerable adaptability. Females as well as males are ridden (Leese, 1927; Sharma and Bhargava, 1963).

The riding camels of the Sind, called Thari (after the desert of that name) or Parkar are similar in quality to the Bikaneri. There are a few riding camels along the coast near the Pakistan/Iran frontier, these being the Mekrani sub-type of the desert–mountain breeds of Baluchistan.

The Rojan is a typical riverine sub-type of the lowland camel but, after suitable periods of adaptation, is also useful in hill work. The head is well

fig. 3.3 Indian riding camels of the Bikaneri breed

shaped with short lips, the body is thick-set and heavy with good hind-quarters. Intermediate between the riverine and desert pack sub-types is the Multan, a tall, very powerful, pack camel, obviously rather coarse, with a clumsy head but strong forequarters. The riverine camels of the Sind are very variable, the best being found in the Indus delta around Hyderabad. The biggest and strongest are capable of carrying very heavy loads in level country but do not stand up to hill work. The camels in the lower delta browse on mangroves in the flood season as their normal habitat, where they eat tamarisk trees, is plagued by biting flies. North of Hyderabad the riverine camels are smaller and lighter in build. In east Rajasthan and south-west Uttar Pradesh, south of Delhi in the complex of rivers of which the Ganges is the main output,

fig. 3.4 A Punjabi riverine camel

the riverine camels are very big, as high as 2·13 m at the shoulder, and very good weight carriers. They need to be regularly fed and watered and are, therefore, of little use outside their own habitat. A Punjabi riverine camel is shown in Fig. 3.4.

True mountain camels are generally smaller than lowland types, shorter in the leg and more compact. These mainly derive from northern Pakistan, Afghanistan and southwards towards the Sea of Oman along the Iran/Pakistan frontier which is the home of the Baluchi. The Powindah is such a camel: small, hardy and hairy with rather light bone but with a muzzle finer than is common in mountain camels. These camels are driven rather than led and can be unruly. Another mountain type of similar conformation is the Kala Chitta from the Peshawar area in the north of Pakistan. The Northern Camel of Afghanistan is very big (2·01 m at the shoulder) for a mountain camel yet is of classic type in conformation and with very strong bone. They are heavy, with a mane and considerable amounts of hair on the hump, over the shoulders and under the throat. They are usually dark brown to black in colour, with the long hair being black. The head is rather Bactrian in shape but they are true *Camelus dromedarius* and are owned and herded by men as robust and enduring as the camels themselves.

Camels of western and south-western Asia and the Middle East

Little appears to be known about types and breeds in this vast area. One can assume either that even less differentiation has taken place than elsewhere or else that the recording of information has been difficult. There is, of course, a wealth of information in the books of travellers from the time of Doughty, through Philby and Freya Stark to Thesiger, but this is mainly folkloric in nature and contains little information of value in livestock production work. It is also necessary to note that Arabia, the United Arab Emirates and Iran are just those areas where the camel is undergoing the greatest reduction in numbers and where any breeds which did exist are probably disappearing rapidly.

In Arabia proper (Saudi Arabia) camel breeding was in the hands of only a few tribes, the heaviest and largest camels being from the north. In northern and central Arabia, Leese (1927) says, the best riding camels are bred by the Sherarart and by the Huteym; the latter are found to the north-east of Medina. The whole central desert area of the Nafud is famous for camels. The Howeytat is a recognised riding breed of rather small size. Buraidah has always been a great commercial centre for camel sales. The Nejd, south of Riyadh, the Harb and Muteir are local varieties. Arab riding camels are generally considered to be very fast but not good weight carriers and are grass eaters.

Aden, in the Yemen Democratic Republic, used to be the home of a lightly built riding camel, very hardy and of considerable endurance but not very fast and a poor weight carrier. They have a thin, short coat, pale fawn in colour. The riding camel of Oman is tall and fast, it has staying power provided that it is well looked after; females as well as males are ridden. This camel is trained to carry the head low and not to move the hindlegs on the same side exactly in unison with the forelegs, this, so it is said, to make the gait easier.

From southern Arabia the camels of the Al Murrah (Cole, 1975) are famous in their own region and also have given their name to almost any 'thoroughbred' riding camel wherever it occurs, in India (p. 33) and in north and west Africa (p. 47). In the Empty Quarter of Arabia it is held that riding camels (which, as elsewhere, bear tribal names) are descended directly from the Djinn or spirits of the desert, four particularly fine breeds being the Mahri (of the Al Murrah), the 'Umani, almost as good as the first, the 'Idi and the Dhabi (Bulliet, 1975).

Egyptian camels

Egypt is a camel-importing rather than a camel-breeding country. It has a low density of camels, low camel to human ratios and a low contribution to domestic herbivore biomass, DHB (p. 19). Nonetheless camels are of some importance in two very different situations: the Nile delta and along the ribbon of the Nile where they are used to some extent for cultivation but mainly for water-lifting and milling: and in the desert.

The so-called delta camel is not a typical lowland riverine camel and in fact very few are bred in the delta. This is a camel of very varied origin including Sudanese pack camels of mixed strains; the Maghrabi of Libya, itself a camel from several strains; and the country-bred camels from Upper

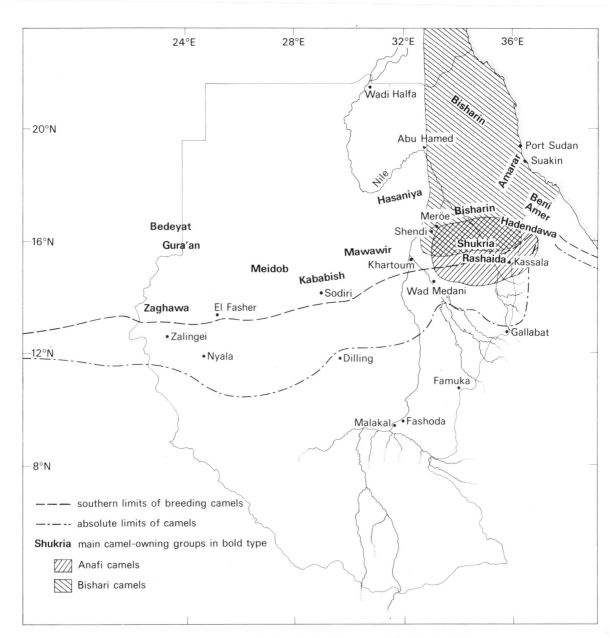

fig. 3.5 The main camel-owning groups in Sudan and the main breeding areas of the Anafi and Bishari riding camels

38

(southern) Egypt. The last are bred, in general, not by the Bedu tribes but by the Fellahin or cultivators. The delta camel should thus not be considered as a distinct breed, even in the vague sense of that term when applied to camels, but as a general-purpose baggage type animal which has become used to green food and plenty of water. It is capable of considerable work output as a result. The appalling specimens paraded before tourists at Giza and at Luxor are not representative of the type.

The oases to the west of the Nile are the homes of good riding types and of medium weight pack animals. In former times many of these animals regularly made the trip on the notorious 'Darb el 'Arbain' or 40-days road between Assiut in Upper Egypt and El Fasher in Darfur. The riding camels bred to the east of the Nile towards the Red Sea coast have much in common with those of the northern Sudan.

Epstein (1971) dignifies the types mentioned for the delta as breeds calling them Sudani, Maghrabi and Fellahi. To these he adds a fourth, the Mowallad, this being a cross between the Maghrabi and Fellahi.

The riding and pack camels of Sudan

Sudan has the second largest number of camels in the world and almost 1½ million km^2 of territory suitable primarily or solely for their use. The approximate southern limit suitable for breeding is about 14°N in the west (in Darfur and Kordofan) and about 16°N in the east. Seasonal movements take camels considerably to the south of these limits, in ever increasing numbers and over longer distances.

While the common classification is into riding and pack types it should be remembered that camels are the basis of the family economy over very large areas and for considerable numbers of people. In such a role they are most important as producers of milk, of some meat for home consumption and for export on the hoof (or on the boat) for slaughter in Egypt, Saudi Arabia and Libya. Fig. 3.5 shows the limits of camel distribution in Sudan and the approximate location of some camel-owning groups and camel breeds.

Riding camels

Most attempts to classify riding camels in Sudan refer only to the Bishari and the Anafi (Bennett, John and Hewison, 1948; Mason and Maule, 1960; Epstein, 1971). Gillespie (1962) who undoubtedly had the longest experience and has given the fullest account of Sudan's riding camels prefers a more detailed classification of the Bishari (in the wider sense) and prefers to make this one of four tribal types which he calls the Red Sea Hills or Beja type. In fact, all the best riding camels in Sudan are found east of the Nile, but the only one bred purely as a riding type, as opposed to selection from within groups, is the Anafi.

The Beja tribes of the eastern Sudan and the Eritrean borderlands breed a distinct type of camel, active, small and hardy. It is not as big as the Omani (p. 37) or Bikaneri (p. 34) camels, nor can it carry as much weight, but it is faster and has more stamina. The Bishari have two types of riding camel, a southern one around Atbara and a northern one in the area of Albai. The former have good conformation but are not as hardy as the northern type and lack their strong feet. The Albai are very much at home in the Red Sea Hills west of Suakin. The Amrat, Aliab and Hamadorab sections of the Bishari have the best northern types while the Eriat and Naafab have the best southern strains. As in Arabia there is a little mythology attached to these camels of which the Kiliwan (a name also given to a strain of Arab horse) and Banagir are owned by the Hamadorab and Aliab sections, respectively.

The Amarar own more camels than the Bisharin although it is said that the camels are not as well bred. Some of those breeds, as Leese (1927) noted, can be separated only by their brands. The camel-owning sections are:

1 the Kurbab - the camels are very small by Sudanese standards but have hard feet.
2 the Nurab - the camels are more variable in conformation and have softer feet as they migrate from the Gash delta, where they spend the summer rains, to the winter-rains grazing in the Red Sea Hills.

The Beni Amer, the Haboub and the Ashraf are

localised in the borderlands of Eritrea and are of mixed pack and riding type.

Three section of the Hadendowa – the Shaabodinab, Ghorhabab and Gemilab – have useful riding camels which are strong and muscular but rather leggy. Their pace is not as smooth as the other Beja breeds and they are not as much in demand as pure riding types.

The Red Sea Hills breeds were the preferred camels for police and army work as they were good stayers even though not very fast. Few detailed descriptions are available of any camels anywhere in terms likely to be understood by livestock specialists or veterinarians. It is perhaps appropriate at this point to give a detailed 'breed standard' of the Bishari (Fig. 3.6) as seen by officers of the Sudan Veterinary Service responsible for the selection and management of government animals.

Head: short, domed forehead, Roman nose, fairly deep muzzle, firm even lips, eyes large and prominent with a bold alert expression, ears small and pointed and kept pricked forward.

Neck: short, muscular, blending well with the shoulders, generally horizontal for about half its length then turning sharply upwards. Full bone and muscle not achieved until 8 years of age.

Shoulders: deep, strong, well covered, the muscles of the chest and upper forearm well developed, elbow well clear of lower chest, a definite slope to the shoulder (the last is desirable in the horse but appears difficult to achieve in the camel).

Chest: wide, ribs well sprung and reaching far back.

Back and loins: former short, latter full and well developed (again difficult to achieve in a camel).

Rump: drooping and of medium length (unlike the horse).

Thighs: broad, full and thick.

Legs and feet: muscular forearm, strong heavy bones and knee joint, hocks fairly straight, strong, close together, rear cannon bone flat to ground, feet even and straight in front, turned out behind, sole tough and horny and showing even wear.

fig. 3.6 A Bishari riding camel from the Red Sea Hills, Sudan

fig. 3.7 An Anafi riding camel from near Kassala in eastern Sudan

Hair: short, more allowed on females and young, castrates may have profuse hair on the hump.

Colour: white to red but usually light sandy dun with some admixture of black hairs.

Locomotion: normal walk and run with each animal having its own best pace but usually about 8 km per hour (in the original version Gillespie (1962) spoke of a camel that had a best pace of 16 km per hour and remarked that such animals are usually not for sale).

The Anafi (Fig. 3.7), as we have said, is the only camel bred specifically as a distinct riding breed. It is bred by the Rashaida in the Butana grassland area east of Atbara and also by the Shukria (Epstein, 1971, gives it this name), Lahawia and Batahin who rear pack camels as well. It is altogether lighter than the Red Sea Hills breeds with a long, narrow head and a low, domed forehead that is a mark of the breed. It is mainly a grazing type and only does really well where grass is available. Its speed has been achieved by sacrificing strength and stamina (it was described by Bennett, John and Hewison (1948) as the cameline equivalent of the the five-furlong (about 1 km) sprinter). It was rarely able to carry the weight of an average officer in the police or army but was often the pride of the traditional owner.

Pack camels

Almost all the tribes of Arab descent in the northern Sudan breed camels. These are generally referred to as 'Gemala' – camel owners, as opposed to the 'Baqqara' – cattle owners. The Baqqara have their main areas of strength in western South Kordofan and in South Darfur; they use camels for pack purposes on occasion but rarely breed them.

The Sudanese pack camel, from whatever source, is normally simply referred to as the Arab. These are fairly big camels often weighing well over 500 kg, usually sandy grey or fawn, occasionally with long hair on the hump and shoulders. The head is big with a pronounced Roman nose (Fig. 3.8) and in good condition the hump is well developed.

In the east the Rashaida have developed (or have retained since their fairly recent arrival in Sudan from Arabia) a distinctive breed of pack camel

fig. 3.8 An Arab pack camel from Sudan

which is named the Rashaidi. The main features which distinguish it from the Arab are its pinkish red colour, its shorter legs and its faster pace. In spite of its slightly smaller size and its relative speed, weight-carrying capacity has not been sacrificed and it is at least as capable as the common Arab in this respect.

Camels in Ethiopia and Eritrea

The central highland mass of Ethiopia is unsuitable for continuous occupation by camels and very few are found there except for specific short-term transport purposes. Camels, therefore, are confined to the peripheral lowlands, the camel-owning groups usually being found not only in political Ethiopia but also in neighbouring countries. The camels of lowland Eritrea have thus much in common with those of the Sudan and those of the Ogaden are identical with the Somali types found in proximity to them.

Various classifications of Eritrean camels have appeared, some based on tribes and some on colours. Droandi (1921) preferred the former system and called the riding types the 'racing' or 'trotting' camels (*il cammelli corridori*). These are mostly found in the Barca or lowland frontier area on the Sudan border. He describes the riding types as being similar to 'Mehari' but refuses to give them this specific name on account of the lack of true breeding lines and the diverse origin of the camels.

He was, of course, basing his classification on the needs of the Italian colonial forces and pointing out possible sources of supply. Among the qualities sought was a regularity of pace and endurance at an average 8–10 km per hour over a whole day's march.

The tribal types are almost all referable to the Sudanese ones. The Bisciari (Bishari) provides the greatest number of riding camels, since they are very easy to train, females as well as males being used for riding. They are tall and fast and usually white in colour. In Eritrea the Amnafi (Anafi) appears to have been subjected to less intensive selection as a pure riding breed than in Sudan, it being described as bigger, stronger but not so fast as the Bisciari. The Amnafi, nonetheless, still provide considerable numbers of riding camels. Other tribal breeds of mixed type but from which riding camels can be selected are: Cabbaci (which appears to be equivalent to the Atbara sections of the Bishari); Beni Amer, very strong camels useful on any kind of terrain, with reasonable speed and described as the true 'country' camels, presumably meaning little real attention is paid to their breeding; and the Sceraf which provide a few very good riding animals. Other riding camels may be selected from the Danakil type but are best used in their own region.

When described by colour (Marchi, 1929) the Anafi is called Tzedi (white) and the Beni Amer is referred to as Cajeh (red) these being the Tigrina (and not Beja) words for these colours. A small camel along the Red Sea coast, known as Grain (sandy) is mainly a pack animal with a few riding types occasionally being selected from among the group.

The Afar or Danakil of the Danakil lowlands (in Italian: *Dancalia*) also keep considerable numbers of camels and fill the gap between the mainly Beja camel owners of the north and the Somali tribes of the south-east. The Afar keep their camels, as do the Somali, almost entirely for milk production but a few males are used for the trade in salt from the Dalol salt plains (Marchi calls the Afar camels Arho after another name for these plains). The Afar camel is very small and capable of carrying weights up to about 120 kg (Wilson, 1976).

The general areas of distribution of Ethiopian camels and of other types found in north-east Africa are shown in Fig. 3.9.

The milk camels of Somalia

Ethnic Somali live not only in Somalia but also in considerable numbers in Kenya and in the Ogaden region, the latter being augmented seasonally by migrants. In total they own more than 5 million camels. A Somali camel is shown in Fig. 3.10.

Unique among camel-owing peoples, the Somali, and the geographically close Afar, maintain large herds of camels almost solely for milk production (Fig. 3.11). Camels are occasionally used for transport purposes but when used in this manner by the Somali themselves it is rarely for anything other than moving camp. Somali camels can be trained as riding animals and a 'saddle' camel is described from Mijirtein (*Miguirtinia* in Italian) right on the Horn of Africa. The British Administration in northern Somalia, the former Somaliland Protectorate, preferred to import riding camels from India, Arabia or Sudan. Perhaps because Somali camels are not used to any extent for pack or riding, a considerable number of

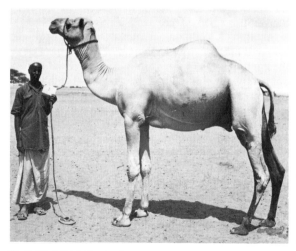

fig. 3.10 A Somali camel

42

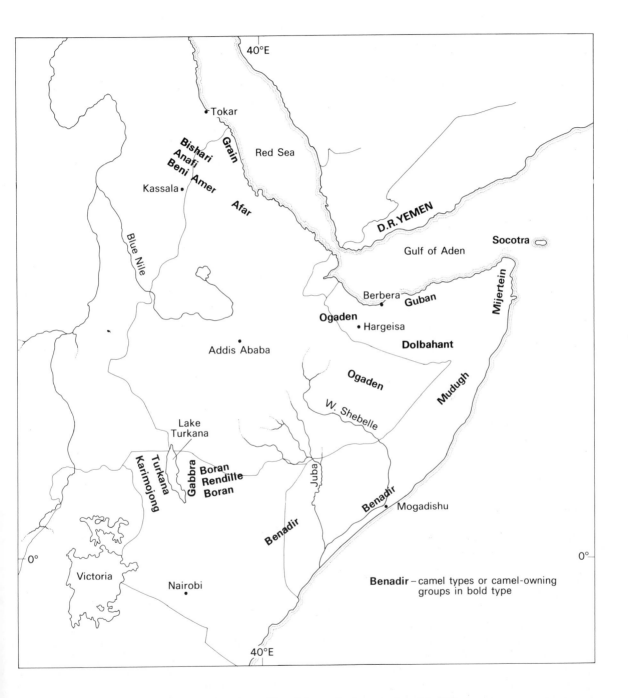

fig. 3.9 Distribution of camel-owning groups and camel breeds in north-eastern and eastern Africa

fig. 3.11 A milking camel of Somalia

males are castrated. These grow very big humps and used to be slaughtered and eaten locally and on ceremonial occasions. In recent years a more commercial attitude has developed and increasing numbers of camels are being sold and exported (Swift, 1979).

Breed classification

The Somali recognise two types, the Gel Ad and the Ayyum (Epstein, 1971). The former is white in colour and is presumably more or less equivalent to the Benadir in the classification in Table 3.5: the Ayyum is darker and said by Epstein to be bigger and worth more than the Gel Ad.

Because the Somali camel is primarily a milk animal there is little differentiation of type and the classification is rather confused. A synthesis of the classifications of Leese (1927), Bettini (1940), Bozzi and Triulzi (1953), and Rossetti and Congiu (1955) is given in Table 3.5 although conceptually the table owes much to Mason and Maule (1960).

A Somali exception: the 'saddle' camel

There are always exceptions to generalisations and the Somali milk camel is not exempt from this. While the British imported riding camels to the part of Somalia they occupied, the Italians selected local animals. These camels belonged in the main to the Mijirtein clan of the Mudayl type. In Somali they are called *recūb* to distinguish them from *safar* – pack camels, and from *bargab* – bulls. It is to be noted that 'saddle' camels were only named as such when they showed characteristics which fitted them to be riding or racing camels.

In general these characteristics are those that we have come to recognise from the riding camels of India and Sudan. The height at the shoulder varies between 1·75 m and 1·90 m, a measurement which confirms the small stature of the camels of northern Somalia. The head is small in relation to the body and set on a fairly short neck, a narrow but deep chest and a long back furnished with a small hump. It should have a tight abdomen, sloping sharply upwards. The legs, especially the hind ones, should be well muscled. The feet should be small, well cushioned and resistant enough to permit passage over any kind of terrain. In short it should have a lively air about it, be nimble, harmonious, slim and elegant and in spite of its small size be possessed of strength and stamina (Tarantino, 1934).

Somali-type camels in neighbouring countries

The majority of camels in Kenya are owned by ethnic Somalis and are mainly of the Benadir type. Other camel-owning tribes are the Rendille, Turkana, Gabbra (whose camels are small and compact), and Boran. In addition to milk, some of these animals are bled (Chapter 10) and some used for pack work. A very few are ridden by police patrols.

There are camels on the island of Socotra which Leese (1927) describes in four words, 'These are hill camels'. The only other apparent source of information (HMSO, 1920) describes them as very fine camels. Little, obviously, is known about them, a fact which may be of minor importance in view of their small numbers.

Table 3.5 A classification of Somali camels by main types, clan groups and locality

Main type	Clan group(s)	Other names	Locality	Notes
Dolbahanta			South-east of Hargeisa (Ain and Nogal Valleys)	similar to Ogaden and Mudugh
Guban			Gulf of Aden coast	small, poorly fleshed; can survive on very poor fodder
Ogaden		Eidime(Beras)	Somalia – Ethiopia border	largest camel in former Somaliland Protectorate: very pale
Mudugh	Mijertein Galjaal Nogal Mudugh	Gel Medu or Eidime (Beras)	extreme North-east Upper Wabi Shebelle South-east of Hargeisa North-central coastal plain	smaller than Benadir; Bozzi and Triulzi (1953) apparently consider Ogaden and Mudugh to be same major type
Benadir	Garre Helai Bimal	Gel Ad Fili Sifdar	Middle Wabi Shebelle, Central Coast Doi Lower Juba	largest camel in whole of ethnic Somali territory: pale coloured, large head, strong neck, good spring of rib, large abdomen and feet, hump varies; Bimal is smallest animal of clan groups; the Sifdar of Bozzi and Triulzi (1953) is bred by Garre, Bartireh, Ajurran and Debarre groups and appears equivalent to the Benadir
		Hor Godir	North-central Somalia Mudugh area	classed only by Bozzi and Triulzi (1953) and difficult to identify with any main type of other classifications; possibly pet names as *hor* is badger and *godir* is kudu

The Mediterranean littoral and its hinterland

Libya

The general-purpose pack type of the north-east coastal plains, known in Egypt as in Libya under the general title of Maghrabi has already been dealt with (p. 37). Libya is one of the few African countries in which there has been a significant decline in camel numbers due largely, in all probability, to increased oil revenues.

Formerly the main oases had considerable numbers of camels and these were named after the particular oasis from which they originated. The Fezzan are small to medium sized camels, light in colour and with short hair and, like those of Tripoli, Cussabat, Chanyan and Jebel Tarhum, are dual purpose riding/pack types. The western oases peopled by the Urfilla and the Awlad Busaif breed more specialised riding camels which are in general heavier (500 kg) than most other African riding types.

Tunisia

In Tunisia, as in Algeria and Morocco, if Bulliet (1975) is to be believed, the camel did not replace the wheel which was already too well established by the time camels first arrived (or were re-introduced) in these western countries. Instead the camel was trained to adapt to the wheel and to agricultural work, roles which it still fulfils to-day in populated and cultivated areas. These areas are confined to a small region in the north of the country and along the eastern coast, the camels usually being hand fed and only one or two belonging to any one owner.

It is doubtful if it is valid to classify the camels of Tunisia by breed, a more practical classification would be by area and method of management. Based rather loosely on the work of Burgemeister (1975), three classes can be defined.

1 The camel trained to the plough and the cart.
2 A camel found in the central part of the country in the area of olive and vine culture, used to some extent for cultivation and owned in lots of up to 15 head. These animals forage for themselves but are also fed on barley and prickly pear (*Opuntia indica var. inermis*).
3 In the south on the beginnings of the Grand Erg Oriental, the camels are managed in large herds on open rangeland of two principal types: desert grassland on sandy and stony soils; and salt-bush grazing including species of *Salsola, Suaeda* and *Tamarix*. In addition to providing mounts for the Tunisian forces of law and order these camels are a resevoir of animals for the two categories above.

Algeria and Morocco

Both Algeria and Morocco are countries of very varied habitat from the rich coastal hinterlands known as the *tell*, through the mountains of the Atlas to the vast expanses of the Sahara. All camels appear to be of the lowland/desert type and in general a classification along similar lines to the one proposed for Tunisia would appear to be the most appropriate. Because of the varied habitats, attempts have been made in the past to equate Algerian and Moroccan camels to Indian ones. Leese (1972) suggested that the *tell* camels should be separated into riverine and desert types. More recently it has been said that Moroccan camels have become so acclimatised to the mountains that they are useless in the desert (Epstein, 1971) but it is not clear that these should be labelled mountain camels on account of this.

Local environmental types have always existed in north-west Africa even where the function has remained the same. The example of the caravan trade from Algeria to northern Nigeria demonstrates this. From the Atlas mountains to the Tidikelt group of oases in the In-Salah area the 'Northern' camel was used, a total distance (over 14 degrees of latitute from 36°N to 22°N) of almost 1 200 km. Through the central mountain ranges of the Hoggar and the Aïr the type was referred to as the 'Hoggar' and covered a much shorter distance of about 500 km. The last stage of 700 km from Iférouane through Agadès to Kano was accomplished by the 'Southern' camel (Gautier and Chudeau, 1909). All three types are probably referable to lowland/desert type with a mainly pack function (Fig. 3.12).

The Western Sahara, Mauritania, Mali, Niger and Chad

These are the areas of the romantic novels of the

fig. 3.12 A bank note recognising the importance of camels as pack animals in Algeria

desert, of Beau Geste and of the dashing French camel troops. It is undoubtedly true that the French had some influence on camel breeding in these areas for a short period of time, but few men were involved and the majority of troops were native, mounted on (and responsible for) camels which were their own personal property. These troops were known as Meharists and their camels as Mehari, which in former French Africa means 'thoroughbred' as it does elsewhere among camel-owning peoples. But the camels were a mixed lot, depending much on the locality from which they came, with only a few units having constant blood lines. The most celebrated of these were the Reguib of north-west Mauritania. The heterogeneous nature of the camels is amply illustrated by the standards laid down for remounts for Meharist squadrons: while the best camels go as tall as 2·00 m at the shoulder anything over 1·90 m would be suitable for an officer, 1·85 m for the rank and file and anything less but with a minimum of 1·80 m could be used as pack (Boué, 1950).

Table 3.6 A breed classification of West African camels (*Source*: **Doutressoulle, G.** (1947). *L'Elevage en Afrique Occidentale Francaise*. Imprimerie du Mortainais: Mortains, France; **Boué, A.** (1948). *Les chameaux de l'ouest saharien. Rev. Elev. Méd. vét. Pays Trop*., **2**, 193–201; and others.)

Breed	Locality/Owners	Function	Notes
Steppe	Western Sahara	pack	poor quality, tires easily; badly managed by owners
Awlad Sidi	Western Sahara	pack/riding	better quality, good in both rocks and sand, shoulder 1·80–1·85
Chambi (Bani Abbès)	West of Grand Erg Occidental	pack	solid, small 1·65 at shoulder; vigorous and untiring on dunes
Chambi (El Golea)	Chambi Oasis (South Algeria)	pack/riding	
Saharawi	North of Grand Erg Occidental	pack/riding	good feet, vigorous with easy pace; shoulder 1·85
Ayt Khebbach	Western Sahara	pack	powerful, good bone and muscle; well managed
Mehari Reguibi	Western Sahara (Mauritania)	riding	light coloured, 2·00 at shoulder; 'The Reguibi seduces by his class'
Manga	North of Lake Chad	heavy pack	unfit for hard conditions such as desert or mountain
Tibesti	North Chad/ Toubous	pack/riding	very small but good on sandy or stony desert
Aïr	North Niger/ Tuareg	riding	tall, lightly built; similar to Mehari
Berabish	North-west of Timbuctoo/ Berabish	pack	heavy build, not very tall, capable of heavy loads
Adrar n Iforas	North Mali/ Tuareg	riding	similar to Aïr and Mehari
Azwad	Mali–Niger/ Tuareg	heavy riding	solid, stolid riding animal
Hodh	Mali–Mauritania/ Moor	fast riding	very tall 2·10; similar to other riding types
Gandiol	Mauritania–Senegal	heavy pack	good feed of Senegal river valley results in heavy animal

All West African camels, including the few in Senegal, are of lowland/desert type. They are generally pack or dual-purpose type since caravans and particularly salt transport were (and to a considerable extent still are) more important in the desert economy than warfare. A limited number is selected from within these as riding animals and an even fewer number specially bred as fast riding camels. In Table 3.6 there is a summary of the main breeds of West African camels acording to function and distribution.

Interspecific hybrids

Present-day camels are classed as two species, *Camelis dromedarius* and *C. bactrianus*, because formerly it was thought that hybridisation between them was not possible. On this premise being proved false, it was then assumed that the offspring of the cross must be infertile and that the two-species structure should be maintained. Now that this latter myth has also been dispelled there is no reason, other than established usage, for maintaining the animals as distinct species. We will not enter into the argument as taxonomic considerations, fortunately, do not concern us here.

Most of the scientific work on hybridisation has been done in southern Russia where the two species of camel are sympatric. Crossbreds have been known for a long time in Turkey, in northern Iran and in Afghanistan. In all those areas they fulfil specific roles.

History of hybrids
The development of hybridisation probably began under the Parthians about 2200 BP and grew increasingly important as traffic along the Silk Route increased (Bulliet, 1975). In the first centuries of the Islamic period in Asia, *Camelus bactrianus* continued to be bred south of the main trade routes which passed through northern Iran to east-central Asia but in the later years they were kept primarily to produce hybrids. It is probable that for a considerable period neither the one-humped nor the two-humped species was preferred. During the nineteenth century Syria regularly imported *C. bactrianus* males from Anatolia (Turkey) to produce hybrids while the Kirghiz imported *C.*

dromedarius as studs for their two-humped females. Such importations were necessary as herding of the two species together produced a mixture of varied types of crossbreds many of them being inferior to the first crosses.

Hybrids were more than likely produced in Anatolia, before the Islamic period, directly as a result of the Turkish conquest of Syria. Initially a few male Bactrians were taken to Syria for crossing purposes but later larger numbers of female *C. dromedarius* were imported into Turkey. The characteristic hybrid with the elongated hump (Fig. 3.13) which is generally known as the Turkmen or Turkoman camel is the result.

In the nineteenth century between 8 000 and 10 000 *C. dromedarius* females every year were imported to Anatolia from Syria and Arabia mainly for crossbreeding purposes. At the beginning of World War I the figure was still 7 000–8 000 when exports from Syria and Arabia to Egypt were 32 000 thus giving some idea of the importance of the trade (Bulliet, 1975).

fig. 3.13 Hybrid camel with characteristic hump

Recent scientific research

Almost all experimental work has been done in Russia, the best general access to the results being summarised by Gray (1971).

The usual cross is the male Bactrian on the female dromedary although, as history has shown, the reciprocal cross is possible. The F_1 hybrids are normally fertile. Spermatogenesis in male hybrids is normal but infertility, or a lack of ability to induce conception, does occur. The female hybrid is almost always fertile and will produce offspring resembling the male parent whether she is back-crossed to *C. bactrianus* or *C. dromedarius*. The diploid chromosome number of the hybrids is 74, as in all Camelidae.

The hybrid offspring show heterosis in respect of body size, hardiness, endurance, longevity and of some blood characteristics including haemoglobin content, number of erythrocytes and glutothione content. They resemble the Bactrian in having a hairy chin and hairy legs but there is normally no hair on the shoulder. The single hump is longer and not as high as in the dromedary but it may occasionally show a small indentation towards the front.

The *C. bactrianus* × *C. dromedarius* first-cross hybrid is a strong animal equally suitable for pack or draught. Leese (1972) states they could carry up to 550 kg. Its milk yield and the fat percentage of the milk are intermediate between those of the parents. Wool yield tends towards the higher weights of the Bactrian.

A whole list of nomenclature for various grades of cross is known but economic crossing is confined in practice to the simple hybrid 'bertuar' (*C. bactrianus* × *C. dromedarius*) or to the next generation hybrid 'korspak' (*C. bactrianus* × (*C. bactrianus* × *C. dromedarius*)). Other crosses and particularly the interbreeding of the F_1 give unsatisfactory, weak progeny of poor conformation which are difficult to train (Kolpakov, 1935).

Further reading

Bennett, S. C. J., John, E. R. and Hewison, J. W. (1948). Animal husbandry. In: Tothill, J. D. (ed.) *Agriculture in the Sudan*, pp. 633–667. Oxford University Press: Oxford, UK.

Bettini, T. M. (1940). *L'allevamento del bestiame in Migiurtinia. Agric. colon.*, **35**, 51–77.

Boué, A. (1950). *La remonte d'une unité mehariste: son caractère polymorphe; conditions d'une homogeneité moyenne. Rev. Elev. Méd. vét. Pays trop.*, **4**, 139–144.

Bozzi, L. and Triulzi, G. A. (1953). *Osservazioni sugli animali domestici allevati in Somalia. Riv. Agric. subtrop. trop.*, **47**, 266–294.

Bulliet, R. W. (1975). *The camel and the wheel.* Harvard University Press: Cambridge, Massachusetts, USA.

Burgemeister, R. E. (1975). *Elevage de chameaux en Afrique du Nord.* Office Allemand de la Cooperation Technique: Eschborn, West Germany.

Cole, D. P. (1975). *Nomads of the nomads: the Al Murrah Bedouin of the Empty Quarter.* Aldine Publishing Company: Chicago, USA.

Droandi, I. (1921). *I cammelli corridori del Barca. Agric. colon.*, **14**, 1–47.

Epstein, H. (1971). *The origin of the domestic animals of Africa.* Africana Publishing Corporation: New York, USA.

Gautier, E. F. and Chudeau, R. (1909). *Mission au Sahara.* Paris: France.

Gillespie, I. A. (1962). Riding camels of the Sudan. *Sudan J. Vet. Sci. Anim. Husb.*, **3**, 37–42.

Gray, A. P. (1971). *Mammalian hybrids: A checklist with bibliography.* Common. Bur. Anim. Breed. Genet. Tech. Commun. No. 10. Commonwealth Agricultural Bureaux: Farnham Royal, UK.

Hira, L. M. (1947). Camel breeding in India. *India Fmg.*, **8**, 504–508.

HMSO (1920). *British Somaliland and Sokotra.* Her Majesty's Stationery Office: London.

Kolpakov, V. N. (1935). *Uber Kamelkreuzungen. Berl. Tierärtzl. Wschr.*, **51**, 617–622.

Leese, A. S. (1927). *A treatise on the one-humped camel in health and disease.* Haynes & Son: Stamford, Lincs, UK.

Marchi, E. (1929). *Studi sulla pastorizia della colonia Eritrea.* Istituto Agricolo Coloniale Italiano: Florence, Italy.

Mason, I. L. (1951). *A world dictionary of breeds, types and varieties of livestock.* Common. Bur.

Anim. Breed. Genet. Tech. Commun. No. 7. Commonwealth Agricultural Bureaux: Farnham Royal, UK.

Mason, I. L. and Maule, J. P. (1960). *The indigenous livestock of Eastern and Southern Africa*. Common. Bur. Anim. Breed. Genet. Tech. Commun. No. 14. Commonwealth Agricultural Bureaux: Farnham Royal, UK.

Rossetti, G. and Congiu, S. (1955). *Richerche Zootecnico-Veterinario sugli Animali Domestici della Somalia*. Ispetorato Veterinario: Mogadishu, Somalia.

Sharma, V. D. and Bhargava, K. K. (1963). The Bikaneri camel. *Indian Vet. J.,* **40**, 639-643.

Swift, J. J. (1979). The development of livestock trading in a nomad pastoral economy: The Somali case. In: *Pastoral production and society*, pp. 447-465. Cambridge University Press: Cambridge, UK.

Tarantino, B. (1934). *II cammello da sella (recūb) della Somalia. Riv. zootec.*, **11**, 392-398.

Williamson, G. and Payne, W. J. A. (1978). *An introduction to animal husbandry in the Tropics* (3rd ed.). Longman: London.

Wilson, R. T. (1976). Some quantitative data on the Tigre salt trade from the early nineteenth century to the present day. *Ann. Ist. univ. orient. Napoli*, **36**, 157-164.

Yasin, S. A. and Abdul Wahid (1957). Pakistan camels - a preliminary survey. *Agric. Pakistan*, **8**, 289-295.

Part 2 Biology

4 Anatomy

"The Camel's hump is an ugly lump Which well you may see at the zoo."

The Hump by Rudyard Kipling

A morphological sketch

The camel is the most distinctive of domestic animals; the hump and the long, curved neck are its most noticeable feature. Another striking feature is the presence of the peculiar horny pads on the elbows, stifle and chest (Fig. 4.1).

The legs are relatively long and slender, an adaptation, perhaps, to a long easy gait and to adaptive cooling, and terminate in large disc-like

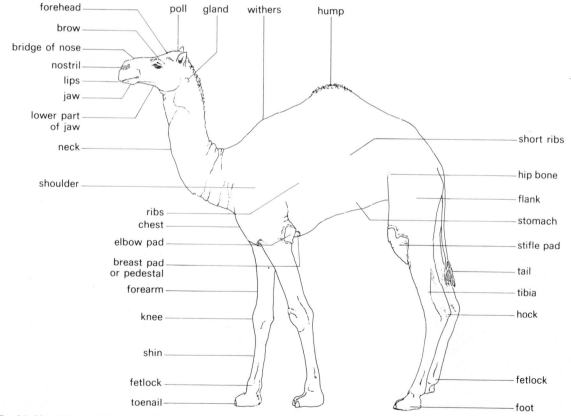

fig. 4.1 Morphology of the camel (*Source*: **Acland, P. B. E.** (1932). Notes on the camel in the eastern Sudan. Sudan Notes Rec. **15**, 119–149.)

feet. The weight of the head and neck have resulted in very heavy forequarters to support this burden: more than 65 per cent of the camel's total weight is supported by the front limbs (Kingdon, 1979). The chest is deep and narrow which allows the balance to be shifted easily so that it is directly over the weight-bearing foreleg during locomotion. The waist slopes sharply upwards and is very constricted, appearing to be loosely connected to the long thin hind legs. The generally rather weak hindquarters are accentuated in riding types.

The head (Fig. 4.2) while often appearing large and ungainly on the end of the long neck, is small in comparison to that of other domestic animals. It bears no horns and has small bluntly-pointed ears. The eyes are large and prominent but the massive supra-orbital processes give some protection and there are long lashes. The nostrils are long slits which can be closed as a protection against sand. The upper lip is split and hairy, extensible and slightly prehensile: it is very sensitive. The lower lip is large and pendulous. The male and female both have two glands behind the poll. These are modified sweat glands whose physiology will be discussed in detail in Chapter 5.

The skin is supple, covered over the most part of the body with short fine hairs, which may be longer in cooler climates or during the cool season in hot areas. The longer hair is usually confined to the hump and the shoulders but this varies between individuals. The hair colour is generally brown, varying from a deep chocolate almost black colour, through reds, rusts, fawns to almost white in some types. Some two-coloured animals occur, particularly in the western Sudan and Chad (Fig 4.3). The tail is short and hairless except for a row of hairs down each side and a less noticeable row along the upper surface.

The female has a four-quartered udder. The testicles of the male are positioned high up in the groin (as in the pig or dog) and the opening of the sheath is directed backwards.

General anatomy

This section deals in general with the anatomy of the hard and soft parts. The digestive system and dentition, the lower limbs, feet and locomotion are rather peculiar in the camel and are treated separately below. The anatomy of the reproductive system is described in Chapter 6.

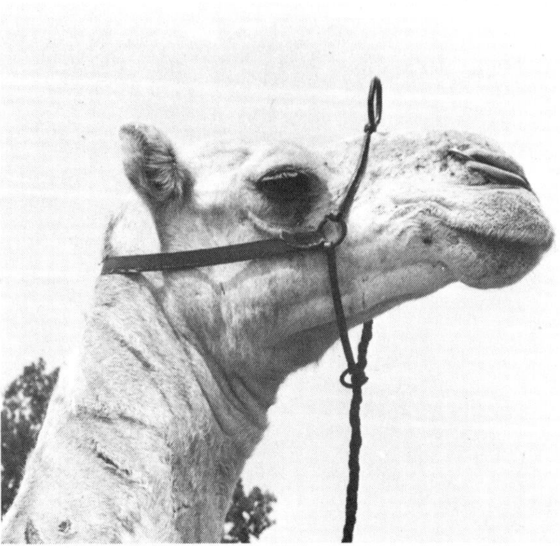

fig. 4.2 Head of a camel showing large supra-orbital processes and eyelashes, slit-like nostrils and lips

fig. 4.3 A piebald camel from Darfur, Sudan

The skeleton

The skeleton of the camel is shown in Fig. 4.4.

The head The skull of the camel is more nearly comparable with that of the horse than with that of any other domestic animal (Leese, 1927). The occipital crest is prominent and is responsible for the peak-shaped poll of the camel; the bone is very massive, up to 75 mm thick between the apex of the crest and the cranial cavity. The posterior surface of the occipital bone has a rough projection to which the strong ligament, the *ligamentum*

nuchae, is attached: this ligament is largely responsible for supporting the weight of the head and neck. The temporal fossa is very wide; the width of the frontal bones is responsible for the 'beetling brows' above the eyes. The frontal sinus, in which are often found the larvae of the camel bot fly (see Chapter 8) lies immediately below the facial portion of the frontal bone. Each sinus is triangular in shape. The orbital cavity (the eye socket) is very deep.

The bone structure of the face results in the hollow between the bridge of the nose and the eye

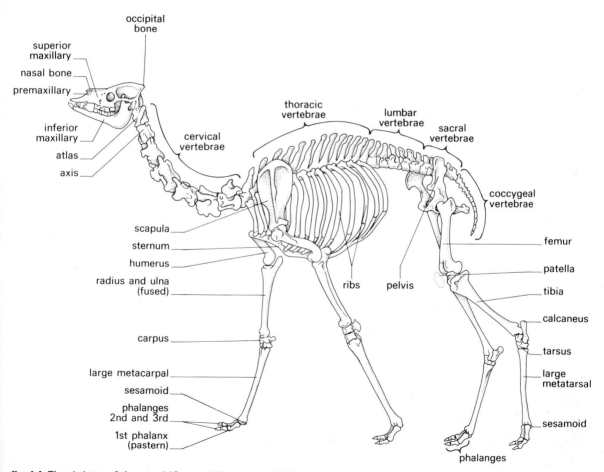

fig. 4.4 The skeleton of the camel (*Source*: **Kingdon, J.** (1979). *East African Mammals*, Vol. III, Part B *Large mammals*, Academic Press: London.)

socket seen in the living animal. The nasal bone is often convex giving rise to the bulge or Roman nose. The nasal cavities are narrow. The socket of the upper incisor or canine tooth is in the premaxillary bone and the rest of the teeth are lodged in the superior maxillary bone. The hard palate is narrow, in particular behind the first premolars. The inferior maxillary is long and constricted, and carries the lower teeth.

The vertebral column, ribs and sternum   The vertebral anatomy of *Camelus* spp. is similar to that of most of the other domestic species of mammal with the exception of that of the horse in which the thoracic vertebrae are more numerous. The comparative formulae are shown in Table 4.1. The formula for the camel is based on the work of Kanan (1960) as are the descriptions which follow in this section. In fact, most sources are in agreement on the anatomy although there is occasionally dispute as to the number of coccygeal vertebrae, this being given as 15-18 for example by Leese (1927).

The bones of the cervical vertebrae are massive, elongated and narrow which, of course, accounts for the length of the neck. It needs to be noted, however, that, as in the giraffe, they are the same in number as the majority of other animals. The neural spines (or supra-spinous processes) on these vertebrae are low, resembling those of the horse, but the transverse process of the sixth vertebra

bears a quadrilateral boney plate directed downwards, as in bovines. The atlas (the first cervical vertebra) is shorter than the others while the axis, or second vertebra, is intermediate in length. The anterior articular surfaces are less convex and the posterior ones less concave than in short-necked animals which, together with strong intervertebral discs, allows very large lateral movements of the neck.

The thoracic vertebrae are short, although still longer than in the horse, and constricted in the middle. The neural spines are long, laterally compressed and with a distinct backward slope. The spines of all the vertebrae are similar in length. Neither these nor the lumbar vertebrae take any part in the formation of the hump which consists entirely of soft tissue.

The lumbar vertebrae are rather long and thick, constricted in the middle and dorsally flattened. With the exception of the first of them the neural spines are all directed forwards and become successively shorter towards the rear. The oblique processes are strong and impart considerable rigidity to the spine. The transverse processes are long and occasionally suffer necrosis from the pressure of the pack or saddle.

The four sacral vertebrae are fused into a single body but the neural spines are relatively free from each other and quite short.

The coccygeal vertebrae have complete arches but lack articular processes.

Table 4.1 Comparative vertebral formulae of the common domestic animals. (*Source*: **Kanan, C. V.** (1960). Notes on the vertebral column, ribs and sternum of the camel. *Sudan J. Vet. Sci. Anim. Husb.*, **1**, 84–91; **Sisson S. and Grossman, J. D.** (1975). *The anatomy of the domestic animals.* L. B. Saunders: London.)

Animal species	Number of vertebrae				
	Cervical	Thoracic	Lumbar	Sacral	Coccygeal
Camel	7	12	7	4	14–9
Cattle	7	13	6	5	20–18
Sheep	7	13	6–7	4	18–16
Pig	7	14–15	6–7	4	22–20
Horse	7	18	6	5	21–15

There are 12 pairs of ribs of which 8 are sternal and 4 asternal. They show very little curvature which accounts for the lack of the barrel chest in the camel. The rib bones are laterally compressed so that the intercostal spaces are narrow. A rudimentary thirteenth rib is sometimes present (Leese, 1927) but does not articulate with a vertebra. Articulated ribs are thus always 12 in number in the camel.

The sternum is large with seven sternebrae, increasing in size from front to rear, except for the last which is about equal in size to the fifth.

The limbs In the forelegs the upper edge of the shoulder blade, the scapula, is very convex with a marked constriction just above the shoulder joint. The humerus is similar to that of other domestic animals. The radius and ulna are unusual in that they are bound together to form a single bone – the long bone – except for a small division near the lower and where the two bones are distinguishable. This long bone is often over 0·5 m long and very slender for its length and the weight it has to bear. The toes are reduced to two, there being no vestigial digits behind the leg. There are three phalanges in each digit; there is only one in the short pastern, the other two being horizontally disposed in the foot.

The pelvis of the camel is very short, the ilium has a flat upper surface and the socket of the hip joint is very deep. The femur is slender and slightly bowed forward, the large trochanter is not prominent. The patella is long and narrow but is not rudimentary. The tibia is long and slender but otherwise normal while the fibula is a small irregularly-shaped bone. The tarsus of the camel is peculiar in that it has two ginglymoid or hinge joints, rather than one, as is normal. This adaptation allows very free movement, necessary not only for keeping the foot flat on shifting sand but also for flexing the limb when the camel is moving into or out of the sitting position. The phalanges are similar to those of the foreleg but are slightly smaller.

Musculature and tendons
These parts exhibit few special peculiarities. The muscles of the neck are weakly developed as are those of the hindquarters. In the latter the adductor muscles are particularly weak.

The extensor muscles of the limbs are rather special with one for each digit and one common to both digits. The flexor is a tendonous band from the posterior of the carpus which bifurcates behind the metacarpus to the first phalange of the digit. The musculature of the hind limbs is more or less analogous to that of the fore limbs. In the couched position the Achilles tendon is exposed over the end of the tibia before it enters the hock: a tendency for this tendon to slip over the outer side causes lameness on occasions.

The lateral swaying of the camel due to its gait is minimised by the narrow chest; the trapezius and deltoid muscles thus require little contraction to shift the animal's centre of gravity over the limb which is on the ground at any given moment. The powerful nuchal ligament which supports the head and neck, continues over the withers and to the sacrum.

The hump
Most of the fatty tissue of camels is stored in the hump rather than being diffused throughout the body. This is an adaptation to heat transmission (see Chapter 5); similar systems can be found in the fat tails or rumps of certain desert sheep. In addition there are fat deposits on occasions under the skin, around the heart and kidneys and sometimes under the peritoneum, behind the eye and in the temporal fossa. The fat is very white and soft.

The hump is composed of fibrous and fatty tissue. The fibrous part is more noticeable in front and along the vertebrae, where it largely consists of the cervical ligament. In the upper part of the hump the tissue is mostly fat but this depends on the state of health of the camel. Thus the camel's hump does not resemble that of the zebu which is basically muscular. The hump tissue is covered by a very dense aponeurotic layer which attaches it to the vertebrae; this is followed by a layer of lamella cells and finally by the skin which is very elastic over the hump itself. The size and shape of the hump vary from animal to animal and depend much on its condition: the skin expands or contracts easily with the hump.

In very fat camels there is some subcutaneous

fat deposited over the withers and this may be regarded as the rudiment of a second hump.

Nervous, lymphatic and circulatory systems

These are similar to those of other domestic animals. The brain is longer (150 mm) and narrower than those of the ruminants in general and is thus similar in shape to that of the horse; it weights about 450 g.

The lymphatic system is characterised by few ganglia with conglomerations in the usual areas (Fig. 4.5). The peculiarities here are the location of the external thoracic and lower cervical ganglia in the front of the chest. The mesenteric ganglia have a particular distribution in the abdomen. The cer-

vical glands are very small and there is a large kidney-shaped iliac lymph gland instead of the normal group of such glands.

The camel's heart is slightly pointed at the apex and has only two ventricular grooves. It contains a floating bone. The jugular veins are of very large diameter and lie on the underside of the neck for three-quarters of its length, being protected by the transverse processes of the cervical vertebrae. Sacrificing the camel by the usual method of cutting the jugular high on the throat is thus not possible and it is necessary to cut these veins at the junction of the chest and throat. The posterior tibial artery is very exposed when the camel is couched, this being the easiest artery to use when counting

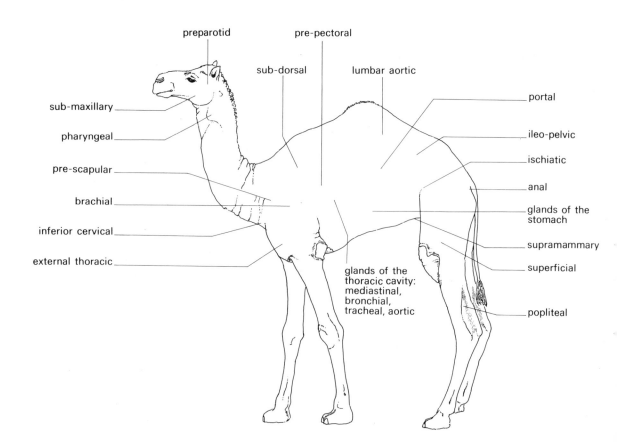

fig. 4.5 The lymphatic system of the camel (*Source*: **Curasson, G.** (1947). *Le chameau et ses maladies*. Vigot Frères: Paris, France; **Leese, A. S.** (1927). A treatise on the one-humped camel in health and disease. Haynes & Son: Stamford, Lincs, UK.)

heartbeat. The red corpuscles of the camel are elliptical and biconvex and measure about 8μ in length.

The blood volume of camels, of which some details are given in Table 4.2, appears to be in the same range as that found in other domestic animals, equivalent to just under 10 per cent of the liveweight (Hassan, 1968) with a specific gravity in the region of 1·05. These determinations were carried out using radioactive iodine as a tracer and must be considered to be more realistic figures than earlier reports of 4·2–4·5 per cent for young animals and 3·4–3·6 per cent for older animals (Boué, 1948) which were estimated on the amount of blood collected at slaughter.

The respiratory system
The nostrils are long, slit-like and set obliquely; they can be closed at will. The sinuses are well separated from each other and are subdivided in themselves. The frontal sinus communicates with the superior meatus of the nasal cavity by a curved slit. The larynx is long, with a large opening into the epiglottis; the thyroid is domed in shape. The larynx is a rather simple organ which accounts for the limited voice range of the camel. The trachea is 130–150 cm in length, narrow and cylindrical. It lies in the lower part of the neck on the right side; it is wholly cartilaginous in the neck. A third small bronchus is present on the right side.

The lungs are entire and not lobed; large amounts of connective tissue occur between the lobules. The top of the right lung which takes its bronchus direct from the trachea is more developed than the left one. The pleural cavities do not interconnect.

The diaphragm has well-developed pillars and is attached to the tenth, eleventh and twelfth ribs. It contains a floating bone against the opening of the vena cava.

The skin, skin glands and pads
The skin is attached rather tightly to the underlying tissue and is relatively immobile.

This is a disadvantage when the animal is attacked by biting and flying insects, particularly in view of its short and ineffectual tail. The animal is thus reduced to stamping, kicking and throwing its head about in the effort to remain comfortable, apparently often without much success. The skin is thicker over the back than elsewhere and particularly over the hump when this is in decline. The epidermis is well developed; the dermis is compact and hard and is rich in elastic fibres which have long papillae; the sub-epidermal tissue is very hard. Sweat glands occur sparsely all over the body but sweating is restricted to very hot periods and to times when the animal is excessively tired.

The poll glands are more active under conditions of heat and fatigue than at any other time except when the male is in rut. They are thus probably modified sweat glands. Contrary to general belief, they are found in both sexes although they are less active in castrates and females than in males and the fluid emitted has a much less noticeable odour. The glands are situated towards the top of the back of the neck and cover an area of about 6 by 4 cm. They can be distinguished from

Table 4.2 Blood volume of camels (*Source*: **Hassan, Y. M.** (1968). Blood volume determination in camels (*Camelus dromedarius*). *Isotopenpraxis*, **4(2)**: 73.

Female camel age (years)	Total plasma volume (ml)	Haematocrit value (per cent)	Total blood volume (ml)	Blood volume (ml per kilogram)	Implied liveweight (kg)
2	18 210	30	26 014	93·23	280
10	22 053	32	32 430	92·65	350
13	20 733	34	31 414	94·00	335

the surrounding skin, particularly in males, by their slight elevation, their colour and the comparatively few hairs they carry.

The pads are modified skin and occur at the points where the camel is in contact with the ground when couched. The dark horny membrane of which they consist is generally about 7 mm thick. It is elastic and grows from a vascular secreting membrane beneath which there is a foundation of fibro-cartilaginous tissue. The largest pad is generally referred to as the pedestal and is on the chest below the sternum; there are in addition pads on the elbows and stifles and less important ones on the knees and outside the hocks. In young animals the pads are less developed and covered with short hair which wears away after a few months.

The digestive system

The buccal cavity

The upper lip is split, hairy, extensible and slightly prehensile. The lower one, more so in older

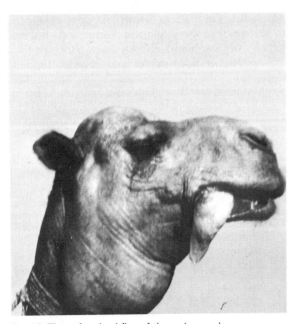

fig. 4.6 The soft palatal flap of the male camel

animals, is pendulous. The upper dental pad is tough and horny, the lining membrane of the cheeks is covered with long conical papillae, directed towards the rear. The hard palate is long, while the soft palate is protrusible (Fig. 4.6) and this has been attributed to its distension by ruminal gases (Leese, 1927). It forms part of the sexual display of the male during rut (see Chapter 6). The tongue is small in relation to the overall size of the camel. It is very mobile and is furnished with between five and seven large-diameter papillae along each side.

Dentition is dealt with separately on p. 60. The salivary glands are little different from those of other ruminating animals. They have been best described by Tayeb (1950). The parotid gland is small and the Stenson's duct opens behind the third upper premolar. The maxillary gland lies under the parotid and beneath the jugular vein but over the pharyngeal lymph gland. The sublingual gland is very small, the molar glands are well developed and there are additional minute glands at the bases of the cheek papillae.

The pharynx and oesophagus

The pharynx is very long and narrow, partly divided into two chambers. The oesophagus is a long tube (1–2 m) of large capacity. The lining has secreting glands which apparently serve the purpose of moistening the often rough forage which is the normal diet of the camel.

The stomachs

As early as 1890 it was considered that the stomach of the tylopods was more primitive than that of the typical ruminant (Boas, 1890) and it was compared with that of certain of the Suiformes (Cordier, 1893). Boas also made the fundamental point that the reticulum of the Tylopoda is not homologous with that of the Ruminantia; since that time the question of terminology has often assumed dominance over the anatomical problems themselves.

Modern authorities (Hansen and Schmidt-Nielsen, 1957; Bohlken, 1960) are in agreement that the compartments of the stomach are not homologous in the Tylopoda and Ruminantia but that it is convenient, where possible, to use the conventional terminology for the different compartments. A further point of controversy is the function and terminology of the water cells of the rumen, first recognised by Pliny in his *Historia Natura* over 2 000 years ago. Hansen and Schmidt-Nielsen (1957) call these 'glandular sac areas' and Schmidt-Nielsen (1964) states that they do not, and indeed are not large enough, to function as water-storage compartments. These glandular sac areas, shown in one view of the stomach in Fig. 4.7, are diverticula which are divided into a number of smaller chambers by folds of mucosa. This mucosa is covered for the greater part by a simple columnar epithelium containing short, straight tubular glands; the number of glands is estimated to be of the order of 100 million. The area of the rumen in the region of the glandular sacs has strong bands of muscle; these were once thought to act as sphincters but this is now known not to be the case. Similar mucosa are found in almost the whole of the reticulum and the whole of the omasum. It is suggested that these glands are for absorption of the fermentation products of the rumen. Alternatively, they may be areas of secretion to augment the functions of the salivary glands and may produce much of the fluid of the rumen. The two functions may not, of course, be mutually exclusive and could be complementary. The interior of the rumen of the Ruminantia contains no analagous structures.

As discussed in Chapter 1, the fact that the parts of the stomach of the Tylopoda and the Ruminantia may not be homologous has been used not only to justify the systematic position of the former but also to support a hypothesis of separate evolution of the ruminating function (Bohlken, 1960). In addition it has been suggested that the actual processes of rumination and of digestion may be different. The comparative morphology of the two types of stomach is shown in Fig. 4.8.

The rumen is of no concern in this argument as it is agreed that it is nothing more than a container for initial storage and fermentation by bacteria and protozoa of the cellulose of the ingested food. The fluid in the stomach of Ruminantia consists of salivary secretions but that in the camel's rumen derives from both the salivary glands and the glandular sacs. In general, the rumen contents are equivalent to 11–15 per cent of body weight (Schmidt-Nielsen, 1964) although levels of up to 20 per cent have been recorded (Wilson, 1978). These figures are of a similar order to those for cattle.

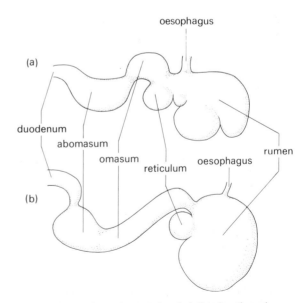

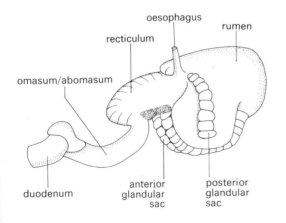

fig. 4.7 The camel's stomach

fig. 4.8 Comparison of stomachs of a) Ruminantia and b) Tylopoda. (*Source*: **Bohlken, H.** (1960). Remarks on the stomach and the systematic position of the Tylopoda. *Proc. Zool. Soc. Lond.* **134**, 207–215.)

There are other minor differences between the tylopod and ruminant stomachs. In tylopods the oesophagus discharges directly into the rumen while in ruminants it joins the stomach between the rumen and the reticulum. A further difference is that the exterior surface of the rumen in tylopods is smooth except for the glandular sac areas, while the rumen of ruminants has strong muscular pillars.

The typical ruminant reticulum has an appearance strongly resembling a honeycomb, covered with horny papillae. The tylopod reticulum shows a structure similar to that of the glandular sacs. This fact has been used to provide further support for the theory of water storage but in fact its volume is only about 2 litres.

The omasum of the Ruminantia is sharply separated from the abomasum and contains a large number of leaves or laminae covered with horny papillae. It is kidney-shaped. The omasum of the tylopod is long and cylindrical and externally cannot be distinguished from the abomasum. Internally, the division is marked by the cessation of the folds of the omasum which contain the tubular secreting glands. In the Ruminantia the abomasum is the only section of the stomach which contains glands, they are mounted on longitudinal ridges or folds. The abomasum of the Tylopoda is very small and has no ridges except in the foetus; it contains two different areas of mucosa, the front two-thirds having fundus glands, the last third having pyloric glands and gastric pits.

The stomach occupies much of the left side of the abdomen in adult camels but, as might be expected, is proportionately smaller in young calves before the ruminating function has developed.

Intestines

The small intestine This measures about 40 m in length in a fully grown camel. The duodenum starts with a dilation and then forms a loop. A common duct from the pancreas and liver opens into this duodenal loop slightly more than 0·5 m from the pyloric constriction of the abomasum. The jejunum occupies most of the abdomen and is situated along the mesentery on the right side. A chain of mesenteric lymph nodes is found along the length of the jejunum and there is a large group of nodes around the anterior mesenteric artery. The lymph nodes of the final part of the small intestine, the ileum, are associated with those of the large intestine.

The large intestine This measures about 20 m in length. The caecum is blind, and is attached to the mesentery at the blind end. For a length of about 4 m the colon is of large diameter and coiled into a mass consisting of a concentric and an excentric spiral. The colon is on the left side of the abdomen in a special mesenteric fold. The colon narrows as it enters the tight part of the spiral, the walls become thicker and it is in this portion that much of the water is reabsorbed from the faeces (see p. 74). The colon bends in the lumbar region before becoming the rectum. The lymph supply is concentrated at the entry of the large intestine between the ileum and the caecum with further lymph glands near the terminal portion of the colon and the rectum.

Liver, pancreas and spleen

The liver is highly lobulated, particularly on the rear lower part. There is a considerable amount of interlobular tissue; this has the appearance of cirrhosis. As in the horse there is no gall bladder; the bile duct is common with the pancreatic duct before entry to the duodenum. The pancreas has only the single duct. The spleen is attached not to the diaphragm but high on the left side of the rumen by its front lower surface. It is crescent-shaped and wider at the rear end than the front; in the healthy camel it weighs 1·0 – 1·5 kg. The peritoneum is similar to that of cattle.

Dentition

In common with other members of the order Artiodactyla, the Suiformes excepted, the camel has reduced dentition. The typical mammal, of which the pig is representative, has 32 deciduous, temporary or milk teeth and 44 permanent ones. In the camel some are absent or modified so that there are 22 deciduous teeth and 34 permanent teeth. The molars are selenodont, that is, with crescent-shaped ridges on their crowns. The standard study of camel dentition is that of Rabagliati (1924), from which much of the information in this section is drawn.

Deciduous, temporary or milk teeth
These teeth in the camel are 22 in number, the dental formula is:

$$\frac{1-1}{3-3} \quad \frac{1-1}{1-1} \quad \frac{3-3}{2-2} = 22$$

incisors   canines   premolars

or in short form as:

$$2\frac{1-1-3}{3-1-2} = 22$$

The relative placement of these teeth in the upper and lower jaws is shown diagrammatically in Fig. 4.9 and comparisons with the dental formulae of the other sub-orders of the Artiodactyla and with the horse are shown in Table 4.3. The camel differs in dentition from the other ruminating animals by the possession of incisors in the upper jaw and of canine teeth in both the upper and lower jaws.

Upper jaw The incisor teeth are much modified; they are just visible through the dental pad and represent the corner incisors of the full mammalian mouth. A pair of lateral incisors may be represented by alveoli, but these never break through the pad and are ignored in the dental formula. There is never any sign of the central

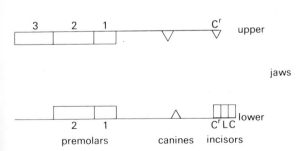

fig. 4.9 Diagrammatic representation of the deciduous teeth of the camel (*Source*: **Rabagliati, D. S.** (1924). *The dentition of the camel.* Government Press: Cairo, Egypt.)

Table 4.3 Comparative deciduous dental formulae of sub-orders of the Artiodactyla and of the horse (Perissodactyla)

Species	Dental formula
Suiformes - pig	$2\dfrac{3-1-4}{3-1-4} = 32$
Tylopoda - camel	$2\dfrac{1-1-3}{3-1-2} = 22$
Ruminantia - sheep	$2\dfrac{0-0-3}{4-0-3} = 20$
Perissodactyla - horse	$2\dfrac{3-0-3}{3-0-3} = 24$

incisors. The incisors are carried on the premaxillary bone. The canines are carried on the superior maxillary bone as are the premolars. The deciduous canines are small, blunt and point backwards slightly; they are somewhat rudimentary although they have very large roots. The first premolars are single teeth; they erupt with sharp cutting edges which subsequently wear to a flat surface with double bumps; these teeth are not replaced by permanent ones. The second premolars are double with marked necks and three fangs with triangular-shaped wearing surfaces. The enamel is folded and shaped rather like the letter B. The second premolars erupt at the same time as the first while the third pair come through later. The third and last pair are larger than the second and have square tables, less well-marked necks and four fangs. The enamel is similarly arranged in B-like folds.

Lower jaw The three pairs of temporary incisors overlap in echelon when newly erupted but separate out into line after wear: in a very worn condition they may be represented by stumps with large gaps between. They have well-developed necks and form an angle of about 45° with the jaw. The centrals are the largest and erupt first. The laterals are next largest and erupt second to be followed by the smaller corners. The canines are peculiar as when they erupt they are the same shape as the corner incisors and lie right up against them. As the jaw grows they separate from the incisors and become triangular in shape; they are much more developed than the canines of the upper jaw. The lower jaw has only two pairs of temporary premolars; the first or front pair are very small for grinding teeth but the second pair are the largest of all the temporary set. The first pair, which erupt slightly before the second, are single with the table surfaces longer than broad when in wear: the front fangs are small and occasionally not even embedded in the jaw. The second pair are typical molar teeth with a crown of three divisions and the enamel arranged like the letter B. The necks of these teeth are poorly developed and they have large double fangs.

Permanent teeth

The permanent teeth number 34 and, following the example given for deciduous teeth, the dental formula is written as:

$$\frac{1-1}{3-3} \quad \frac{1-1}{1-1} \quad \frac{3-3}{2-2} \quad \frac{3-3}{3-3} = 34$$

incisors   canines   premolars   molars

or in shortened form as:

$$2\frac{1-1-3-3}{3-1-2-3} = 34$$

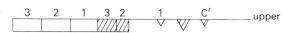

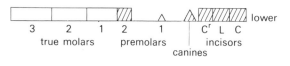

these teeth have temporary predecessors

fig. 4.10 Diagrammatic representation of the permanent teeth of the camel (*Source*: as for Fig. 3.9.)

A diagrammatic representation of these teeth is given in Fig. 4.10 and a comparison with some other animals in Table 4.4. Differences similar to those in the formulae for temporary teeth are apparent in the ones for permanent teeth.

Upper jaw There are no central incisors and for all practical purposes there are no laterals either. The corner incisors are carried on the premaxillary bone but are much modified, being thick, rather pointed and curling backwards slightly. They resemble to some extent the canines (although they are much smaller) and are often referred to as the first pair of 'tushes'. There is no neck between the crown and fangs. The true canines are large, massive, inclined slightly forwards and may be up to 4 cm in length. They are narrow laterally and are sharp both in front and behind. The canines have no neck and the fangs are enormous, as indeed they need to be to fulfil their function of tearing heavy food from trees and as fighting weapons, particularly in males.

The upper jaw has three pairs of premolars, the first pair being set apart, forward and resembling the canines to some extent. They are set in the arch of the superior maxillary and do not contact the lower first premolars. They are usually blackish in colour. This first pair may be absent, especially in females. The second pair are single teeth with triangular wearing surfaces, the apex of the

Table 4.4 Comparative permanent dental formula of the sub-orders of the Artiodactyla and the horse.

Species	Dental formula
Suiformes – pig	$2\dfrac{3-1-4-3}{3-1-4-3} = 44$
Tylopoda – camel	$2\dfrac{1-1-3-3}{3-1-2-3} = 34$
Ruminantia – sheep	$2\dfrac{0-0-3-3}{4-0-3-3} = 32$
Perissodactyla – horse	$2\dfrac{3-0-3/4-3}{3-0-3-3} = 40-$

triangle to the front. There are well-developed necks between the crowns and the three fangs. The third set of premolars are also single teeth but much larger than the second pair. They also have three fangs. The tables are semi-circular or elliptic but wear to a triangle.

There are three pairs of permanent true molar teeth, normally lying immediately behind the premolars although there is sometimes a gap. All the true molars are double teeth and they increase in size from first to third, the first pair themselves being double the size of the last premolars. All the teeth are longer than broad when new, the tables of the first pair becoming square with use. All the teeth have four fangs, the ones on the third pair being broader lower down giving a pyramid shape to the tooth. The necks are absent in the third pair and are less distinct in the second than in the first pair. The enamel in all the molars is arranged in the shape of a B.

Lower jaw The lower incisors overlap when new and come up behind their temporary predecessors. On wear they become separated and eventually may remain as stumps. The centrals are broad and leaf-shaped, with slightly serrated sharp edges. They are convex from top to bottom and laterally, when viewed from the front, and have ridged anterior surfaces. The cutting edges are higher on the inner side than on the outer. The necks between the crown and the fangs, which are single, are not very evident. The laterals are similar but more convex, smaller and with a more marked neck. The corners are again smaller, with a well marked neck and are the least convex of all the incisors.

There is one pair of canines which are shorter and thicker than those of the upper jaw. The lower canines have less massive fangs and may be placed a little in front of the upper ones. They are often filed or cut off by the camel's owner.

There are two pairs of premolars with the first pair, as in the upper jaw, being placed well forward. The first premolars are often referred to as 'tushes'. They are dark, thick, and shorter than those of the upper jaw. Occasionally they may be duplicated or, particularly in females, absent. They are farther forward than the corresponding

first premolars in the upper jaw. The second premolars are single teeth with two fangs as opposed to the three fangs of those in the upper jaw. They are the smallest grinding teeth of the lower jaw and have flat wearing surfaces, and a well-marked neck.

The first pair of true molars in the lower jaw are the smallest of the true molars found in either jaw. They are smaller than the corresponding pair in the upper jaw, very long from front to back and do not become square on wearing. The necks are distinct and there are only two fangs. The second molars are much bigger than the first but again smaller than the corresponding pair above. They are long with a poorly developed neck and double fangs. The third true molars are the largest teeth in the head. The crowns are divided into three sections, like the second lower deciduous premolars, the last division being the smallest. This last pair are very narrow with no neck and have three fangs. All the molars have the enamel in the characteristic B shape.

Occasionally the first temporary premolars in the upper jaw persist. In this case they lie between the first and second pairs of permanent premolars.

While the generally accepted dental formula for camels is 34 there have been occasional efforts to propose a species with 36 teeth (Cauvet, 1929) as pointed out in Chapter 1.

Eruption patterns and ageing

The chronology of eruption of the temporary and permanent teeth is outlined in Tables 4.5 and 4.6. The first permanent teeth to appear are the first pair of molars in the upper and lower jaws at 12–15 months of age and there are no other permanent teeth until the animal reaches at least 2½ years of age.

The upper temporary corner incisors are the weakest in the whole head and have usually disappeared by the time the camel is 1 year old. The upper canines persist until they are replaced by the permanent ones, growing alongside them at 6 to 7 years old. The second premolars usually disappear at about 5 years, before the eruption of the permanent ones; the third premolars disappear at about the same time.

In the lower jaw the incisors are all well up and

Table 4.5 The eruption pattern of the temporary teeth of the camel. (*Source*: **Rabagliati, D. S.** (1924). *The dentition of the camel.* Government Press: Cairo, Egypt.)

Jaw and teeth	Birth	1 week	2 weeks	1 month	3 months	6 months
upper jaw						
incisors, corner					just	up
canines					small	up
premolars 1	gum	just	through	up	up	up
premolars 2	gum	just	through	up	up	up
premolars 3	gum	gum	gum	through	up	up
lower jaw						
incisors, centre	gum	just	through	up	sharp	in
lateral	gum	gum	just	through	overlap	wear
corner	gum	gum	gum	just		
canines					incisor like	up
premolars 1	gum	just	through	up	up	up
premolars 2	gum	gum	gum	through	up	up

Table 4.6 The eruption pattern of the permanent teeth of the camel. (*Source*: as for Table 4.5).

Jaw and teeth	12–15 months	2½ years	3 years	4½ years	5 years	5½ years	6 years	6½ years	7 years
upper jaw									
incisors									
corner							through	up	up
canine							through	up	large
premolars 1								through	dark
premolars 2					gum or	through	up	up	wear
premolars 3					just	through	up	up	wear
molars 1	through	up	up	up	wear	wear	wear	wear	wear
molars 2		just	through	up	wear	wear	wear	wear	wear
molars 3					gum	through	up	up	wear
lower jaw									
incisors									
centre			just		through	up	wear	wear	worn
lateral						gum	up	wear	wearing
corner								through	up
canines							through	up	large
premolars 1								through	dark
premolars 2					just	through	up	up	wear
molars 1	through	up	up	up	wear	wear	wear	wear	wear
molars 2		just	through	up	wear	wear	wear	wear	wear
molars 3					gum	through	up	up	wear

in wear by the time the camel is 1 year old. By the age of 2, they are worn and separate, at 3 years they are well worn. At 4 years the incisors are well worn, irregular and loose and may be reduced to stumps. The centrals persist until about 4 years, the laterals until 5-5½ years and the corners normally until 6-6½ years but these may be lost before the eruption of the permanent ones. All the incisors are replaced from behind. The lower canines persist in excess of 6 years and do not become excessively worn until very late in their life. The first lower premolars persist until 4½ years and are not replaced: the second lower premolars persist to about 5½ years.

The state of wear of the permanent teeth to 7 years of age is shown in general terms in Table 4·6 on p. 62. At 8 years all the teeth are in wear including the last to erupt, the lower corner incisors. At this age the first pair of premolars in each jaw (the second tushes) are nearly at full size and are very dark due to the accumulation of tartar. The true tushes or canines are very large and powerful. In the female the true and false tushes are not as prominent and the first premolars may be absent.

From 9 years onwards all teeth are more or less worn but actual age can only be determined on the basis of considerable knowledge and local experience. As in other animals, the type of fodder and various other factors influence the rate of wear. The incisors do not separate until about 15 years and the gaps gradually increase from this age. From this time the useful life of the camel is limited if it has to fend for itself off natural hard feed. The principal problem in determining the age of a camel using its teeth alone lies in the fact that almost all the milk teeth are badly worn at 4½ to 5½ years old, and this may be taken to indicate considerable age. However, the milk teeth are always smaller than the permanent ones and the experienced observer should have no difficulty in telling the age of a camel from its teeth. General stature and condition can also indicate a camel's age.

Camels may live to 40 years or so but their useful working life, at least as transport or pack animals, is from 6 to 15-20 years. Before 6 years of age they are immature and still have to undergo the difficult period of the change from temporary to permanent dentition. Beyond the age of about 20 years worn teeth and increasing debility limit their overall usefulness.

The foot and locomotion

The foot of the camel is well designed to cope with the loose sandy soils of the desert. The bearing surface of the foot is like a large plate. This plate is able to maintain flat contact with the ground throughout the duration of the stride due to exceptional rotation at the first digital joint. The foot splays out on taking the weight of the camel and thus acts as a firm base for levering the weight forward to the next stride.

The front foot, is about 19 cm long by 16 cm broad and covers an area of about 300 cm^2. The hind foot is smaller and measures about 16 cm long by 14 cm broad, covering an area of about 220 cm^2. The front feet are straight but the hind feet are usually slightly turned out. The stance of the camel is unique for the Artiodactyla in that it is digitigrade and not unguligrade (Dagg, 1974).

The anatomy of the foot

The foot is comprised of only two digits, the third and fourth. All trace of the other digits has disappeared. The foot bones are united to form a cannon bone as in the horse. The first (proximal) phalanx is the only bone in the short pastern of the camel and is rather flattened. The second and third phalanges are the foundation of the foot and both are almost horizontal. The second phalanx is wide and flattened and embedded in the cutaneous pad which forms the sole (Fig. 4.11 and 4.12). The third (distal) phalanx is a small triangular bone, not flattened on the inner surface and not bearing a hoof. It carries a nail on the upper side only. The digits are joined by the cushion and the foot does not appear very cloven.

The foot has been described as resembling a tyre but filled with fat instead of air (Bligh, Cloudsley-Thompson and MacDonald, 1976). The cushion is made up of a number of fatty pads which are soft, semi-fluid and of a lighter-coloured tissue than the general body tissues. These pads, or balls, are separated by cartilage and surrounded by a sheath of collagen; towards the rear of the foot elastin

65

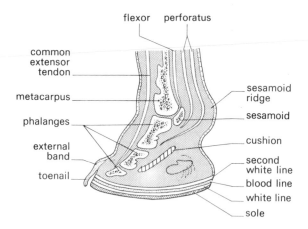

fig. 4.11 The camel's foot. (*Source*: **Droandi, I.** (1936). *Il cammello*. Istituto Agricolo Coloniale Italiano: Florence, Italy.)

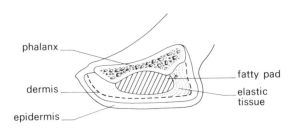

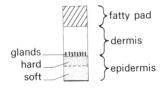

fig. 4.12 Section through the foot of the camel (*Source*: **Bligh, J., Cloudsley-Thompson, J. L. and MacDonald, A. G.** (1976). *Environmental physiology of farm animals.* Blackwood Scientific Publications: Oxford, UK.)

forms a major component of the tissue. The pads are largely composed of neutral triglycerides containing about 75 per cent of unsaturated fatty acids.

The fatty pads are covered by a fibrous rubbery sheath up to 10 mm thick (Fig. 4.12). This is essentially composed of an outer hard and inner soft layer of epidermis about 5 mm thick separated from the dermis by a layer of glands which serve to moisten the pad. The whole serves as a horny but supple sole for the foot.

The camel's foot is excellent for movement on sand. It is less suitable for traversing stony desert although some hardening occurs in animals habituated to this kind of country. It is equally unsuitable, in principle, for travel on slippery or muddy surfaces but some camels become adept at traversing even this kind of terrain.

Locomotion

The exceptional degree of rotation achieved at the fetlock is essential not only for keeping the foot flat on the ground but also in order for the camel to effect its normal gait. The camel is peculiar among domestic animals in that both legs on one side of the body move in unison (and not in opposition as is more normal), a type of locomotion which involves the hind foot being placed well in front of the forefoot on the same side.

Walking stride The long synchronised stride (Fig. 4.13(a)) involves the whole weight of the body being supported for a very considerable part of the time on either the two right or the two left legs (Dagg, 1974). This pacing gait is normal at the walk and is long and slow, averaging 38–43 steps per minute in the adult animal and economy is achieved both in covering distance and in the energy used to attain this.

Pacing gait The pace at trotting speed (Fig. 4.13(b)) is known to horseman as the pace or rack but called by Leese (1927) the jog. It is an unstable gait and is only suitable for flat terrain. This type of gait is not universal in the Camelidae – the vicuña, for example, has the more normal pattern of locomotion (Dagg, 1974).

Significant differences have been noted between the movements of young and old animals and of various trotting actions (Dagg, 1974). The fast run or **gallop** (Fig. 4.13(c)) is not a normal gait for the camel and is rarely used except for exhibitions, races and such. Dagg noted it only in animals chased away from watering points.

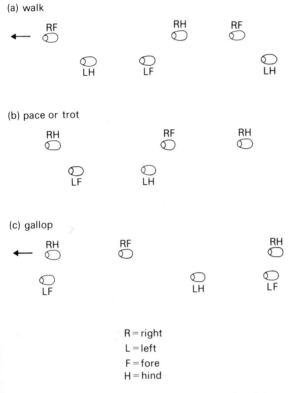

(a) walk

RF ⟵

RH   RF

LH   LF   LH

(b) pace or trot

RH   RF   RH

LF   LH

(c) gallop

RH ⟵   RF   RH

LF   LH   LF

R = right
L = left
F = fore
H = hind

fig. 4.13 Diagrammatic representation of three gaits of the camel (*Source*: a) **Dagg, A. I.** (1974). Locomotion of the camel, *Camelus dromedarius. J. Zool. Lond.*, **174**, 67–78; b) and c) **Cauvet, G.** (1925). *Le chameau*. Baillière: Paris, France.)

The quantitative data on speeds shown in Table 4.7, which are largely calculated from analysis of moving films, are in broad agreement with the earlier less scientific measurements of speed recorded by, for example, Leese (1927) in India and Somalia and by Gillespie (1962) in Sudan (see Chapter 10). If my calculations from Dagg's data are correct they also show another unusual fact about the camel which does not appear to have been noticed before – it increases speed mainly by increasing the speed of limb movement and not by lengthening its stride.

Rising and couching

When **rising** the camel thrusts its head forward with a jerk, rises to its knees and then lifts the hindquarters to the full extent. One foreleg is then lifted until that foot is flat on the ground; this leg is then used to lever up the whole animal until it is erect, the opposite foreleg being the last to touch the ground.

When **couching** one knee is lowered to the ground, followed almost simultaneously by the other. The hind legs are then bent until the stifle pads touch the ground, the forelimbs are settled and finally the bulk of the weight is taken on the breast pad.

Further reading

Bligh, J., Cloudsley-Thompson, J. C. C. and Mac-Donald, A. G. (1976). *Environmental physiology of farm animals*. Blackwell Scientific Publications: Oxford, UK.

Boas, J. E. V. (1890). *Zur Morphologie das Magens de Cameliden und der Tragulidan und über die systematische Stellung letzterer*

Table 4.7 Data on speed, duration and length of stride at various camel gaits. (*Source*: **Dagg, A. I.** (1974). Locomotion of the camel, *Camelus dreomedarius J. Zool. Lond.* **174**, 67–78.)

Gait	Speed		Duration of stride (seconds)	Strides per minute	Implied length of stride (metres)
	m per second	km per hour			
Walk	1·76	6·3	1·67	35·9	2·93
Pace(trot)	3·31	11·9	0·97	61·8	3·21
Gallop	5·20	18·7	0·56	107·1	2·91

Abtheilung. Morph. Jahrb., **16**, 494–524.

Bohlken, H. (1960). Remarks on the stomach and the systematic position of the Tylopoda. *Proc. Zool. Soc. Lond.*, **134**, 207–215.

Boué, A. (1948). *La masse sanguine chez le chameau. Rev. Elev. Méd. vét. Pays trop.*, **2**, 117.

Cauvet, G. (1929). *Dromadaires à 34 dents et dromadaires à 36 dents. Bull. Soc. Hist. Nat. Afrique Nord.*, **20(9)**, 247–256.

Cordier, J. (1893). *Recherches sur l'anatomie comparée de l'estomac des ruminants. Ann. Sci. Nat. (Zool.)*, **16**, 1–128.

Dagg, A. I. (1974). Locomotion of the camel, *Camelus dromedarius. J. Zool. Lond.*, **174**, 67–78.

Gillespie, I. A. (1962). Riding camels of the Sudan. *Sudan J. Vet. Sci. Anim. Husb.*, **3**, 37–42.

Hansen, H. and Schmidt-Nielsen, K. (1957). On the stomach of the camel with special reference to the mucous membrane. *Acta anat.*, **31**, 353–375.

Hassan, Y. M. (1968). Blood volume determination in camels (*Camelus dromedarius*). *Isotopenpraxis*, **4(2)**, 73.

Kanan, C. V. (1960). Notes on the vertebral column, ribs and sternum of the camel. *Sudan J. Vet. Sci. Anim. Husb.*, **1**, 84–91.

Kingdon, J. (1979). *East African mammals* Vol. III part B *Large mammals*. Academic Press: London.

Leese, A. S. (1927). *A treatise on the one-humped camel in health and disease*. Haynes & Son: Stamford, Lincs, UK.

Rabagliati, D. S. (1924). *The dentition of the camel*. Government Press: Cairo, Egypt.

Schmidt-Nielsen, K. (1964). *Desert animals: physiological problems of heat and water*. Oxford University Press: Oxford, UK.

Tayab, M. A. F. (1950). *La cavité buccale du chameau. Rev. Elev. Méd. vét. Pays trop.*, **4**, 147–160.

Wilson, R. T. (1978). Studies on the livestock of Southern Darfur, Sudan. V. Notes on camels. *Trop. Anim. Hlth Prod.*, **10**, 19–25.

5 · Physiology

"The camel can store in special compartments in its stomach vast amounts of water which it drinks when it can find it. It then makes use of this water when there is none in the deserts where it normally finds itself."

Pliny "Historia Naturalis"

General physiology of camels in the desert environment.

Until approximately 30 years ago the physiology of the camel was the subject of much speculation but of very little knowledge. Since that time, largely thanks to the work of Schmidt-Nielsen and his team (mainly in north-west Africa) and to Macfarlane and his co-workers (in Australia) much more is known and understood about the camel's adaptation to a desert life.

The brief summary which follows is drawn basically from Schmidt-Nielsen and Schmidt-Nielsen (1952) while the layout of the two subsequent sections is based on Macfarlane (1968).

The requirements for survival in hot arid areas are in general similar to those in other terrestrial environments. Temperature must be maintained and water must be conserved and, in large mammals particularly, there is often interaction and trade-off between the two. Small mammals escape the worst effects of temperature and dehydration by burrowing into the soil but obviously an animal the size of a camel cannot do this. However, its size and shape can be of advantage. Fig. 5.1 shows that the camel loses body heat by sweating more efficiently than smaller mammals. In most mammals fat is spread over the body surface just under the skin. This reduces the rate of evaporation of sweat. In the camel the fat is concentrated in the hump which enables sweat to be evaporated easily over the rest of the body surface. The camel's coat is fairly sparse which allows sweat to evaporate at the surface of the skin. In mammals with very thick coats evaporation occurs at the ends of the hairs, a less efficient process.

The combined attributes of the camel give it a greater comparative advantage than other mammals have achieved. For example, the camel can lose 25 per cent of its body weight over a period of time, without losing its appetite for food and can then make up this amount in just 10 minutes by drinking (p. 77). Donkeys are almost as efficient in this respect but the majority of animals die when they lose 12–15 per cent of their body weight.

In other animals water lost is drawn from the body tissues, the interstitial tissues and the blood plasma. As a result the blood becomes viscous and the heart can no longer pump it fast enough to transfer the deep body heat to the surface for evaporation. Explosive heat death then occurs. In camels very little water is drawn from the blood, which remains fluid and can thus continue its function of heat transfer.

Other adaptations to the desert environment in camels are listed below.

1 The body temperature can vary over a wide range under conditions of dehydration; the large mass of the camel acts as a heat buffer.

2 The camel is able to concentrate its urine to a considerable extent, urea is reabsorbed from the intestines and transferred back to the stomach for reconversion to protein.

Energy balance

Body size and metabolic rate

Body size, as Fig. 5.1 has shown, is very important in the turnover of energy, but is even more important in its effect on the metabolic rate. In mammals this is an exponential rather than a direct relationship. Metabolic rate is a function of mass raised to

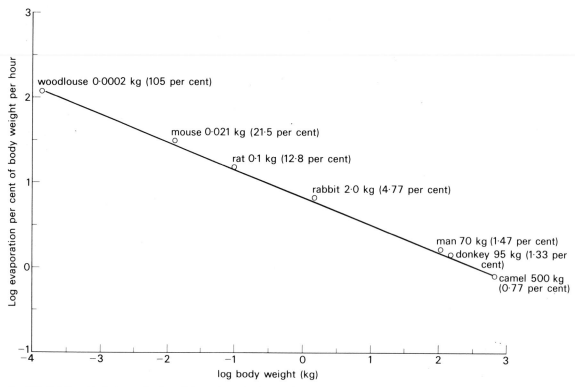

fig. 5.1 Relationship between body weight and required water loss to preserve a constant body temperature in desert conditions (*Source*: **Schmidt-Nielsen, K. and Schmidt-Nielsen, B.** (1952). Water metabolism in desert mammals. *Physiol. Rve.*, **32**, 135–166.)

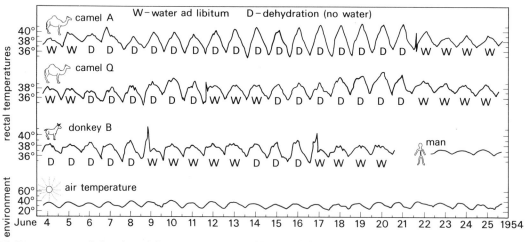

fig. 5.2 Temperature variations in camels, donkeys and man (*Source*: **Schmidt-Nielsen, K., Schmidt-Nielsen, B. Jarnum, S. A. and Houpt, T. R.** (1957). Body temperature of the camel and its relation to water economy. *Amer. J. Physiol.*, **186**, 103–112.)

the power of 0·75 and is usually expressed as $W^{0·75}$. Water turnover is also an exponential function of mass and is proportional to $W^{0·82}$. Metabolic rate and water turnover are thus related, and in large mammals where W is high there is a considerable saving, particularly during evaporative cooling.

Heat and temperature relations
The camel is able to save considerable amounts of energy by allowing its body tempeature to rise during the day, thus absorbing heat which would otherwise have to be dissipated by some form of cooling. The variations in the camel's temperature were formerly thought to be an indication of poor thermoregulation. It is now realised, however, that the rises in temperature indicate a sophisticated control mechanism rather than poor regulation.

In a camel watered daily (hydrated) the diurnal temperature variation is of the order of 2 °C which implies a heat storage of $4·2 \times 10^6$ J if the camel weighs 500 kg. In the dehydrated camel, however, when energy conservation becomes important, the temperature can fluctuate over a range of more than 6 °C. The camel is able to store $1·26 \times 10^7$ J of energy in this way. To dissipate this energy the camel would require to sweat 6 litres of water. Fig. 5.2 compares the temperature fluctuations of camels, donkeys and humans in the same environment.

The ability of the camel to raise its temperature also has the advantage of reducing heat gain. This is because the raised temperature reduces the heat gradient between the body and the air, and heat flow is proportional to the gradient. The energy gained during the day can be dissipated at night when ambient temperatures are lower.

Under conditions of dehydration and intense heat the camel also adopts behavioural mechanisms to conserve energy. The camel sits down in the early morning before the ground has warmed up. It tucks its legs underneath its body so that it absorbs little heat from the ground by conduction. The camel orientates itself towards the sun presenting the least possible body area for the absorption of radiant heat. Any heat absorbed from the ground or the sun would have to be dissipated later in the day. The camel may gradually change its position

during the day to follow the trajectory of the sun (Schmidt-Nielsen *et al.*, 1957a). A group of animals may lie down together (Gauthier-Pilters, 1958) thus presenting an even smaller target area for heat accumulation.

The camel's metabolic rate increases in the normal way as the temperature rises. The Q_{10} is slightly over 2 (Schmidt-Nielsen *et al.*, 1967).

Hair and skin
Theoretical considerations suggest that desert animals exposed to high levels of solar radiation and high temperatures should possess smooth reflective coats and black skins. In addition the coat should not be so thick as to prevent evaporation at the skin surface but not so thin as to allow too much heat to strike the body surface. High albedo values are achieved if the coat is light in colour while the black skin absorbs much of the ultraviolet light that penetrates the coat, preventing damage to tissue proteins.

The camel conforms well to these requirements in its normal summer coat which rather is dense, not too long (at least on the flanks) and normally of a light colour. The skin is black. A camel in its

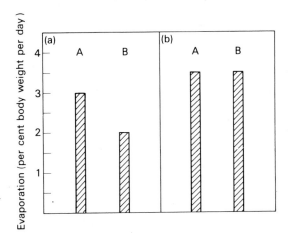

fig. 5.3 Comparative evaporation rates in summer between shorn and unshorn camels: a) camel A (shorn) evaporates more than camel B (unshorn); b) both camels shorn so both lose the same amount, the increased evaporation is due to higher ambient temperatures.

natural summer coat has fur about 30 mm thick on the flanks and straight short hair about 15 to 20 mm long on the belly and legs. Such an animal is able to maintain a lower body temperature than a camel with its fur shorn to 5-10 mm and since there is less heat to be dissipated requires to expend less energy (Schmidt-Nielsen *et al.*, 1957a). In fact, a camel in its natural summer coat evaporates much less water than a shorn camel (Fig. 5.3). When the same camel is shorn, water expenditure rises, and this demonstrates the effect of the coat on this aspect of energy conservation.

If the coat is too thick it may reduce evaporative heat loss at the body surface. The coolest point in a water/water vapour chain is at the point of change. If evaporation occurs at the skin surface while the fur remains dry, the heat flow from the environment, through the fur to the body is reduced. If the fur is too thick to allow evaporation at the skin surface the water from the skin wets the fur. Evaporation then occurs at the fur/air interface not at the skin surface. The resulting accumulation of heat has then to be dissipated by the expenditure of energy.

Evaporative cooling

Two main sources for evaporative cooling are via the respiratory tract and through the skin by sweating. Respiratory cooling as a means of heat dissipation is achieved by an increase in the respiratory rate. The normal respiratory rate in camels in the Sahara on cool mornings varies from 6 to 11 respirations per minute with an average of about 8 (Schmidt-Nielsen, 1964) but appears to be slightly higher, averaging 10 to 12, in Australia (Macfarlane, 1968). At high temperatures the rate increases to 8-18 (average 16) in the Sahara and to somewhere in the region of 20-24 in Australia. None of these rates significantly achieves increased evaporation, which requires rates of between 300 and 400 per minute in the dog. Higher rates obviously utilise much more energy than the lower ones. Camels avoid this energy expenditure by sweating through the skin since the nature of the coat allows efficient heat loss by this means. Camel sweat is high in potassium (about four times as much as sodium) and in hydrogen carbonate ions. The pH is 8·2-8·5 (Macfarlane, Morris and Howard, 1963).

Water balance

Water is essential to life and the camel has often to survive on limited quantities for long periods of time. To do this it has developed not only a very low rate of water use but mechanisms for restricting water loss as soon as its intake is reduced.

Water content

To dispel misunderstandings that have arisen in the past it is necessary to state that the camel does not store water, either in the stomach or in the hump, and that its body water content is in the normal range for all terrestrial mammals (Schmidt-Nielsen *et al.*, 1956a).

The hump is mainly comprised of fat and thus the metabolic water content is high. Complete oxidation of fat in the hump, say about 20 kg, would release a total of just over 21 kg of water. However, the cost in energy would be enormous, and more water would be lost through the lungs than would be made available from the hump. In fact,

Table 5.1 The water balance from oxidation of fat and starch at an estimated metabolic level of 41 868 × 10³ J (*Source*: **Schmidt-Nielson, K.** (1964). *Desert Animals*. Oxford University Press: Oxford.)

Substrate	Amount used (kg)	Oxidation water formed (kg)	Oxygen required in process (litres)	Water evaporated from lungs (kg)	Net water deficit (kg)
Fat	1·06	1·13	2 130	1·8	0·67
Starch	2·39	1·33	1 980	1·7	0·37

oxidation of an equivalent amount of starch yields less water but as less oxygen is needed the net gain is greater (Table 5.1). However, in normal metabolisms more starch is oxidised than fat, and more water is derived from starch than fat. Although there is a net loss of water used in oxidation the negative balance is less unfavourable for starch.

The camel's stomach contains a large amount of fluid secreted by the glandular sac areas (p. 59). The composition of this fluid is shown in Table 5.2. Its content is similar to that of saliva, while its osmotic concentration approaches that of blood (Schmidt-Nielsen, 1964). The sodium concentration in this fluid is high while the potassium and chloride concentrations are low. It is probable that the hydrogen carbonate concentration is also high as the pH of the fluid is 7·6–8·0. The sodium hydrogen carbonate would neutralise the acid products of rumen fermentation. The liquid is a rather startling green colour and has a strong odour but in emergency could certainly be used as a drinking water supply for humans with no other source.

The total water content in a camel may be as high as 75 per cent of body weight in a hot dry period, but this will drop to around 50 per cent in winter cold periods. Water content is modified by both the gut content and the fatness of the animal. In summer in India body water and intracellular fluid accounted respectively for 63·1 per cent and 44·5 per cent of total body weight while blood and plasma volumes are respectively 7·8 and 4·7 per cent (Ghosal, Appanna and Dwaraknath, 1974). In winter there were significant reductions in total body water, intracellular fluid, blood and plasma volume but an increase of intestinal fluid.

The increase of total body water induced by heat and malnutrition has been interpreted as advantageous under conditions of water shortage and represents an efficient regulatory mechanism. In a fully hydrated camel in which 70 per cent of the live weight is water, the body weight is accounted for by the following percentages:

the fluids of the alimentary canal	12
body cells	34
intracellular water	14
plasma	5

This is about the same percentage as for cattle in a tropical environment.

Water conservation

Water is lost from the body by evaporative cooling, in the urine and in the faeces. The camel is able to allow considerable temperature variation and by sweating instead of panting is able to achieve considerable savings not only of energy (p. 71), but also of water. The structure and function of the kidney are of extreme importance in water conservation. The long loops of Henle in the medulla have the function of urine concentration and the more loops there are the greater the degree of concentration that can be achieved. The ratio of medulla to cortex thickness is a useful index of potential reabsorption ability and this has recently been shown to be 4:1 in the camel (Abdalla and Abdalla, 1979).

The kidney controls water loss in two ways – by the absolute concentration achieved and by reduction in flow of urine. Camels are not the most efficient animals at concentrating urine. For example,

Table 5.2 Composition of rumen fluids, blood plasma and water. (*Source*: **Schmidt-Nielsen, K., Schmidt-Nielsen, B., Houpt, T. R. and Jarnum, S. A.** (1956). Water balance of the camel. *Amer. J. Physiol.*, **185**, 185–94).

Fluid	Na (mN)	K (mN)	Cl (mN)	Osmotic concentration (milliosmoles)
Rumen fluid	106·9	17·6	17·6	281
Sac fluid	109·4	17·6	17·5	282
Blood plasma	156·3	45·6	109·6	338
Water	1·4–1·9	(0)	1·46–2·34	

merino sheep in Australia can achieve a concentration of 3·5–3·8 osmoles per litre while camels in the same environment concentrate to 3·1 osmoles. The osmolality of plasma does not increase at the same rate during dehydration as that of urine. Dehydration results in the urine to plasma (u/p) ratio being increased from 5 to 8 (Maloiy, 1972a). Reduction in urine flow is thus the most important water conservation measure in the camel.

Concentration of urine not only serves to conserve water but allows camels to drink water even more concentrated than sea water and to eat very salty plants that would otherwise be poisonous. A peculiar variation occurs in the ratios of the salts excreted in the camel's urine. In most urine samples potassium is the dominant ion excreted but when the camel feeds on certain types of fodder, sodium can become the dominant ion (Schmidt-Nielsen et al., 1957b). Table 5.3 gives data on two urine samples and a comparison with sea water. The chloride concentration may reach a level of 1 068 mN per litre in animals deliberately fed salt (Charnot, 1958). In addition as urine flow is decreased there may be a change in the balance of ions excreted. Charnot (1958) found that the chloride concentration remained about the same, potassium doubled, sodium increased by 9 times and that of sulphate was increased 16 times. In a well-watered camel, sulphate is an insignificant ion in the urine but this massive increase suggests an extraordinary ability of the camel kidney to eliminate sulphate

The products of nitrogen metabolism are normally excreted in the form of urea by terrestrial animals. As can be seen from Table 5.3 urine concentrations of this compound can reach high levels. As the volume of urine output decreases urea content increases. There are differences, however, in growing animals with high protein requirements and these will be discussed on pp. 78–79.

The amount of urine flow is variable in camels as in other animals but the camel's bladder is very small in relation to the size of the animal. The bladder is thus emptied frequently where food and water intake are normal but the total urine volume, even in this state, rarely exceeds 7 litres per day. Individual discharges of urine are of low volume, varying from a 1–2 ml up to about 400 ml. The urine is voided in a series of distinct jets and the total process takes a considerable time. In the Sahara, a camel weighing 300 kg, fed on dry dates and hay but watered daily, had a daily urine output of 0·75 litres per day but during dehydration this output was reduced to 0·5 litres per day (Schmidt-Nielsen et al., 1956b). Normal urine flow in camels in arid areas is about 2 ml per minute or 3 litres per day in Australia (Macfarlane, 1968), a figure within the range of 1·5–5 litres per day given by Charnot (1958). During dehydration antidiuretic hormone (vasopressin) secreted from the neurohypophysis inhibits urine flow in the kidney (Siebert and Macfarlane, 1971). High concentrations of vasopressin in the plasma do, on the other hand, lead to an increase in the excretion rate of potassium, and of sodium to a lesser extent, which requires that the rate of water flow must be increased to cope with the increased electrolyte load (Fig. 5.4). The conserved sodium is retained mainly in the extramedullar fluid and is used later for osmotic readjustment when water becomes available.

A reduction in urine flow is also achieved by reducing the glomerular filtration rate from a norm of 55–65 ml per 100 kg body weight per minute to 15 ml per 100 kg per minute. The initial glomerular filtration rate in camels is about one-half that of sheep and cattle and its flow reduction is much more efficient. In camels it is reduced to one-quarter of the initial flow compared to about one-third for the other animals. Total urine flow in camels may be as low as 0·5–1·5 ml per minute with relatively low urine concentrations of 2–2·5 osmoles per litre (Siebert and Macfarlane, 1971).

Faecal water loss is also small in camels. Final reabsorption of water occurs in the colon and

Table 5.3 Concentration of urine samples from Saharan camels compared with that of sea water. (*Source*: as for Table 5.1)

Sample	Na (mN)	K (mN)	Cl (mN)	Urea (mN)
Camel 1	834	77	970	229
Camel 2	11	902	492	1 415
Sea water	470	10	548	

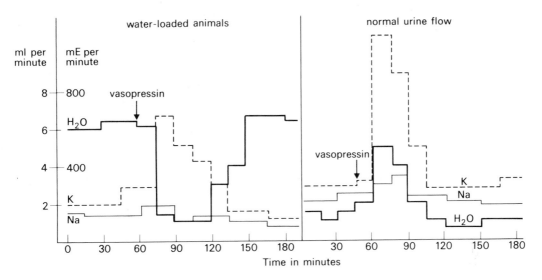

fig. 5.4 The effects of vasopressin on water flow and electrolyte excretion (*Source*: **Macfarlane, W. V.** (1968). Comparative functions of ruminants in hot environments. *In*: Hafez, E. S. E. (ed.) *Adaption of domestic animals*, pp. 264–276. Lea & Febiger: Philadelphia, USA.)

camels are again more efficient in their conservation mechanisms than other animals. Table 5.4 gives some comparative data on this aspect of water economy; the figures for the camel in this table are lower than some other figures from the same region of 168 g per 100 g for dehydrated animals and 268 g per 100 g for animals watering freely (Charnot, 1958). Australian figures give water contents as low as 38–40 per cent after 5 days of water deprivation (Macfarlane, 1968), a similar figure being obtained in Kenya (Maloiy, 1972a; 1972b). The dry weight of camel dung produced per day is of the order of 1 000 g; the water voided with it varies from 400 ml to 2 680 ml.

The results of these conservation measures mean that camels have a lower turnover of water than other animals. It should be noted that while camels have a lower rate of turnover on the basis of actual body weight they are slightly less efficient in terms of metabolism at $W^{0.82}$ (188 ml per $kg^{0.82}$ per day) than tropical goats (185 ml per $kg^{0.82}$ per day) and only slightly more efficient than sheep (197 ml per $kg^{0.82}$ per day) (Fig. 5.5).

Table 5.4 Comparative water excretion in faeces, expressed as grams water per 100 grams dry faeces. (*Source*: as for Table 5.1).

Animal and diet	Water excretion
Camel, hay and dates, no water	76 ± 2·5
Camel, hay and dates, watered daily	109 ± 5
Donkey, hay and dates, watered daily	181 ± 12
Kangaroo rat, barley, no water	83
White rat, barley, water	225
Man, mixed diet	200
Cow, grazing	566

Dehydration and weight loss

In cool temperatures averaging less than about 22 °C camels can go for long periods without drinking, obtaining sufficient water from their food to maintain a physiological balance. When day temperatures reach 40 °C and temperatures at

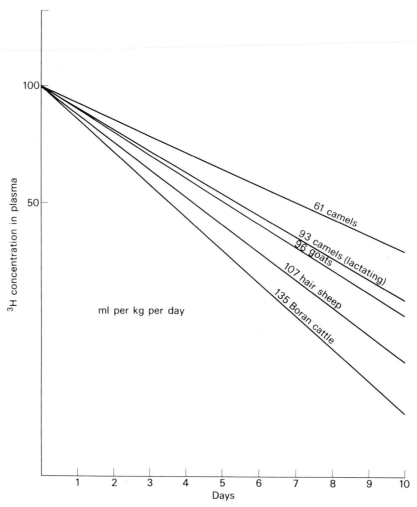

fig. 5.5 Turnover of water (expressed as tritium oxide concentration in tropical ruminants) (*Source*: **Macfarlane, W. V. Morris, R. J. H. and Howard B.** (1962). Water metabolisum of Merino sheep and camels. *Australian J. Sci.*, **25**, 112-121; and as for Fig. 5.4.)

night do not fall below 25 °C a steady loss of water from the body occurs through evaporative cooling, urine and faeces. If this is not made up by drinking, loss of body weight results. Camels are able to tolerate this dehydration much better than other animals as exhibited by their ability to go on grazing normally for long periods. As we have shown they also lose less weight as a proportion of their initial weight. Some comparative total weight losses per day are: 6·1 per cent in cattle, 4-5 per cent in sheep and about 2 per cent in camels. At these rates of loss, losing in total about 28-32 per cent before death supervenes, cattle would die in 4 days without water, sheep in about 7 and camels in

15 or more (Macfarlane, Morris and Howard, 1962; Siebert and Macfarlane, 1975). The sources of these losses are interesting:

cattle

body solids	⅓
alimentary tract and intracellular spaces	⅓
interstitial spaces and plasma	⅓

camels

body solids and plasma	very little
alimentary tract and intracellular spaces	½
interstitial spaces	⅓

These changes for the camel are shown pictorially in Fig. 5.6 for three camels which averaged a weight loss of 20 per cent after 9 days of dehydration. Cattle under dehydration lose 20 per cent of the plasma volume, and packed cell volume (PCV) rises by 20 per cent while albumin concentration, increases by only 8 per cent and total protein by only 29 per cent. In cattle as in most other animals the turgidity of the blood results in the heart's being unable to pump it to the surface fast enough to achieve sufficient cooling of the body and explosive heat death occurs. In camels while plasma volume falls it does not do so to the same extent and the PCV does not rise, due to the ability of the camel's red cells to shrink to a greater extent. In addition total proteins in camels' blood increase by more than 70 per cent including a rise in albumin of more than 20 per cent. The albumin in the plasma increases the osmotic pressure which is instrumental in holding fluid in the vascular spaces, even perhaps drawing it from the gut, and circulation can thus be maintained.

When water becomes available camels rehydrate very rapidly. Schmidt-Nielsen (1964) reports camels taking in more than 25 per cent of their body weight regularly and more than 30 per cent on some occasions. He suggests that camels immediately drink enough water to replace the amount lost through dehydration and has records of camels drinking 104 litres at a single session. Gauthier-Pilters (1958) has a record of 186 litres, in two bouts of 94 litres and 92 litres, being taken by a camel in one period of 24 hours after 5 days of

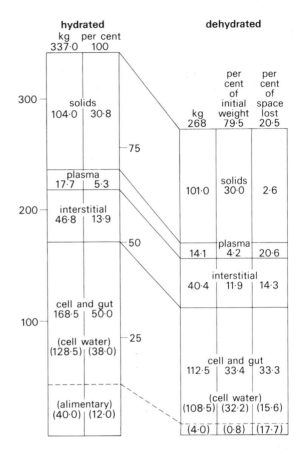

fig. 5.6 Mean body composition of three camels before and after 9 days without water. (*Source*: **Macfarlane, W. V., Morris, R. J. H., and Howard, B.** (1963). Turnover and distribution of water in desert camels, sheep, cattle and kangaroos. *Nature*, Lond., **197**, 270–271.)

thirst. Such a rapid ingress of water would normally place great strain on the regulatory mechanisms, were it immediately to enter into the system, causing the blood corpuscles to swell and break. This does not appear to be important in the camel as the resilient corpuscles are capable of reverting to their original size and shape even after rupturing (Peck, 1939). In fact, camels have the most resilient corpuscles in a series of 15 domestic and laboratory animals (Perk, Frei and Herz, 1964).

Other work (Macfarlane, Morris and Howard, 1962) has shown that camels do not necessarily rehydrate to the full extent immediately. Initially they may take in only about 60 per cent of the weight lost and may not achieve equilibrium for 18–24 hours. The arrival of water in the alimentary tract results in a fall of plasma sodium and a concentration of the plasma as water and salts passes into the alimentary tract. A gut fluid isotonic with the blood is achieved. During this time urine flow and sodium and potassium excretion remain low (Fig. 5.7) and only increase when tissue equilibrium is achieved. These flows are once again inhibited when further water is taken in to restore the original weight loss.

As a brief comparative summary to these last two sections on energy balance and water relations Table 5.5 shows some of the ways tropical animals have found solutions to the problems encountered.

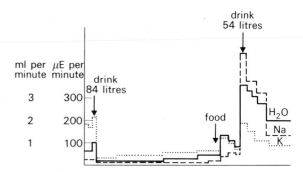

fig. 5.7 Effects of rehydration in the camel on water and electrolyte output. (*Source*: as for Fig. 5.4.)

Nitrogen metabolism

All vertebrates rely on the kidney for nitrogenous excretion. Normally, as urine flow decreases, urea

Table 5.5 Comparative effectiveness of energy and water conservation measures in tropical domestic animals (*Source*: **Macfarlane, W. V.** (1968). Comparative functions of ruminants in hot environments. *In*: Hafez, E.S.E. (ed.) *Adaptation of domestic animals*, pp. 264–276. Lea and Febiger: Philadelphia, USA.)

Animal species	Coat		Evaporative cooling		Water conservation		Coat colour
	reflect-tance	insul-ation	respi-ratory	sweat-ing	renal	faecal	
Sheep (Merino)	+	+++	+++	+	++	++	white
Sheep (hair)	++	++	++	++	++	++	dark
Goat	++	+	++	++	++	++	dark
Bos taurus (shorthorn)	++	+	++	++	+	+	white
Bos indicus *Bibos banteng*	+++	±	+	+++	+	++	black
Buffalo			+	+++	+	+	black
Camel (subtropical)	++	+		+++	+++	+++	black
(equatorial)	+++	±		+++	+++	+++	black

+++ major effect, high efficiency
 ++ moderate activity
  + some effect
  ± little action

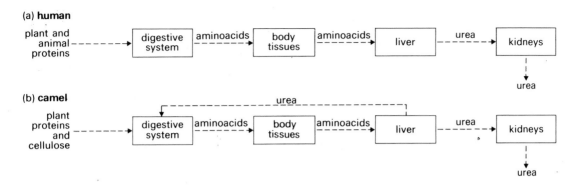

(a) **human**

plant and animal proteins → digestive system → aminoacids → body tissues → aminoacids → liver → urea → kidneys → urea

(b) **camel**

plant proteins and cellulose → digestive system → aminoacids → body tissues → aminoacids → liver → urea → kidneys → urea (with urea feedback from liver to digestive system)

fig. 5.8 Nitrogen metabolism in man and in the camel. (*Source*: **Schmidt-Nielsen, K.** (1959). The physiology of the camel. *Sci. Ameri.* **200**, 140–151.)

concentration increases and this is true for all mammals including camels. In camels with high protein requirements, such as young growing animals and lactating females the output of urea falls as urine volume is reduced. This is particularly the case in animals on low-protein diets, and again urea appears in the urine when protein intake is increased. In one experiment (Schmidt-Nielsen *et al.*, 1957b) the concentration of urea in the urine dropped to 1·5 mM per litre, lower than that found in the blood, which is in the range of 2–10 mM per litre. The total urea excreted was less than 1 g in 24 hours. This corresponds to a metabolism of only 2·5 g protein per day, which is obviously far too low. When 475 mM of urea were injected into the blood stream only 30 mM were recovered in the urine thus showing active synthesis into protein. This results from urea entering the rumen fluid where it is converted by bacteria to protein (Fig. 5.8). Farther along the digestive tract the bacterial protein is digested by the camel and the urea returns via the blood stream to the alimentary canal to be used again. It is not clear whether the regulation of urea excretion by the kidney involves active transport or whether it is a simple diffusion process.

While camels are best known for their ability to reduce urea output this phenomenon is not solely confined to them. It has been shown for example (Payne, 1965) that *Bos taurus* cattle are able to reduce Urea-N output from 36·1 g to 2·3 g daily when deprived of water or when water intake is significantly reduced due to longer than normal intervals between waterings.

Blood chemistry

In recent years a considerable amount of research has been carried out on the blood chemistry of the camel. Much of this has taken place in India, Egypt and Sudan, and to a lesser extent in Israel. Unfortunately, many of the results appear to be contradictory, the anomalies perhaps arising from different methods of analysis and the difficulties of reproducing the same conditions in exactly the same way. Some of the differences can be explained by seasonal and nutritional factors and by the effects of sex and the rut but many anomalies are unexplained.

Dehydration is the principal factor affecting blood chemistry. Although it is known that PCV remains almost constant (p. 77), what happens to total serum proteins is not established. Reports from Macfarlane in Australia and other workers in India (Ghosal, Appanna and Dwaraknath, 1975) indicate a rise in total serum proteins but a Sudanese worker has recorded a lowering of total serum proteins, due to a fall in globulins while albumin rose from 40·7 to 75·5 per cent (Hassan, 1971). In these experiments the erythrocyte (red cell) count, which is normally about $7·24 \times 10^6$ per 100 ml of serum (Banerjee, Bhattacharjee and

Singh, 1962), rose slightly. This rise may be related to the longer half-life (12 days) and survival time (150 days) of red blood cells during dehydration when compared with 8 and 120 days respectively in hydrated camels (Yagil, Sod-Moriah and Meyerstein, 1974). The lengthening of survival time may contribute to the water conservation ability. In the same series of experiments the acid – base parameters were also studied. The pH rose from 7·25 to 7·32 and pCO_2 from 29·4 to 48·0 mm of mercury. Sodium and magnesium rose while blood pO_2 and calcium levels fell. These changes have also been interpreted as an additional mechanism to conserve body water (Yagil, Etzion and Berlyne, 1975).

Blood sugar has a fairly wide range of levels ranging from 74 to 140 mg glucose per 100 ml (Chavanne and Boué, 1950; Kumar and Banerjee, 1962; Maloiy, 1972b; Yagil and Berlyne, 1977). In general it seems that blood glucose levels are higher in females than in males and slightly lower in the dry season than when feed is green. The levels are higher and more variable than those found in cattle under similar conditions. When large infusions of glucose are given to fully hydrated camels, the glucose is readily removed in the urine with only a slight increase in blood levels. Following dehydration, blood glucose levels increase considerably but excretion in the urine is reduced. Conversely insulin levels fall with dehydration but injection of glucose leads to the balance being restored. These data have led to the conclusion that camels are not only acclimatised to conserving body water under desert conditions but are able to adapt very quickly to acute non-physiological stresses to prevent loss of body water.

The specific gravity of whole blood is about 1·05 in both summer and winter in India, that of serum 1·02 and of plasma 1·03. Haemoglobin values are about 11·7 g per 100 ml, red cells 5·54 – 7·2 × 10^6 per millilitre and white cells 11·8 – 18·1 × 10^3 per millilitre. None of these is affected by age or sex of the animal.

Chloride levels are generally higher in camels than in other species. They rise with maturity, but are not affected by pregnancy, lactation or health. Inorganic phosphorus is also higher than in other species (Ayoub, Awad and Bayyazeed, 1960;

Banerjee, Bhattacharjee and Singh, 1962; Bhattacharjee and Banerjee, 1962; Ghosal, Appanna and Dwaraknath, 1973; Lakhotia, Bhargava and Mehrotra, 1964). Copper and iron (essential for haemoglobin) and zinc (for some enzymes) are present at different levels in comparison with other domestic animals, as shown in Table 5.6: copper is generally higher, iron is intermediate and zinc is low.

Table 5.6 Copper, iron and zinc values in the serum of farm animals in Egypt (*Source*: Moty, I. A., Muller, A. el and Zaafer, S. A. (1968). Copper, iron and zinc in the serum of Egyptian farm animals. *Sudan Agric. J.*, 3, 146 – 151.)

Animal (number in sample)	Copper	Iron	Zinc
	(gamma/100 ml)		
Buffalo (30)	72 ± 7·4	254 ± 17·0	144 ± 5·0
Cow (29)	64 ± 4·4	162 ± 14·0	144 ± 4·2
Sheep (32)	82 ± 4·4	182 ± 6·0	160 ± 4·8
Camel (19)	83 ± 6·7	186 ± 3·9	135 ± 4·1

Further reading

Abdalla, M. A. and Abdalla, O. (1979). Morphometric observations on the kidney of the camel *Camelus dromedarius*. *J. Anat.*, **129**, 45 – 50.

Ayoub, M. H., Awad, Y. L. and Bayyazeed, L. A. (1960). Calcium level in Egyptian farm animals. *Indian J. Vet. Sci.*, **30**, 43 – 49.

Banerjee, S., Bhattacharjee, R. C. and Singh, T. I. (1962). Hematological studies in the normal adult Indian camel (*Camelus dromedarius*). *Amer. J. Physiol.*, **203**, 1185 – 1187.

Bhattacharjee, R. C. and Banerjee, S. (1962). Biochemical studies on Indian camel (*Camelus dromedarius*). *J. Sci. Indust. Res.*, **21C**, 106 – 107.

Charnot, Y. (1958). *Répercussion de la déhydration sur la biochimie et l'endocrinologie du dromadaire*. Theses, Université de Paris VIe: Paris, France.

Chavanne, P. and Boué, A. (1950). *Taux normaux de l'urée et du glucose sanguin chez le droma-*

daire nord-africain. Rev. Elev. Méd. vét. Pays trop., **4**, 183.

Gauthier-Pilters, H. (1958). *Quelques observations sur l'écologie et l'éthologie du dromadaire dans le Sahara nord-occidental. Mammalia*, **22**, 294–316.

Ghosal, A. K., Appanna, T. C. and Dwaraknath, P. K. (1973). Studies on the seasonal variations in the blood constituents of Indian camel (*Camelus dromedarius*). *Indian J. Anim. Sci.,* **43**, 642–644.

Ghosal, A. K., Appanna, T. C. and Dwaraknath, P. K. (1974). Seasonal variations in water compartments of the Indian camel. *Brit. Vet. J.,* **130**, 2.

Ghosal, A. K., Appanna, T. C. and Dwaraknath, P. K. (1975). A note on the effect of short-term water deprivation on certain blood characteristics of the camel. *Indian J. Anim. Sci.,* **45**, 105–108.

Hassan, Y. M. (1971). A note on the effect of dehydration on a camel. *Sudan J. Vet. Sci. Anim. Husb.,* **12**, 111–112.

Kumar, M. and Banerjee, S. (1962). Biochemical studies on the Indian camel (*Camelus dromedarius*). 3. Plasma insulin-like activity and glucose tolerance. *J. Sci. Indust. Res.,* **21C**, 291–292.

Lakhotia, R. L., Bhargava, A. K. and Mehrotra, P. N. (1964). Normal ranges for some blood constituents of the Indian camel. *Vet. Rec.,* **76**, 121–122.

Macfarlane, W. V. (1968). Comparative functions of ruminants in hot environments. In: Hafez, E. S. E. (ed.) *Adaptation of domestic animals*, pp. 264–276. Lea and Febiger: Philadelphia, USA.

Macfarlane, W. V., Morris, R. J. H. and Howard, B. (1962). Water metabolism of Merino sheep and camels. *Aust. J. Sci.,* **25**, 112–121.

Macfarlane, W. V., Morris, R. J. H. and Howard, B. (1963). Turnover and distribution of water in desert camels, sheep, cattle and kangaroos. *Nature, Lond.,* **197**, 270–271.

Maloiy, G. M. O. (1972a). Renal salt and water excretion in the camel (*Camelus dromedarius*). *Symp. Zool. Soc. Lond.,* **31**, 243–259.

Maloiy, G. M. O. (1972b). Comparative studies on

digestion and fermentation rate in the free-stomach of the one-humped camel and the zebu steer. *Res. Vet. Sci.,* **13**, 476–481.

Payne, W. J. A. (1965). Specific problems of semiarid environments. *Qual. Plant. Mat. Veg.* **12**, 269–294.

Peck, E. F. (1939). Salt intake in relation to cutaneous necrosis and arthritis of one-humped camels (*Camelus dromedarius*) in British Somaliland. *Vet. Rec.,* **51**, 1355–1360.

Perk, F., Frei, Y. F. and Herz, A. (1964). Osmotic fragility of red blood cells of young and mature domestic and laboratory animals. *Amer. J. Vet. Res.,* **25**, 1241–1248.

Schmidt-Nielsen, K. (1964). *Desert animals: physiological problems of heat and water*. Oxford University Press: Oxford, UK.

Schmidt-Nielsen, K. and Schmidt-Nielsen, B. (1952). Water metabolism in desert mammals. *Physiol. Rev.,* **32**, 135–166.

Schmidt-Nielsen, K., Schmidt-Nielsen, B., Houpt, T. R. and Jarnum, S. A. (1956a). The question of water storage in the stomach of the camel. *Mammalia*, 20, 1–15.

Schmidt-Nielsen, B., Schmidt-Nielsen, K., Houpt, T. R. and Jarnum, S. A. (1956b). Water balance of the camel. *Amer. J. Physiol.,* **185**, 185–194.

Schmidt-Nielsen, K., Schmidt-Nielsen, B., Jarnum, S. A. and Houpt, T. R. (1957a). Body temperature of the camel and its relation to water economy. *Amer. J. Physiol.,* **188**, 103–112.

Schmidt-Nielsen, K., Schmidt-Nielsen, B., Houpt, T. R. and Jarnum, S. A. (1957b). Urea excretion in the camel. *Amer. J. Physiol.,* **188**, 477–484.

Schmidt-Nielsen, K., Crawford, E. C., Jr, Newsome, A. E., Rawson, K. S. and Hammel, H. T. (1967). Metabolic rate of camels: effect of body temperature and dehydration. *Amer. J. Physiol.,* **212**, 341–346.

Siebert, B. D. and Macfarlane, W. V. (1971). Water turnover and renal function of dromedaries in the desert. *Physiol. Zool.,* **44**, 225–240.

Siebert, B. D. and Macfarlane, W. V. (1975). Dehydration in desert cattle and camels. *Physiol.*

Zool., **48**, 36–48.

Yagil, R., Sod-Moriah, U. A. and Meyerstein, N. (1974). Dehydration and camel blood. I. Red blood cell survival in the one-humped camel (*Camelus dromedarius*). *Amer. J. Physiol.*, **226**, 298–300.

Yagil, R., Etzion, Z. and Berlyne, G. M. (1975). Acid-base parameters in the dehydrated camel. *Tydschr. Diergeneesk.*, **100**, 1105–1108.

Yagil, R. and Berlyne, G. M. (1977). Glucose loading and dehydration in the camel. *J. Appl. Physiol.*, **42**, 690–693.

6 Reproduction and breeding

*"The sexual life of the camel is
stranger than anyone thinks
At the height of the mating
season . . . ."*

Barrackroom ballad to the
tune of the Eton Boating Song

The female reproductive tract and genitalia

Fig. 6.1 shows the female reproductive organs of the camel.

Ovary, Graafian follicle and corpus luteum

The ovaries are flattened, lobulated and reddish brown in colour, and each is enclosed in an ovarian bursa. It is similar in structure to that of other domestic animals but, unlike buffaloes and cows, medullary tubes (normally seen only in the embryos of these two species) are present in four out of five camel ovaries. As these tubes are often of an actively secreting nature they may not be just vestigial embryonic structures but could fulfil an active endocrine function (Tayeb, 1950; Shehata, 1964; Nawito *et al.*, 1967).

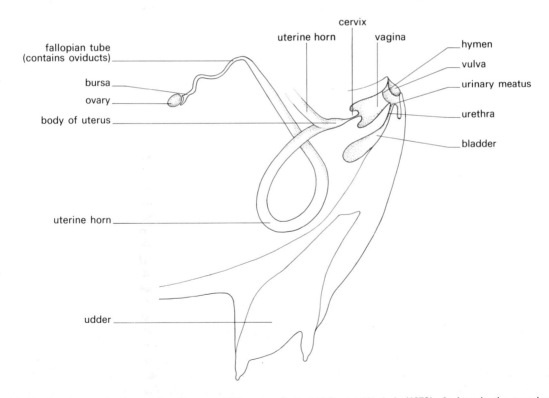

fig. 6.1 The female reproductive organs. (*Source*: **Williamson, G. A. and Payne, W. J. A.** (1978). *An introduction to animal husbandry in the tropics*. Longman: London.)

The size of the ovary is of the order of 15 mm $\times$ 30 mm $\times$ 35 mm and its weight is between 5 and 15 g. The size and weight depend to some extent on the activity. Non-functioning ovaries may weigh as little as 3·7 g, those with Graafian follicles 5·5 g and those containing a corpus luteum of pregnancy about 8 g (Shalash and Nawito, 1964; Chahrasbi, Radmehr and Goulbazhagh, 1975).

Graafian follicles occasionally persist into pregnancy but in non-pregnant females are distributed randomly over the ovarian surface. They are opaque and spherical and up to 18 mm in diameter.

The ovarian activity is mainly follicular rather than luteal and a corpus luteum is usually seen only during pregnancy (p. 87), occasionally two corpora lutea are present (Shalash and Nawito, 1964; Musa and Abusineina, 1978b). Corpora lutea, however, occasionally may be present without pregnancy (Abdo, Al-Janabi and Al-Kafawi, 1969; Nawar, Abul-Fadle and Mahmoud, 1978). Both the Graafian follicles and the corpora lutea are limited in position to the cortical stroma and project prominently from the surface, as in the female pig (Abdalla, 1965).

The oviducts

The oviducts, which are 170–280 mm in length, follow a tortuous course to the horns but more so in the ovarian part of the Fallopian tube and the ampulla than in the isthmus. They are soft and flabby except in the area of the isthmus where there is a thick, fibrous muscle layer. The fimbriae lie in the bursa at the ovarian end of the tubes (Tayeb, 1953; Abdalla, 1967). Unlike in other mammals the oviducts are enlarged at the uterine end, this unique arrangement allowing prolonged storage of large numbers of spermatozoa (Steklenev, 1968).

The uterus and placenta

The camel has a bicornate uterus which is T- rather than the normal Y-shaped. The body is rather short, reddish in colour and smooth, the left horn being longer than the right. The uterus is usually abdominal in position and increases in weight during follicular activity.

The placenta, as in all Camelidae is diffuse and epitheliochorial in nature, without cotyledons. Per-

haps surprisingly this was one of the earliest scientific facts known about the camel, being first recorded almost 140 years ago (Savi, 1843).

The vagina and cervix

The cervix consists of out-growth ridges arranged in 3 or 4 rows and the vagina is some 300–350 mm in length lined with mucosal folds. It is wide and extensible and with advancing pregnancy the uterine weight tends to stretch the mucosal folds. The canals of Gartner are large and the Bartholin glands are also well developed (Tayeb, 1953).

The vulva

The vulva is 30 to 50 mm deep with thick velvety lips, the clitoris being very small. The urethra is short and the opening of the urinary meatus is small. The hymen, or its remnants mark the separation between the vulva and the vagina (Tayeb, 1953).

Mammary glands

The udder has four quarters, the front two are separated more distinctly from each other than they are from the two smaller rear quarters. The udder is covered by a thin black skin. The teats are small and have three small openings.

The follicular wave and the reproductive cycle in females

The follicular wave

The regular and recurring hormonally controlled sequence of events which culminates in the spontaneous release of an ovum (or of ova) is known as the oestrus cycle. The term oestrus cycle, properly used, thus refers to animals which are spontaneous ovulators, this type of ovulation being the norm in the majority of animals.

In a few mammals including cats, the rabbit and the camel, rupture of the follicle does not occur spontaneously, coitus being required to induce release of the ova. In these animals the neuro-endocrine reflex involving the initiation of luteinising hormone release is delayed until coitus occurs. This type of cycle, involving reflex or induced ovulation is more properly known as a follicular

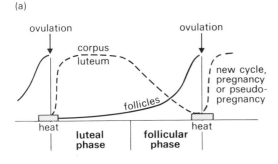

(a)

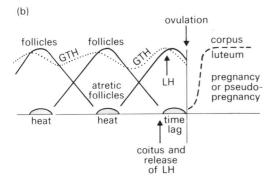

(b)

fig. 6.2 A comparison of events in: a) spontaneous, and b) induced ovulation in oestrus cycles and follicular waves. (*Source*: **Nalbandov, A. V.** (1976). *Reproductive physiology* (3rd ed.) W. H. Freeman & Co: London, UK.)

wave. A comparison of the principal events involved in spontaneous and reflex ovulation is shown in Fig. 6.2.

Phases of the follicular wave
In the spontaneous ovulators the oestrus cycle occurs in four distinct phases known as pro-oestrus, oestrus, meta-oestrus and di-oestrus. In induced ovulators and specifically in the camel, there are also four distinct phases but the normal terminology is not appropriate (Nawito, Shalash, Hoppe and Rakha, 1967). The four phases of the follicular wave in camels are:

1 Mature follicular stage, equivalent to oestrus or heat. The camel should not be considered to be in continuous oestrus in spite of the fact that ovarian maturity is follicular. Unlike the rabbit, which will accept the male at any time, the female camel will accept the male only during the mature follicular stage. There is no normal luteal phase.

2 The atritic follicular stage commences after a varying period of time if mating does not occur. Atresia is probably due to degeneration and phagocytosis of the granulosa of the follicles or to the extravasation of blood and the formation of blood follicles.

3 The non-follicular stage.

4 The growing follicular stage.

Duration of the wave, polyoestrus and seasonality
It has long been accepted that camels are polyoestric but it was also thought that oestrus occurred only at certain times of the year, in Iran for example in the cold season (Islamy, 1950) and in Pakistan from December to March (Yasin and Abdul Wahid, 1957). A fuller treatment of geographical variation in breeding seasons is given on pp. 96–97.

In Egypt large numbers of animals were examined in slaughterhouse studies and it is these studies which have contributed most to an understanding of the follicular wave phasing (Nawito, Shalash, Hoppe and Rakha, 1967). Follicular wave activity was shown by these studies to occur all the year round although the length of the whole wave, the phasing and the duration of oestrus vary considerably. Fig. 6.3 shows some of the changes that occur in the length of the wave and of the phases at different seasons. Follicular activity is at its greatest in winter and spring, roughly from December to March or April in Lower (northern) Egypt and the total cycle is longer at this period. During the summer, mature follicles are found in only a few animals (i.e. the phase lasts for only a very short time) and the growing follicular stage is prolonged in relation to the cycle as a whole. Generally, in summer the wave is often incomplete and oestrus does not occur.

In Egypt, the mean duration of the follicular wave was 24·2 days with oestrus lasting 4·6 days within a range of 0–15 days. These figures have been confirmed by more recent work both in Sudan where the length of the wave was 28 days with

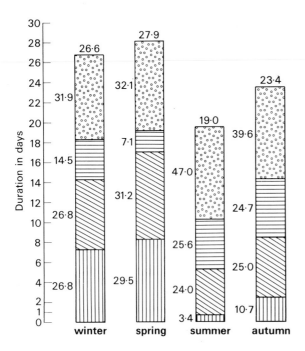

follicular stages:

[∘∘∘] growing-follicular

[≡] non-follicular

[◫] atretic-follicular

[⊞] mature-follicular

fig. 6.3 Seasonal effects on duration of total time and individual phases of the follicular wave: figures on top of columns – duration in days of total waves; figures at sides – per cent of total time occupied by each stage (*Source:* **Nawito, M. F. Shalash M. R. Hoppe, R. and Rakha, A. M.** (1967). Reproduction in the female camel, *Bull. Anim. Sci. Res. Inst.* Cairo, No. 2.)

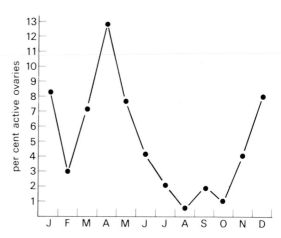

fig. 6.4 Variation in the activity of camels' ovaries by month of year (*Source:* **Shalash, M. R. and Nawito, M. F.** (1964). Some reproductive aspects in the female camel. *Ve Congr. Rep. Anim. I.A. Trento.* 2, 263 – 273.)

These show clearly that pregnancy (and therefore copulation, a fact which also has implications for male sexual physiology, see p. 90) can occur at any time of the year but for general practical purposes it would be correct to consider the camel a seasonal breeder throughout most of its normal range.

External signs of oestrus or heat

Anatomical, physiological and behavioural signs of heat are evident. The intensity of heat varies both individually and seasonally. In India, for example, 14, 31 and 55 per cent of female camels exhibited weak, moderate or intense signs respectively.

Camels in heat become restless, bleat continuously and associate with the male; the tail is lifted and flapped and they urinate little and often. The lips of the vulva swell and open and close irregularly. There is usually a more or less copious emission of mucus, foul smelling to humans but presumably a powerful and attractive olfactory stimulus for the male camel.

Vaginal examination reveals that it is pink-coloured and moist, although the degree of wetness decreases as heat progresses. The cervix is moist and relaxed. Rectal examination will reveal that the uterine horns are turgid at the beginning of heat – although not so much as in the cow – and

oestrus normally lasting 4 – 6 days within a range of 1 – 7 days (Musa and Abusineina, 1978b) and in India where wave duration was 23·4 days and oestrus averaged 5·0 days within a range of 3 – 6 days (Joshi, Vyas and Pareek, 1978). The only disagreement is the one of Matharu (1966) who says oestrus occurs every 15 days.

Table 6.1 shows some data on ovarian activity by seasons and Fig. 6.4 is based on a monthly analysis of these figures relating to total ovarian activity.

Table 6.1 Variation in ovarian activity determined from post-mortem examinations in Egyptian slaughterhouses (*Source*: Nawito, M. F., Shalash, M. R., Hoppe, R. and Rakha, A. M. (1967). Reproduction in the female camel. *Bull. Anim. Sci. Res. Inst.* (*Cairo*), No. 2.)

State of ovaries	Percentage of ovaries			
	Winter (n = 467)	Spring (n = 601)	Summer (n = 237)	Autumn (n = 423)
Non-functioning	31·7	29·6	67·5	46·8
Follicles less than 10 mm diameter	6·4	4·0	6·7	8·7
Follicles greater than 10 mm diameter	9·4	11·3	7·6	5·0
Corpora lutea	52·5	55·1	18·1	39·5

Graafian follicles but not corpora lutea can be felt on the ovary (Joshi, Vyas and Pareek, 1978).

Pregnancy and parturition

Initiation and maintenance
Ovulation is induced by copulation, the ova being shed about 32–40 hours afterward, under the influence of the luteinising hormone (LH). The LH induces corpus luteum formation. Fertilisation of the ovum need not, of course, occur after every mating but induction of the corpus luteum takes place. A sterile mating is normally followed by pseudo-pregnancy with resultant initiation of the corpus luteum which regresses after a time. In the Egyptian studies a corpus luteum lasted for 32 days but it is possible in this case that fertilisation did take place followed by early embryonic mortality.

In the case of fertilisation the corpus luteum persists in the ovaries throughout the full term of gestation. It is not certain whether the corpus luteum is required to maintain pregnancy (as, for instance, in rabbits and rats) or whether its loss after a certain period (as in the sheep and the horse) would be of no consequence. In these early Egyptian studies (Nawito, Shalash, Hoppe and Rakha, 1967) corpora lutea were found only in pregnant females but later studies, also in Egypt, have demonstrated some mature corpora lutea in non-pregnant camels in the spring (Nawar, Abul-Fadle and Mahmoud, 1978). These, of course, may

have resulted from pseudo-pregnancy or early embryonic death as regressed corpora lutea, occasionally two or three in the same ovary (indicating that either of the above events had occurred) were found throughout the year. The presence of corpora lutea does not necessarily prevent follicular growth and Graafian follicles were seen in 4·8 per cent of pregnancies in Egypt, such activity also being not uncommon in early gestation in Sudan.

Location in the uterus and multiple ovulation
The left ovary apparently is more active than the right; a very high percentage of pregnancies occur in the left horn of the uterus, for example 98·6 in Sudan (Musa and Abusineina, 1976), and 99·24 in Egypt (Shalash and Nawito, 1964). Migration of the ovum is a not infrequent occurrence, 37·7 per cent of foetuses and corpora lutea occurring on opposite sides and indicating that the right ovary is not entirely useless.

Multiple ovulation, as represented by multiple corpora lutea, occurs in about 12·5 per cent of cases in Egypt but only 0·13 per cent had twin foetuses with the same percentage of triple foetuses. These were in the early stages of pregnancy. There were no multiple births but this was to be expected since the studies took place in the slaughterhouse. The figures do, however, support the hypothesis of high mortality of the ova or the early embryo.

In Sudan the twinning rate has been given as 0·4 per cent (Musa and Abusineina, 1976), without any indication of numbers involved. Leese (1927) – who has perhaps not had as much attention in this book as he might have had but whose contribution to the knowledge of camels is not to be underestimated – never saw or heard of twins.

Duration of pregnancy and sex ratio of young

Most general references to the duration of pregnancy simply state 12–13 months. There is perhaps good reason behind this apparent vagueness: the published literature is certainly rather conflicting. Most of the available data are given in Table 6.2. Leese (1927) implies a gestation period of 385 days, longer by 15 days for the first parity when compared with subsequent ones but a more recent study (involving only 33 camels) showed no significant differences in gestation length whether between parities or between sexes of offspring (Mehta, Prakash and Singh, 1962). Gestation length has a high rate of heritability with an h^2 of 0·18 (Ram, Singh and Dhanda, 1977). The little evidence that is available suggests that the gestation of Bactrians may be longer than that of dromedaries.

The primary sex ratio does not differ from the expected unity; the few data available are shown in Table 6.3.

Table 6.3 Sex ratio *in utero* or at birth in the camel.

Ratio males: females	Source	Notes
1·00 : 1·03	Sharma, Bhargava and Singh, 1963	n = 205: dystokia, abortions and still-births not included.
1·00 : 1·11	Shalash and Nawito, 1964	n = 516: *in utero*
1·28 : 1·00	Musa and Abusineina, 1976	no sample size given (calculated from percentages given in original).

Pregnancy diagnosis

Various methods for the determination of pregnancy have been developed.

Changes occur in both the specific gravity and the pH of the cervical mucus about 6 weeks after the start of pregnancy. In the follicular stage the specific gravity is usually less than 1·009 with a neutral or slightly acid reaction (pH 7·0 or less). From 6 weeks the specific gravity varies from 1·009

Table 6.2 Gestation period in the dromedary

Number of days	Area	Source	Notes
336	Negev, Israel	Bodenheimer, 1954	
350	—	Jennison, 1927	
362	Tunisia	Burgemeister, 1975	three individuals 355, 363 and 367 days
370		Iwema, 1960	
365–395	Pakistan	Yasin and Abdul Wahid, 1957	12–13 months in original
370/385	—	Leese, 1927	longer period first parity
370–390	India	Matharu, 1966	
389–390	India	Mehta, Prakash and Singh, 1962	
395	Turkestan	Abdunazarov, 1971	about 13 months in original
403/405	India	Ram, Singh and Dhanda, 1977	males shorter (n = 56)

to 1·014 and the pH varies from 7·05 to 8·2. (Nawito, Shalash, Hoppe and Rakha, 1967). While this appears to be a very precise method it might not be very practical under field conditions.

Vaginal temperature, in view of the normal variations in camels, is of no use for determining pregnancy and no positive results have been obtained in the use of vaginal smears.

The Cuboni test carried out on a series of slaughtered animals was of some use, but the results are not very reliable until at least the mid-term of pregnancy. Some positive urinary oestrogen can be detected when the crown–vertebral length of the foetus exceeds 350 mm (equivalent to a pregnancy already advanced by almost 6 months) but certain positive reactions did not arise until the crown–vertebral length exceeded 600 mm, by which time the foetus is 7 months or more (El-Ghannam, El-Azab and El-Sawar, 1974).

By the latter time it would hardly be possible to avoid detecting pregnancy by rectal palpation. In fact, by this time the uterus has descended into the abdomen and the foetal head and forelegs can be distinguished with ease. This represents one period in a series of 13, corresponding roughly to months of pregnancy, described for clinical pregnancy diagnosis in Sudan and listed below (Musa and Abusineina, 1978a).

1st month: there is one corpus luteum at least in the ovaries, no evident sign of pregnancy.
2nd month: uterus is still within the pelvic cavity; in the early stage of this period the pregnant horn is slightly bigger and softer than the non-pregnant.
3rd month: pregnant horn is obviously bigger than non-pregnant; whole uterus is soft.
4th month: cervix at pelvic brim: the ovary on the gravid side is out of reach: vaginal scrapings show only epithelial cells.
5th month: uterus is in the abdomen; a small degree of fluctuation can be noticed; foetus occasionally is detectable.
6th month: uterus is in the abdomen with dorsal surface a little below the level of the pelvic floor.
7th month: uterus is in the abdomen below the level of the pelvic floor but still can be reached

by the hand; foetal head and forelegs can be detected.
8th month: foetal head, neck and forelegs can be felt.
9th month: foetal movements are observable and can possibly be balloted at the apex of the right flank; slight udder development possible.
10th month: foetal movements are obvious; presentation can be determined; balloting fairly certain; udder possibly developing rapidly.
11th month: udder well developed but no milk.
12th month: almost fully developed young; some changes in anatomy indicating pre-calving condition.
13th month: normal signs of approaching parturition; note that in the camel there is no mucal discharge resulting from the breaking of the cervical seal.

Several practical camel men (Leese, 1927, Mares, 1954) assert that it is possible to detect pregnancy from as early as the fifteenth to twentieth days. A pregnant camel will always lift her tail, and perhaps curl it over to the right, when handled about the neck by a man or when approached by a male camel. It is asserted by these practical men that this is a sure sign of pregnancy but this method may be regarded by some as not scientific and in fact Musa and Abusineina (1978a) have noted this tail-lifting behaviour in non-pregnant camels (in both oestrus and non-oestrus) as well as in pregnant ones.

Parturition

Early signs of approaching parturition are often more or less suppressed although comparable to other herbivorous species. There is faint oedema of the udder and vulva from between 5 and 10 days before parturition. While it is possible during this time to feel the slackening of the sacro-sciatic ligaments, such a change is not visible to the eye. Some 3–5 hours before parturition, the female begins to act in a slightly more agitated way: interrupting feeding, lying down and getting up and ruminating during the day (an event otherwise unusual). Contrary to the popular belief which is that females wander off to calve, less than 25 per cent do so in Tunisia, birth in the morning in the middle of the herd being not unusual. Mid-morning births are commonest, also, in Turkestan (Abdunazarov, 1971). Birth pangs are not very evident. Fig. 6.5 gives the phasing of a number of births observed in detail. The actual birth takes place either from the normal sitting position or lying on the side, oscillation between the two positions often occuring. Birth in a standing position is probably uncommon.

The birth proper takes only a few minutes if the presentation is normal. In cases of malpresentation or when other problems arise - about 30 per cent of all times (Fig. 6.5) - the birth takes longer and assistance needs to be given. The camel rises immediately after the birth is completed; the umbilical cord is broken in the usual way. According to Burgemeister (1975), on whose work this section is based, the female neither licks the young nor eats the afterbirth, although earlier work in Tunisia noted both activities (El Fourgy, 1950).

The first post-partum oestrus may occur within 14 to 30 days of parturition (Yasin and Abdul Wahid, 1957; Abdunazarov, 1971). The timing of post-partum oestrus and its intensity are probably very much dependent on the time of year. Total suppression or silent or near-silent heats are likely to occur.

The male reproductive organs

The penis

Externally the penis is covered by a triangular-shaped sheath which opens to the rear. To the rear of the sheath are four vestigial teats. Because of the backward facing sheath the male camel urinates towards the rear but erection of the organ for copulation is accompanied by the effects of powerful protractor muscles which withdraw the sheath. In erection the penis is thus directed forwards in the normal way. The penis has a characteristic S-shaped flexure in front of the scrotum, not behind it as in the bull. The approximate length in African camels is about 600 mm (Tayeb, 1951/52; Mobarak, El-Wishy and Samira, 1972) although it may be shorter (374–500 mm) in Indian camels (Khan and Kohli, 1973b). The glans is transverse and hook-shaped with a definite neck between the glans and the body of the penis. The urethral opening is very small.

The scrotum and testicles

The scrotum is high in the perineal region as in the dog or pig, not pendulous as in the bull or ram. The scrotum is divided so that each testicle is contained in a separate pouch.

The testes are small in relation to the size of the animal. They are about 50 mm broad and 45 mm deep and vary in length from 70 to 100 mm. They are ovoid in shape and lie obliquely in the pouch. The front edge is nearly straight and linked to the

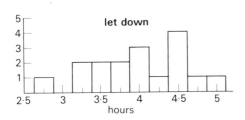
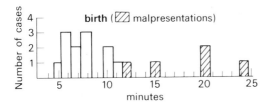
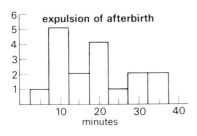

Time

fig. 6.5 Duration of events associated with parturition in 17 camel births in southern Tunisia (*Source*: **Burgemeister, R. E.** (1975). *Elevage de chameaux en Afrique du Nord.* Office Allemand de la Cooperation Technique: Eschborn, West Germany.)

epididymis. The weight of each testis is in the region of 80–110 g, the left one tending to be bigger than the right (Tayeb, 1951/52; El-Wishy and Omar, 1975). Weight undoubtedly varies seasonally. For example, in Morocco both testes together weighed less than 140 g between May and November and more than 165 g (maximum 253 g) from December to mid-May (Charnot, 1963a). The increase in weight is due largely to an increase in interstitial tissue. The body of the epididymis accounts for almost 50 per cent of total testicular weight.

The seminiferous tubules have a small diameter which is significantly less when the camel is not in rut. Season does not have any effect on the size of the spermatozoa although it does on their numbers. The sperm are smaller than those of the bull or the buffalo, being slightly less than 50μ in length. The head is elliptical rather than ovoid as in other Artiodactyla and represents about 10 per cent of the total length of the sperm (Abdel-Raouf and El Naggar, 1965; Khan and Kohli, 1973a).

Semen transport and storage

The vas deferens is very convoluted in the camel in its early course but becomes straighter farther down. It is enclosed in a spermatic cord which is thickened as a result of these convolutions and which is 450–500 mm in length. The spermatic cord also carries, as usual, the associated blood, lymph and nervous apparatus. The prostate gland is disc-shaped and slightly bilobed, it measures about 374 mm × 50 mm. The gland is located on the upper side of the pelvic urethra and is dark yellow. Towards the end of the urethra and on either side of it is the bulbo-urethral or Cowper's gland, each unit being almond-shaped, white in colour and measuring 12 mm × 25 mm. The secreting canals open into the urethra. There are no seminal vesicles (Tayeb, 1951/52). Sperm is stored in the body of the epididymides.

The rut and the sexual cycle in males

The period of heightened sexual activity which occurs in the male camel is generally known as the **rut** in both English and French. In much of India it is known as *musth* (the same term being applied to

the male elephant in an analagous condition), as *heg* in Arabia, *waghogh* in Somalia and *riwiss* in many Tuareg dialects.

Physical signs

The manifestation of rut in the male is accompanied by many of the signs which would be normally considered masculine: fighting instincts are aroused, control is difficult or impossible, bulls in rut at the same time are hostile to each other and noisy.

In general, rutting males in a mixed herd are more preoccupied with the females than with other males. It is usual, after the initiation of rutting, for one male to become dominant due to his size or fighting ability. Subdued males quickly go out of rut or show reduced activity.

Males in full rut grind their teeth, suck air, belch, draw the head back, lash the tail, crouch with jerky movements of the pelvis and generally make themselves look ridiculous. As the season advances bulls lose condition, not only for the obvious reason but also because they tend to go off feed. The camel tends to urinate more than normal and will even pass semen. The tail is not lifted to urinate and may be be waved about vigorously. Leese (1927) recommends tying the tail 'to one side by means of a cord to the hair of the hump, otherwise everything in the vicinity, including the load and the attendants, is liable to be covered with the urine, dung and semen which the animal splashes about at this time'. Diarrhoea is a frequent accompaniment of rut. Figure 6.6 shows a male camel in full rut drawing his head back and raising his upper lip.

In addition to the secretions of the poll glands which are copious, red-coloured and smelly at this time, there are also secretions from the salivary glands. As a slight digression, a description of the poll glands was one of the earlier pieces of scientific work concerning the camel and it was known also that the glands were present in females (Pocock, 1910). It is rather strange that Leese (who said that poll glands were present only in males) either was unaware of this work – which seems unlikely – or preferred to ignore it.

The soft palate is evaginated frequently during rut, due probably to the expelling of gases from the

fig. 6.6 Rutting male camel approaching a female.

rumen but there is also an actual increase in length (Charnot, 1963b). Dependent upon the age when castration occurs, castrated animals may also have increased palatal length (although it is never evaginated) which might indicate that once growth has occurred complete regression is not possible.

Physiology of the rut

Rut appears to be elicited by environmental factors in the immediate vicinity as the timing of rut varies geographically. Nutritional and/or climatic factors are undoubtedly involved.

The onset of rut is marked by increased activity in the α and β secreting cells in the anterior pituitary; testicular weight increases and growth of the soft palate takes place (Charnot and Racadot, 1963; Charnot, 1964). The increased weight of the testes is due mainly to an increase in the amount of interstitial tissue and spermatogenesis is much increased at this time. It slows down, but does not stop completely when external signs of rut are not present. In effect, the male camel, like the female, is capable of breeding although it is not likely to do so, throughout the year. Neither the physical nor the physiological attributes of rut are as pronounced in dehydrated animals as in regularly watered ones (Charnot, 1965).

In rutting camels the seminiferous tubules have a greater diameter (209 – 220 μ) than the tubules of camels not in rut (190 – 203 μ) and spermatogonia, spermatids and spermatozoa are all more numerous in rut. The number of spermatozoa per gram of testicular tissue varies from about 27 – 30 million in quiescent bulls to 36 – 47 million in animals in rut (Osman and El-Azab, 1974; Abdel-Raouf, El-Bab and Owaida, 1975). Even the highest of these figures is still only about one-third the value for semen of cattle.

In addition to seasonal changes in physiological factors there are long-term ones. Seminiferous tubule diameter increases up to about 9 years of age and the numbers of spermatozoa increase up to the following year and then decline gradually. Conversely there is little variation in total germinal cells - spermatogonia, primary spermatocytes and spermatids - between 6 and 18 years (Abdel-Raouf, El-Bab and Owaida, 1975).

The rut is the one factor which appears to affect the composition of the blood, at least significantly. Some of these changes are shown in Table 6.4; the decrease in haemoglobin and the increase in leucocytes (white blood cells) are highly significant. The other changes, including the lower number of erythrocytes (red blood cells) were not statistically significant.

Table 6.4 Changes in blood constituents of male camels before and after the rut. (*Source*: **Khan, A. A. and Kohli, I. S.** (1973). (*Source*: A note on variations in blood serum cholesterol in the camel (*Camelus dromedarius*). *Indian J. Anim. Sci.*, **43**, 1094–1095, **Khan, A. A. and Kohli, I. S.** (1977). A note on some haematological studies on male camels (*Camelus dromedarius*) before and during rut. *Indian J. Anim. Sci.*, **48**, 325–326.)

Constituent	Unit	Before rut		During rut	
		range	mean	range	mean
Erythrocytes	10⁶ per mm³	7·0–11·5	8·8	6·5–9·9	8·4
Leucocytes	10³ per mm³	6·5–13·6	10·5	10·5–19·2	14·6
Haemoglobin	g per 100 ml	11·0–14·0	12·6	9·6–11·8	10·8
Cholesterol	mg per 100 ml	49·8–85·3	65·6	75·3–116·3	92·1
Lymphocytes	per cent	43–59	51	47–59	53
Monocytes	per cent	7–18	13	5–11	7
Neutrophils	per cent	23–34	27	24–34	29
Eosinophils	per cent	5–11	9	4–15	9
Basophils	per cent	1–3	2	1–3	2

Copulation

Copulation in the camel is the subject of much mythology. The sexual act in the camel is unusual to the extent that it is effected with the female in the couched position but both male and female face in the same direction. The position is shown clearly in Fig. 6.7(a) for the approach stages and Fig. 6.7(b) for full coitus.

The female in heat presents a series of stimuli to the male based on sight, sound and smell. The male, in a highly excited state, courts the already receptive female in various ways – kicking, smelling and biting the vulva, rubbing her along the back with the underside of his neck and finally forcing her to the couched position. This last usually is not difficult since most oestrus females are not unwilling.

fig. 6.7 Copulatory position of the camel : a) approach stage, and b) full coitus

The male mounts (or in this case it might be more appropriate to say descends) the female by straddling her with his forelegs. The rear of the male is lowered resulting from a flexure of all the joints of the hind legs until finally he is in position with his stifle pads on the ground.

Intromission is effected after the vulva has been found as a result of rotational movements of the penis along its longitudinal axis. Camel owners often assist at penetration. It should be evident, nonetheless, that human help is not an absolute requirement: if it were, to give one example, there would be no feral camels in Australia. On the other hand a certain awkwardness in this respect, coupled with the restricted breeding season does help to control matings to the camel owners' advantage.

Copulation, prior to ejaculation, is accompanied by penal strokes, although these are not very violent. One complete act is comprised of three or four separate entries. The duration of copulation varies from about 7 to 35 minutes but averages 11–15 (Singh and Prakash, 1964; Matharu, 1966; Khan and Kohli, 1973b; Burgemeister, 1975). The female will ruminate during the act and the male will evaginate the palate. Copulation may be repeated at frequent intervals, interrupted in free-ranging herds by secondary sexual displays such as fighting. If allowed, a bull may spend all day with one cow to fall off her, finally, exhausted and unable to stand.

The ejaculate varies in volume from 5 to 22 ml, increasing in volume and in motility for the first few ejaculations. The semen is milky white in colour, viscous, with a pH in the alkaline range from 7·2 to 8·8, averaging 7·8 (Khan and Kohli, 1973b). Conclusion of the act is accompanied by much bellowing, gurgling and frothing at the mouth by the male and a more or less continuous bleating by the female.

If the male is not allowed to tire himself out by overworking individual females he can be expected to serve up to 70 females in a rutting season (Matharu, 1966) at the rate of as many as three a day (Burgemeister, 1975). In traditionally managed herds the ratio of males capable of breeding to breeding females may be much less. This cannot be considered a true breeding ratio in view of the heirarchical structure among male camels leading to suppression of the rut in weaker and younger males.

Sexual maturity in males and females

Sexual maturity, the ability to conceive or to cause conception, is attained before full physical maturity. In camels it may be correlated not only with absolute age and condition but also with the other factors affecting the onset of the breeding season such as nutrition and climate.

Males

Rut first appears in males as early as 3 years. At this age, long before physical maturity, they have little chance of serving cows in a large herd of mixed sexes and rut is suppressed until some years later. In single sex herds 6 years is a normal time for bulls to attain a reasonable level of activity but full overt sexual activity may be delayed until 8 years. Physiological capacity may increase up to 10 years and remain at a more or less constant, fairly high, level until 18–20 years (Leese, 1927; Yasin and Abdul Wahid, 1957; Matharu, 1966) and see p.92.

The short breeding season, the complicated copulation pattern and the heirarchical system allow considerable scope for management of male camels (p. 140).

Females

Puberty in females can occur as early as 8–12 months (Abdunazarov, 1970) and in Turkestan first calving takes place at 3 to 4 years of age. A later sexual maturity would appear to be more normal, probably at about 3 years. Some owners may allow breeding at this age but, in general, breeding is delayed until the cow has reached her nearly mature physical size. In a few areas cows may be bred at 4 years to calve down at approximately 5, but delay for a further year to drop the first calf at 6 years is by no means unusual.

Cow camels will breed without problems up to at least 20 years old and even up to 30 years (Leese, 1927; Yasin and Abdul Wahid, 1957; Matharu, 1966).

Table 6.5 Geographical variations in the breeding season of camels with some known or inferred climatic and nutritional data at the onset of breeding

Male in rut	Females in heat	Area	Source	Climate	Nutritional status
Nov – Mar		India	Matharu, 1966		
Nov – Feb		India	Singh and Prakash, 1964	daylength decreasing then increasing	'depending on level of nutrition' but not specified.
Oct – Mar		India	Khan and Kohli, 1972		
	Dec – Feb	India	Joshi, Viyas, Pareek, 1978	increasing daylength	
	Dec – Mar	Pakistan	Yasin and Abdul Wahid, 1957.		
mid-Jan – end May		Turkestan	Abdunazarov, 1970	very cold becoming warm: rapidly increasing daylength	probably poor, at least in early period
	Jan – Feb	Iran	Islamy, 1950	'only when weather is cold': rapidly increasing daylength	
Jan – Mar		S. Israel	Volcani, 1952;	cool to warm; rain; increasing in daylength	short growing season, rising plane
Mar – Apr		Egypt	Abdel Raouf and El Naggar, 1964		
	Mar – May	Egypt	Shalsh and Nawito, 1964	increasing daylength: warm to hot	
Spring		Egypt (+ Sudanese camels)	Osman and El Azab, 1974		
	Nov – Apr	S. Tunisia	Burgemeister, 1975	daylength decreasing then increasing; rain; cool to warm	fairly good
Dec – May		Morocco	Charnot, 1963a	daylength decreasing, then increasing; cool to hot	fairly good
Nov – Apr		Morocco	Charnot, 1965		
	Aug – Sept	Mali	Swift, 1979	daylength decreasing; rain	good
	Feb – Mar	Mali	Swift, 1979	daylength increasing; warm to hot	depends on winter conditions
June		Somalia	Leese, 1927	daylength static	
Sept – Nov		Somalia	Leese, 1927	daylength slowly decreasing	good
	Jun-Sept	Australia	McKnight, 1969	daylength increasing	

Geographical variation in the breeding season

Briefly, the camel can be described as a seasonal breeder with a marked peak in sexual activity. Occasionally, and particularly in specific climatic zones, a lesser peak also occurs. Both males and females show low levels, at least physiologically, of breeding activity throughout the year. The breeding peak, therefore, can be considered facultative rather than required.

The variation in the timing and length of the season clearly demonstrate that local environmental factors trigger off the start of increased sexual activity. What the exact factors are, whether they are climatic or nutritional, and how strong the relative effects are is not clear. Table 6.5 brings together most of the data on breeding seasons that are available together with climatic data at the onset of the breeding season and nutritional status, where these are known or can be inferred. The results are far from consistent. It is not clear why breeding seasons occur when they do. In some areas the reason advanced is the state of the vegetation; an improving plane of nutrition certainly is an important factor in many localities. It is inconceivable, however, that camels would be on an increasing plane of nutrition in Turkestan in early January but it would certainly be cold, as in nearby Iran where the short season occurs only in the cold weather. Photoperiod can probably be discounted altogether as it can shorten to a minimum or lengthen rapidly or slowly to more or less maximum and slowly decrease. One factor which almost certainly affects the rut is the presence of females, the rut starting earlier in mixed herds than in bachelor herds.

The prolonged breeding season in Somalia can be explained by the nature of the country. Some areas are close to the equator where double rains occur in spells of 6-8 weeks and about 12 weeks with a short dry season of about 3 months and a long one approaching 5 months. The Horn and the Gulf of Aden coast have winter rainfall while the Ogaden plains in the Somali/Ethiopia border region have summer (July–August) rains. Leese (1927) noted with respect to Somalia that nutritional effects were important and that the breeding season depended on the area in which the animals happened to be. This implies that the rut is not necessarily static in individuals. This implication is not supported by observations in Israel where camels from winter rain areas, when moved to summer rain areas ceased to breed (Bodenheimer, 1953). It is highly likely that these latter effects are only temporary. There is ample evidence that the breeding season can adapt to change. Camels in Australia adapted to a complete 6 month change of climatic and nutritional regime. The Australian experience is supported by evidence from zoos throughout the world which shows that in general the Camelidae - dromedary, Bactrian, guanaco, llama, alpaca and vicuña - in such conditions maintain a short breeding season adapted for latitude (Schmidt, 1973). But even in zoos, there are some anomalies with e.g. camels having been born in the London zoo in February, April and September (Zuckerman, 1953).

Other anomalies remain in pastoral populations. Of the two short breeding seasons that exist in northern Mali the one in August and September might well be controlled by nutritional factors, but temperatures are medium increasing, daylength is shortening, and insolation medium. These conditions are in complete contrast to those which prevail during the other less pronounced Malian breeding season in February and March. At this time temperatures are hot to torrid, humidity is low increasing, insolation intense, daylength increasing, nutrition poor. These two seasons (but not the analysis of climate) are taken from Swift (1979) who is of the opinion, based on his own interpretations of the literature, that rut and oestrus are the results of the effects of fresh grazing at the end of the cold season in the winter/spring rainfall zone, or alternatively, follow the main rains in the summer rainfall zone each year.

Such a conclusion is somewhat simplistic and certainly does not hold for all areas in which breeding camels are found. Another analysis has suggested that the 'pattern of the reproductive cycle appears to relate to the harsh environment in which the camel progenitors evolved' and that 'when rutting season exists it is probably elicited by influences similar to those which induce the advent of oestrus in the female' (Novoa, 1970).

That rut and the follicular wave are hormonally controlled is not in question. The question which still has to be answered is what are the external factors which initiate the hormonal release?

Reproductive success and fertility rates

The long gestation period and the closed breeding season impose restrictions on the maximum fertility rate. In addition to these factors the high rate of egg and early embryonic mortality impose further limitations (Nawito, Shalash, Hoppe and Rakha, 1967; Nawar, Abul-Fadle and Mahmoud, 1978).

The conception rate varies with the time of service, the optimum time being the first or second days which require.an average of 1·87 and 1·75 services respectively per conception. The third to fifth days require 2·75, 2·12 and 2·71 services respectively for successful conception (Gupta, Chowdary and Barhat, 1977). Using these figures in conjunction with certain others in this chapter it is possible

to construct a simple model of maximum reproductive rate over a number of years. Fig. 6.8 shows part of such a model cycle for two areas, the one (for example Somalia) with two distinct rutting/breeding seasons in June and in September – November and the other (for example, India or Pakistan) with a single season of four months, say December – March. The assumptions are that the first post-partum oestrus occurs 21 days after parturition, that the follicular wave last 25 days, that service is always achieved on the first day requiring 1·87 services for conception to occur and that gestation lasts 390 days. The calving dates of cows from the two areas based on the model are shown in Table 6.6 on the assumption of a 20-year productive life. In effect the single-season area can achieve a maximum calving rate of 66 per cent while the two-season area could achieve 75 per cent.

These theoretical rates of reproduction are unlikely to be achieved in the long term. Long-term fertility levels are affected by nutritional factors

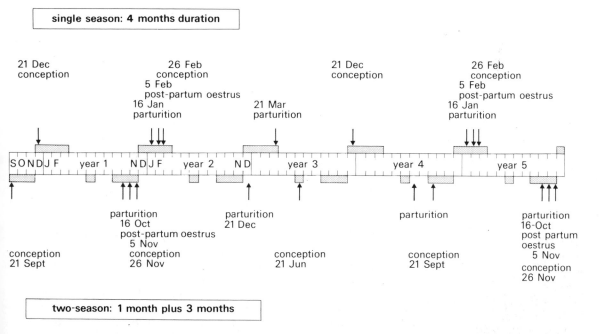

fig. 6.8 Model of theoretical maximum calving in single season and two-season breeding areas

Table 6.6 Sequence of calving dates over 20 year productive life based on model in Fig. 6.8

Two-season area	Year	One-season area
16 Oct	1	
21 Dec	2	16 Jan
	3	21 Mar
16 July	4	
16 Oct	5	16 Jan
21 Dec	6	21 Mar
	7	
16 July	8	16 Jan
16 Oct	9	21 Mar
21 Dec	10	
	11	16 Jan
16 July	12	21 Mar
16 Oct	13	
21 Dec	14	16 Jan
	15	21 Mar
16 July	16	
16 Oct	17	16 Jan
21 Dec	18	21 Mar
	19	
16 July	20	16 Jan

place early in the first season so that there will still be some males in rut after she has calved the next season. The model in Fig. 6.8 clearly demonstrates this.

Calvings, in practice, thus occur every 2 years, even in two-season areas. Some field data to support this conclusion is shown in Table 6.7. Actual long-term calving percentages are probably nearer to 40 per cent (and may even be lower) than to 50 per cent. However, even under field conditions, high calving rates in individual years may follow a series of poor calving seasons in earlier years. Some controlled data on calving rates relating to Tunision army camels and Tunisian camels under range conditions are shown in Table 6.8. Rates of up to 70 per cent are possible in single years (Wilson, 1978).

Neo-natal deaths and losses and those in calves up to 1 year old may be as high as 50 per cent of calves born. Levels of losses of 30 per cent would be quite normal. Where the growing season is restricted, late and out-of-season calvings are more likely to result in losses from low lactation yields and poor feed availability. These losses further reduce the effective reproduction rate with consequent further long-term effects on herd dynamics.

perhaps related to the climate and disease factors, including diseases causing sterility or reduced fertility. Reported reproduction rates depend very much on whether abortions and stillbirths are included or not. In a Tunisian example there were no stillbirths or abortions included in the total of 73 pregnancies while in Somalia of 186 pregnancies a total of 34 resulted in either abortion or stillbirth and in Mali 15 of 77 pregnancies failed for one or other of these reasons.

In practice in two-season areas two calves may occasionally be dropped in 2½ years but according to Leese (1927) this required good conditions and a good cow, and should not be allowed to occur more than once or twice in her lifetime. He considers that to 'go empty each alternate year seems to be a provision of nature to protect her from a strain she could not endure under ordinary desert conditions'. In single-season areas, he goes on to say, if two calves are required in 2 years it is necessary that the first of the two conceptions should take

Table 6.7 Reported intervals between calvings in camels in Mali and Kenya (*Source*: **Bremaud, O.** (1969). *Notes sur l'élevage camelin dans les districts du nord de la Republique du Kenya.* Institut d'Elevage et de Medécine Vétérinaire des Pays Tropicaux: Maisons Alfort, France; **Swift, J. J.** (1979). *The economics of traditional nomadic pastoralism: The Tuareg of the Adrar n Iforas (Mali).* Ph.D. Thesis, University of Sussex: Brighton, UK.

Calving interval (months)	Per cent of animals	
	Kenya (n = 26)	Mali (n = 43)
12 – 15	11·5	20·9
16 – 23	3·9	27·9
24	53·8	44·2
25 +	30·8	7·0

Table 6.8 Calving rates (per cent of breeding females) recorded for camels in Tunisia. (*Source*: Burgemeister, R. E. (1975) *Elevage de chameaux en Afrique du Nord*. German Bureau for Technical Cooperation: Eschborn, West Germany.)

	Herd	
Year	Tunisia army	Traditionally owned
1969/1970	23·1	
1970/1971	30·8	
1971/1972	15·4	
1972/1973	57·8	42·3
1973/1974		14·3
Average	31·8	28·3

Further reading

Abdalla, O. (1965). Anatomical study of the female genital system of the one-humped camle I. Ovaries. *Sudan J. Vet. Sci. Anim. Husb.,* **6**, 41 – 52.

Abdalla, O. (1967). Anatomical study of the female genital system of the one-humped camel (*Camelus dromedarius*). II. The oviducts. *Sudan J. Vet. Sci. Anim. Husb.,* **8**, 67 – 77.

Abdel-Raouf, M. and El Naggar, M. A. (1964). Studies on reproduction in camels (*Camelus dromedarius*) 1. Mating techniques and collection of semen. *J. Vet. Sci. U.A.R.,* **1**, 113 – 119.

Abdel-Raouf, M. and El Naggar, M. A. (1965). Studies on reproduction in camels (*Camelus dromedarius*) 2. The morphology of the camel spermatozoon. *J. Vet. Sci. U.A.R.,* **2**, 1 – 11.

Abdel-Raouf, M., El-Bab, M. R. F. and Owaida, M. (1975). Studies on reproduction in the camel. 5. Morphology of the testis in relation to age and season. *J. Reprod. Fert.,* **43**, 109 – 116.

Abdo, M. S., Al-Janabi, A. S. and Al-Kafawi, A. A. (1969). Studies on the ovaries of the female camel during the reproductive cycle and in conditions affected with cysts. *Cornell Vet.,* **59**, 418 – 425.

Abdunazarov, N. H. (1970). Biological characteristics of reproduction in the one-humped camel (trans.). *Trudy Turkmen-Sel'kluz Inst.,* **15**, 134 – 141 (in Russian, abstracted in Animal Breeding Abstracts, Volume 41).

Abdunazarov, N. H. (1971). Calving season and parturition in Turkmen dromedaries (trans.). *Trudy Turkmen Sel'kluz Inst.,* **16**, 29 – 37 (in Russian, abstracted in Animal Breeding Abstracts, Volume 42).

Bodenheimer, F. S. (1953). *Problems of animal ecology and physiology in deserts*. Desert Research, Spec. Publ. No. 2. Research Council of Israel and UNESCO: Jerusalem, Israel.

Bodenheimer, F. S. (1954). Problems of the physiology and ecology of desert animals. In: Cloudsley-Thompson, J. L. (ed.) *The biology of deserts*. Institute of Biology: London.

Burgemeister, R. E. (1975). *Elevage de chameaux en Afrique du Nord*. Office Allemand de la Coopération Technique: Eschborn, West Germany.

Chahrasbi, H., Radmehr, B. and Goulbazhagh, F. (1975). Anatomy and histology of the reproductive organs of the Iranian camel (*Camelus dromedarius*). 1. Ovary. *J. Vet. Fac. Teheran Univ.,* **30(4)**, 42 – 50.

Charnot, Y. (1963a). Synchronisation of growth of the palatal expansion and the testis during the sexual cycle in the dromedary. *Bull. Soc. Sci. nat. phys. Maroc.,* **43**, 49 – 54.

Charnot, Y. (1963b). The development of the soft palate and physiological states in the dromedary. *J. Physiol. Paris,* **55**, 226 – 227.

Charnot, Y. (1964). The testicular cycle of the dromedary. *Bull. Soc. Sci. nat. phys. Maroc.,* **44**, 37 – 45.

Charnot, Y. (1965). *Endocrinologie sexuelle et déshydration chez le dromadaire mâle. C. R. Séances Soc. Biol.,* **159**, 1103 – 1105.

Charnot, Y. and Racadot, J. (1963). *Mise en évidence de categories cellulaires distinctes dans la lobe antérieure de l'hypophyse du dromadaire. Bull. Microsc. appl.,* **13**, 144.

El Fourgy, M. (1951). *Le chameau Tunisien*. Thèse, Ecole Nationale Vétérinaire Alfort; Maisons Alfort, France.

El-Ghannam, F., El-Azab, E. A. and El-Sawar,

M. (1974). Preliminary study on the application of Cuboni test to pregnancy diagnosis in the camel. *Zuchthygiene*, **9**, 41-46.

El-Wishy, A. B. and Omar, A. M. (1975). On the relation between testes size and sperm reserves in the one-humped camel (*Camelus dromedarius*). *Beit. Trop. Ländw. Veterinärmed.*, **13**, 391-398.

Gupta, A. K., Chowdary, M. S. and Barhat, N. K. (1977). A note on optimum time for service in camel (*Camelus dromedarius*). *Indian J. Anim. Sci.*, **48**, 324-325.

Islamy, A. (1950). Riding camels around Khash and Iranshah. *Rev. Fac. Méd. Vét. Teheran*, **12(2)**, 87.

Iwema, S. (1960). The ship of the desert. *Veet. Zuiv.*, **3**, 390-394.

Jennison, C. (1927). *Table of gestation periods and number of young*. A & C. Black: London.

Joshi, C. K., Vyas, K. K. and Pareek, P. K. (1978). Studies on oestrus cycle in Bikanir she-camel (*Camelus dromedarius*). *Indian J. Anim. Sci.*, **48**, 141-145.

Khan, A. A. and Kohli, I. S. (1972). A study on sexual behaviour of male camels (*Camelus dromedarius*) Part I. *Indian Vet. J.*, **49**, 1007-1012.

Khan, A. A. and Kohli, I. S. (1973a). A note on biometrics of camel spermatozoa (*Camelus dromedarius*). *Indian J. Anim. Sci.*, **43**, 792-795.

Khan, A. A. and Kohli, I. S. (1973b). A note on the sexual behaviour of male camels (*Camelus dromedarius*). *Indian J. Anim. Sci.*, **43**, 1092-1094.

Leese, A. S. (1927). *A treatise on the one-humped camel in health and disease*. Haynes & Son: Stamford, Lincs, UK.

McKnight, T. L. (1969). *The camel in Australia*. Melbourne University Press: Australia.

Mares, R. G. (1954). Animal husbandry, animal industry and animal disease in Somaliland Protectorate. *Br. Vet. J.*, **100**, 411-423.

Matharu, B. S. (1966). Camel care. *Indian Fmg.*, **16**, 19-22.

Mehta, V. S., Prakash, A. and Singh, M. (1962). Gestation period in camels. *Indian Vet. J.*, **39**, 387-389.

Mobarak, A. M., El-Wishy, A. B. and Samira, M. F. (1972). The penis and prepuce of the one-humped camel (*Camelus dromedarius*). *Zentralbl. Vet. Med.* **19A**, 787-795.

Musa, B. E. and Abusineina, M. E. (1976). Some observations on reproduction in the female camel. *Acta Vet.*, **26(2)**, 63-67.

Musa, B. E. and Abusineina, M. E. (1978a). Clinical pregnancy diagnosis in the camel and a comparison with bovine pregnancy. *Vet. Rec.*, **102**, 7-10.

Musa, B. E. and Abusineina, M. E. (1978b). The oestrus cycle of the camel (*Camelus dromedarius*). *Vet. Rec.*, **103**, 556-557.

Nawar, S. M. A., Abul-Fadle, W. S. and Mahmoud, S. A. (1978). Studies on the ovarian activity of the dromedary (*Camelus dromedarius*). *Zeitsshrift für Mikroskopisch-anatomische Forschung*, **92**, 385-408.

Nawito, M. F., Shalash, M. R., Hoppe, R. and Rakha, A. M. (1967). Reproduction in the female camel. *Bull. Anim. Sci. Res. Inst.* (Cairo), No. 2.

Novoa, C. (1970). Reproduction in the Camelidae: A review. *J. Reprod. Fert.*, **32**, 3-20.

Osman, A. M. and El-Azab, E. A. (1974). Gonadal and epididymal sperm reserves in the camel, *Camelus dromedarius*. *J. Reprod. Fert.*, **38(2)**, 425-430.

Pocock, R. I. (1910). On the specialised cutaneous glands of ruminants. *Proc. Zool. Soc. Lond.*, **1910**, 1840.

Ram, S., Singh, B. and Dhanda, O. P. (1977). A note on genetic studies on gestation length, birth weight and intra-uterine development index in Indian camels (*Camelus dromedarius*) and factors affecting them. *Indian Vet. J.*, **54**, 953-955.

Savi, P. (1843). *Sugli involucri fetali del Camelus dromedarius. Miscellanea Medico-Chirurgico, Farmaceutiche*: Pisa. (quoted by Novoa, 1970).

Schmidt, C. R. (1973). Breeding seasons and some other aspects of reproduction in captive Camelidae. *Intnl. Zoo. Yearb.*, **13**, 387-390.

Shalash, M. R. and Nawito, M. F. (1964). Some reproductive aspects in the female camel. *Ve Cong. Rep. Anim. I. A. Trento.*, Vol. II, 263-273.

Sharma, V. D., Bhargava, K. K. and Singh, M.

(1963). Secondary sex ratio of normal births in Bikaneri camels. *Indian Vet. J.,* **40**, 561 - 563.

Shehata, R. (1964). Medullary tubes in the ovary of the camel and other mammals. *Vet. Rec.,* **76**, 750 - 753.

Singh, V. and Prakash, A. (1964). Mating behaviour of camel. *Indian Vet. J.,* **41**, 475 - 477.

Steklenev, E. P. (1968). Anatomical-morphological characters and physiological functions of the oviducts in the genera *Lama* and *Camelus. VIᵉ Cong. Rep. Anim. I. A*: Paris, France.

Swift, J. J. (1979). *The economics of traditional nomadic pastoralism: The Tuareg of the Adrar n Iforas (Mali).* Thesis, University of Sussex: Brighton, UK.

Tayeb, M. A. F. (1950). *Etude sur l'anatomie de l'ovaire et du corps jaune de la chamelle. Rev. Elev. Méd. vét. Pays trop*, **4**, 177 - 182.

Tayeb, M. A. F. (1951/52). *L'appareil génital mâle de chameau. Rev. Elev. Méd. vét. Pays trop.,* **5**, 203 - 212.

Tayeb, M. A. F. (1953). *Les organes genitaux de la chamelle. Rev. Elev. Méd. vét. Pays trop.,* **6**, 17 - 21.

Volcani, R. (1952). *Seasonal activity of gonads and thyroids in camels, cattle, sheep and goats.* Thesis, The Hebrew University: Jerusalem, Israel.

Wilson, R. T. 1978). Studies on the livestock of Southern Darfur, Sudan. V. Notes on camels. *Trop. Anim. Hlth Prod.,* **10**, 19 - 25.

Yasin, A. S. and Abdul Wahid (1957). Pakistan camels - a preliminary survey. *Agric. Pakistan,* **8**, 289 - 295.

Zuckerman, S. (1953). The breeding seasons of mammals in captivity. *Proc. Zool. Soc. Lond.,* **122**, 827.

7 Foods and feeding

"Even this class of animal cannot ruminate on nothing and it is a positive fact that in the Bayuda I did not see five camels in a thousand chewing the cud. Poor brutes! It would have been precious hard for them to do so on starvation diet and empty stomachs, for even a camel must feed regularly and have food inside him before he can chew the cud."

Leonard, 1894

Nutritional physiology

Almost everywhere and in everything one reads about the camel there is an apology for the lack of data or for the little work that has been done on it. That this is in great part not true is evident from the contents of this book. If, however, there is a basis of truth in these statements it applies to nutritional requirements and standards more than to any other facet or our knowlege of the camel. Only one, rather dated, attempt to apply nutritional standards has been made (Leitch, 1940) and, as the author admits, this was based almost in its entirety on the rations given by Leese (1927).

This lack of information is hardly surprising. The camel is rarely managed on an economic basis or for considerations of monetary profit and loss. Almost without exception knowledge of the nutritional physiology of the camel is a result of the interest in the more general physiology which so peculiarly adapts it to the desert environment. Most of what little knowledge we possess relating to nutrition is mentioned in Chapter 5 and concerns mainly the rumen sac areas and urea metabolism (Hansen and Schmidt-Nielsen, 1957; Schmidt-Nielsen *et al.*, 1957). In this chapter it is assumed that the general features of nutrition, digestion and energy requirements are similar to those of other ruminating animals with a similar digestive system.

The foregoing remarks do not mean that no research at all has been done on digestion in camels. It has been shown of the New World Camelidae that they are significantly more efficient in the digestion of dry matter, fibre, cellulose and crude protein than sheep (and also than ponies and elephants) (Hinz, Schryver and Halbert, 1973). It was suggested that the greater efficiency may be achieved because of the more rapid frequency of contraction in the forestomach and of the ruminating cycle as a whole. While other results confirm the more rapid turnover of rumen contents in the camel, they indicate that at least on low quality, dry grass hay, zebu steers are more efficient at digesting dry matter than camels (Maloiy, 1972). More recently, in apparently the only study involving the technique of a canula in the intestine, the pattern of absorption of monosaccharides and disaccharides was studied (Toofanian and Aliakbari, 1977). The results indicated that there was high lactose and low maltose and sucrose activity in the small intestine. In Australia the rumen fluid of camels on a rather atypical diet was analysed. They eat mainly the leaves of eucalyptus with very low nitrogen content (Williams, 1963). This showed 360–1 230 mg of nitrogen per litre and 98–185 mM of volatile fatty acids per litre. These figures are within the range found in cattle and sheep fed on diets high in fibre and low in nitrogen. The relative proportions of the various acids, with ethanoic (acetic) acid accounting for 77 per cent, proprionic acid, 16 per cent and butanoic and other higher acids only 7 per cent are also similar to those in other ruminating animals.

Some of these results, particularly those relating to digestibility of fibre and cellulose illustrate the need for more detailed research. In addition, they point to the errors which may arise when one interpolates from results obtained on other animals. These points apply throughout this chapter.

Nutrition of the calf

In common with all mammals the new-born camel requires milk. As with all ruminating animals, the rumen, rumen function and rumen fauna are not developed until some time after birth. This means that milk is essential for baby camels as their stomachs cannot digest plant material. Unfortunately, the young camel is generally in competition with humans for milk from the day of its birth. In addition some camel-owning groups deprive the calf of colostrum, for which there is usually little competition, but which is essential for the transfer of certain antibodies and contains essential proteins and mineral matter. The main physical properties of camel colostrum are shown in Table 7.1. Normal milk replaces colostrum secretion within 5–7 days of birth, as can be seen from Table 7.2, and it is essential that camel calves should have free access to the dam during this period. It is perhaps the forbidding of this access which results in the high percentage of neo-natal deaths in camels in some traditional camel-owning societies. Compared with colostrum from cattle that of the camel is higher in total solids, protein and ash and

Table 7.1 Physical properties of colostrum of the camel. (*Source*: **Ohri, S. P. and Joshi, B. K.** (1961). Composition of colostrum of camel. *Indian Vet. J.*, **38**, 604–607.)

Property	Quality
Colour	yellowish white
Odour	faintly abnormal
Taste	unpleasant
Viscosity at 26·7 °C	1·72 times that of water
Specific gravity	1·079
Refractive index	1·382
Boiling point	98·9 °C
pH	5·9 (acid)
Titratable acidity	0·38 per cent

Table 7.2 Composition of camel colostrum at various stages after birth (*Source*: as for Table 7.2.)

Time after calving hours (days)	Specific gravity	Titratable acidity (per cent as lactic acid)	Moisture per cent	Total solids per cent	Fat per cent	Total proteins per cent	Lactose per cent	Ash per cent
Birth	1·079	0·38	75·2 (72·1–83·7)	24·8 (21·3–27·9)	0·15 (0·1–0·4)	17·8 (15·8–19·5)	4·25 (3·98–5·13)	2·00 (1·44–2·80)
6	1·077	0·31	78·7	21·3	0·2	14·5	4·3	2·40
12	1·067	0·19	79·6	20·4	0·3	13·5	4·6	1·90
24(1)	1·057	0·15	83·1	16·9	0·3	11·3	4·0	1·22
30	1·056	0·18	84·0	16·0	0·6	10·1	4·2	1·02
36	1·054	0·21	85·0	15·0	0·8	8·5	4·8	0·98
48(2)	1·038	0·21	87·3	12·7	0·4	6·5	4·8	0·97
72(3)	1·037	0·20	87·5	12·5	2·1	4·5	4·9	0·96
96(4)	1·034	0·17	87·1	12·9	2·2	4·1	5·7	0·97
120(5)	1·031	0·14	87·1	12·9	2·7	4·0	5·3	0·94
168(7)	1·031	0·14	87·1	12·9	1·8	3·9	5·4	0·85
Whole milk[1]			86·9	13·0	4·15	3·4	4·5	0·7

[1]mean of ranges in Table 10.4 on p. 157

achieves the normal amount of fat rather slowly (Ohri and Joshi, 1961).

The dam does not lick the young calf dry but does mark the scent and usually refuses to accept any other calf. The normal tricks to induce acceptance of a calf can be attempted but calves may have to be hand-fed and are often given very dilute milk or even plain water. Conversely a camel with excess milk may provoke digestive upsets in her young: it may then be necessary to restrict access.

Young camels should generally be allowed free access to their dams even where there dams are working (Fig. 7.1). They begin to follow their dams at an age of a few weeks if allowed to do so naturally and quickly start foraging for themselves. Weaning is usually spontaneous and, where a young camel is deprived of much of its mother's milk, does not provide any serious check in growth. In camels which are allowed free or almost free access to their dams, weaning can provide a fairly severe check in growth (Field, 1979).

fig. 7.1 Young camel following its dam in Lebanon.

The food of camels

Types of food

One thinks of camels as eaters of browse, their heads always in the air, their necks stretched, their tongues extended to grasp a thorny twig. While this is a true picture it is not the whole truth.

Camels are able to live on browse to a greater extent even than goats. Anatomical adaptations such as the mobile and prehensile split upper lip, the long tongue and the horny nature of the inside of the mouth mean that a browsing rather than a grazing diet is most suitable for the camel. Some camels, nonetheless, obtain almost all their food from grasses or herbs. The Bikaner desert of India/Pakistan and the Ogaden of Somalia/Ethiopia are well-known grazing areas as well as seasonal grazing areas in the Empty Quarters of both Southern Arabia and Mauritania.

In reality, as one might expect from the seasonal movements which are the norm for camels, the diet is rarely constant for very long periods of time.

During some periods feeding may be limited to only a few species and on occasions even confined to a single one. Camels are selective feeders not only with regard to plants but also in respect of the parts of the plants they eat. Table 7.3 shows, variations in the annual feeding cycle of camels on the saharan vegetation of Mauritania.

Energy values and protein content of feed.

It has been normal to express the nutritional value of a feed either in starch equivalent (SE), in total digestible nutrients (TDN) or in forage units (FU). Recent practice is to give the nutritive value in net energy, expressed as megajoules per kilogram of dry matter of feed: this system will be adopted here to indicate the value of camel fodder.

Net energy is a measure of the energy in the feed available to the animal and can be computed from various sources. A starch equivalent of 0·101 is equivalent to one megajoule (MJ). Digestible crude protein is a function of crude protein (CP) and is usually given in tables; it can be calculated from

Table 7.3 Changes in the foods and feeding regime of camels in an annual cycle: a West African example. *Source: Gauthier-Pilters, H. (1969). Observations sur l'ecologie du dromedaire en Moyenne Mauritanie. Bull IFAN 31A, 1259-1380.)*

Biotope	Live dune or sandy desert	Stony desert on various soil types	Rocky plateaux	Dry wadi beds
Main type of feed	grazing (grasses + some herbs)	grazing (grasses + herbs) and browse	browse, mainly confined to favourable sites	browse, trees as well as bush
Principal species	*Aristida pungens* + other *Aristida* (Graminae), *Cyperus conglomeratus* (Cyperaceae), *Neurada procumbens* (Neuradaceae), *Leptadenia pyrotechnica*	*Panicum turgidum* + *Aristida* (Graminae), several species of Chenopodiaceae *Acacia* spp. (Leguminosae), *Ziziphus* (Rhamnaceae), *Capparis decidua, Maerua crassifolia* (Capparidaceae)	similar to stony desert, depending on soil type, but more browse and less grazing	*Balanites aegyptiaca* (Zygophyllaceae), *Salsola* spp. (Chenopodiaceae), species of Capparidaceae, *Tamarix* spp.
Cover density	2-10 per cent	5-15 per cent	3-6 per cent	often little ground cover

the equation:

$$DCP = 9 \cdot 29 \, (CP) - 35 \cdot 3$$

DCP is expressed as a percentage of the dry matter (DM) of the food. The nutritional ratio is an index of the dietetic value of a forage. It is usually expressed as a ratio and is calculated as DCP in g per kg DM divided by net energy per kg DM. Table 7.4 indicates in more or less subjective terms the value of fodder with various levels of these factors computed for cattle; and Table 7.5 gives some analyses of species and groups of species eaten by camels.

There are indications that the energy requirements of animals in the Tropics are less, perhaps considerably less, than for animals in temperate regions. For lack of evidence we must use, at least for the time being, the standards required for temperate livestock.

Additional factors governing nutritional status are palatability and appetite which contribute to voluntary intake. There is a maximum voluntary intake for each species but this varies within fairly narrow limits depending on climatic conditions, palatability, health of the animal, and so on. The voluntary intake is usually expressed as kg DM per 100 kg liveweight and is generally greater for smaller species than it is for larger ones. Although there are no figures for camels it is probable that

Table 7.4 Indications of fodder quality with respect to Net Energy and Digestible Protein contents (*Source*: **Boudet, G. & Rivière, R.** (1968). *Emploi pratique des analyses fourragéres pour l'appréciation des pâturages tropicaux. Rev. Elev. Méd. vét. Pays trop.*, **21**, 227–266.)

Quality	Net energy (MJ per kg DM)	Digestible Protein (g per kg DM)	Nutritional Ratio
Poor	< 3·10	< 25	< 8·06
Fair	3·10 – 3·45	25 – 34	8·06 – 9·86
Good	3·45 – 4·15	34 – 53	9·86 – 12·77
Excellent	> 4·15	> 53	> 12·77

the voluntary intake is in the region of 2·5 kg per 100 kg liveweight. There is some evidence that dry matter intake can be increased to cope with higher demands for energy, as during work, but in practice this is not very great and increased demands for energy or protein need to be met by better quality feed rather than an increase in quantity.

Energy and protein requirement for various functions

If little is known about the nutritional physiology of the camel it is probably true to say that even less is known about its requirements for energy. What has been done in the way of studies on feeding behaviour is, if not contradictory, at least confusing. Estimates of daily intake vary from 4–55 kg of wet material. The lower figure would not provide maintenance for even a small dromedary. The camel is peculiar in being able to maintain its appetite even under severe dehydration. In common with other animals under conditions where food is in short supply camels are able to survive on diets well below maintenance requirements and compensate rapidly when conditions improve. However, because of their large size, camels should require less feed for maintenance (per unit of weight) than smaller animals such as sheep and goats. Thus, a given amount of available food will support a greater weight of camel than of other species of domestic livestock. In the requirements calculated in the remainder of this section these aspects are ignored, on account of lack of data, and calculations are based on equivalent factors in cattle (MAFF, 1973).

Maintenance

Energy and protein are required for maintenance, that is for the minimum survival level of an animal, before any form of production can take place. Larger species of animals generally require less energy and less protein per unit weight than smaller ones. The same rule applies within species, the larger animals requiring less energy (and less protein) than the smaller and younger ones. For the purpose of determining energy requirements it is considered that the 'work' the camel does in foraging for its daily feed and water requirements

Table 7.5 Chemical composition and nutritive value of some camel browse species (*Source:* **Le Houérou H. N.** (1980). Chemical composition and nutritive value of browse in tropical West Africa. In: Le Houérou (ed.) *International symposium on browse in Africa, 5–12 April 1980, Addis Ababa.* International Livestock Centre for Africa: Addis Ababa, Ethiopia.

Family and species	Dry matter	Crude protein	Crude fibre	Fat	Nitrogen-free extract	Ash	DCP g per kg DM	Net energy MJ per kg DM	Nutritive ratio DP/NE
Asclepiadaceae: *Leptadenia hastata* (green leaves)	21·00	13·9	14·6			15·6	97	6·7	14·48
Boraginaceae: *Cordia* sp. (dry and green leaves)	63·3	8·9	18·6		50·1	16·1	51	6·0	8·50
Capparidaceae: *Boscia* spp. *Cadaba* spp. *Capparis* spp. *Crataeva* spp. *Maerua* spp. (leaves and fruit)		20·7	17·4	2·7	45·4	13·9	151	5·6	26·96
Combretaceae: *Combretum micranthum* (leaves and twigs)	47·7	16·7	20·9	2·9	50·3	9·6	105	5·6	18·75
Guiera senegalensis (twigs, flowers, fruit and leaves)	57·6	13·4	24·9	4·6	50·8	6·2	89	5·5	16·18
		16·8	22·7	3·1	48·2	6·8	121	5·8	20·86
Leguminosae: *Acacia raddiana* (pods)	81·3	16·5	18·3	2·6	54·9	6·4	120	6·1	19·67
Rhamnaceae: (*Ziziphus* spp)		13·6	13·4	3·8	60·4	8·5	91	7·0	13·0
Salvadora persica (twigs, leaves, fruit)	30·1	13·4	12·2	2·5	44·2	29·1	91	4·8	18·96
Balanites aegyptiaca (flowers, leaves, fruit)	51·1	12·3	14·6	4·7	51·3	13·4	84	6·1	13·77
All browse species		12·5	18·3	4·2	53·2	10·9	82	6·0	13·67
Dry season grasses	81·7	3·1	39·8			7·7	trace	2·8	

is part of its maintenance requirement. The energy and protein requirements, along with those for milk and work are shown in Table 7.6.

Milk production

Requirements for milk production are fairly high in terms of energy. To produce 1 litre of milk a 400 kg animal needs the equivalent of about one-ninth of the total energy required for maintenance. Milk is much more expensive in terms of protein, each litre requiring about one-fifth of the protein required for maintenance of the average breeding female. Based on the figures given in Table 7.6 some calculations for a 400 kg lactating female in terms of energy and protein are given in Table 7.7. The daily requirements at a peak lactation yield of 15 litres of milk are unlikely to be obtained, either for energy or protein, from free-range fodder and camels have to draw on body reserves to meet high short-term nutritional demands.

Work

From the little evidence available (see Table 10.9) camels are more efficient at producing draught power than any other domestic animal with the possible exception of the horse. They can maintain a sustained pull of somewhere between one-fifth and one-seventh of their weight at a speed of about 1 m per second.

A 500 kg male or castrate camel can produce a tractive effort of an average of one-sixth of his weight, i.e. 83 kg equivalent to a power output of 455 watts. Assuming that energy is converted into power at an efficiency of 20 per cent, the energy expended is equivalent to 2·275 kW or 136·5 kJ per minute or 8·2 MJ per hour. It is probable that output in the form of work requires little extra in the way of protein. The energy requirement for working animals using various assumptions is shown in Table 7.8. The energy expended by pack animals is not known but, although Gauthier-Pilters (1969) did not remark any difference in feeding between her pack and riding animals and the herd animals studied, it is probably reasonable to assume that energy requirements per hour are of the same order as for draught.

No calculations are made for growing stock but it should be borne in mind that the requirements for protein are appreciable during this phase.

Tables 7.7 and 7.8 clearly show the differing

Table 7.6 Probable energy and protein requirements of camels performing various functions

Function and animal class and weight	Daily requirements	
	Energy MJ ME	Protein g DCP
Maintenance		
500 kg male or castrate	54	300
400 kg breeding female	45	260
300 kg 'average' camel at MPW	36	210
Milk production		
1 litre milk	5	50
Work		
1 hour work 500 kg draft or pack animal	8·2	probably none

Table 7.7 Energy and protein requirements for breeding females of 400 kg liveweight

	Requirement	
	Energy MJ ME	Protein g DCP
Daily maintenance	45	260
1 litre milk	5	50
Daily requirement for maintenance plus peak yield of 15 litres milk	90	1 010
Annual requirement for one female for maintenance plus lactation yield of 1 500 litres milk	23 925	169 900
Average annual requirement for breeding female assuming 50 per cent reproduction rate	20 175	132 400

requirements for energy and protein. Working camels have high energy requirements relative to protein while for lactating camels the opposite is true. It is probable that camels that feed mainly on browse can fulfil their requirements for protein on natural fodder. Working camels in traditionally owned herds are almost always worked for only short periods in any year. This suggests that camels cannot obtain sufficient energy from natural fodder to work as pack or riding animals for long periods. This is supported by the fact that supplementary feeding in traditional herds is confined almost entirely to working animals.

Minerals and vitamins

There is little to show that the mineral and vitamin requirements are different in camels from those of other animals. Serum levels of copper, iron and zinc (Table 5.6 on p. 80) are of the same order as in other animals (Moty, Mulla and Zaafer, 1968); sodium, potassium and calcium show similar values in all species. Inorganic phosphorus and

chloride are higher in camels than in other animals (Ayoub, Awad and Bayyazeed, 1960; Bhattacharjee and Banerjee, 1962). Vitamin requirements, as revealed by blood and milk analyses (Khan and Appanna, 1967; Ghosal and Dwaraknath, 1976) also show no abnormalities.

For practical purposes, normal feeding will ensure adequate levels of minerals and vitamins except where known deficiencies or imbalances occur.

Salt requirements

The camel's need for salt is universally recognised by camel owners and they will often go to great lengths and considerable expense to get it. Some indication of its value in relation to that of a camel is given on p. 145 and all modern users of camels for transport or military purposes stress the need for it.

The fact remains that most camels are probably short of salt unless they are given continuous free access to it. The normal allowances of 30–60 g per day are quite inadequate for normal metabolism, and feed including only this amount predisposes animals to contagious necrosis of the skin and to lameness which is probably associated with arthritis (see Chapter 8). When given salt in quantities equivalent to 140 g per day there is an immediate improvement in both these conditions (Peck, 1938). Camels given free access to salt after being regularly fed 30 g per day immediately consume huge quantities for the first few days (Figure 7.2) and then maintain levels of consumption of about 120 g per day even when feeding on salt bush such as *Salvadora indica*. Camels previously suffering from contagious necrosis of the skin show continued improvement on high salt diets and their skin becomes pliable and lustrous. This occurs even when they are fed supplementary rations which are reduced in energy and protein.

The implications of salt deficiency on general health and on productivity are considerable. At present it is doubtful if many camels are given enough salt to fulfil their total requirements and this means that production is less than it could be. It should be noted that the apparent requirements for salt by camels, for maintenance alone, are between 6 and 8 times those normally considered adequate for other livestock.

Table 7.8 Energy and protein requirements for working camels of 500 kg liveweight

	Requirement	
	Energy MJ ME	Protein g DCP
Daily maintenance	54	300
1 hour work	8·2	
Daily requirement for camel for maintenance and 10 hrs work	136	300
Annual requirement for one camel for maintenance and 8 h work in 250 days of the year	36 110	109 500
Annual requirement for one camel for maintenance and 6 h work in 60 days of the year	22 662	109 500

Calcium/phosphorus ratio

For camels feeding on browse, minerals other than salt are generally adequate. This is shown by the general lack of obvious metabolic disorders and results from the fact that browse is rich in minerals. This is particularly the case when browsing on the family Capparidaceae which includes some of the preferred and most palatable camel browse including species of the genera *Boscia, Cadaba, Capparis, Maerua*, etc. Many of these contain up to 20 per cent mineral matter. In Africa, plants of this family contain an average of 14 per cent mineral matter (Table 7.9).

The main problems with the Capparidaceae and with browse in general is the imbalance in calcium and phosphorus; the ratio is 11·2:1 (Le Houérou, 1980). The leguminous browse has a more favourable ratio of about 5:1 but this is still considerably in excess of the best ratio which is somewhere in the region of 2:1 or less. The calcium/magnesium ratio is generally more favourable, this is of the order of 2·8:1. The mineral content and the ratio varies from area to area and wherever possible local data should be used in making any estimations or calculations of nutrient value.

Metabolic disorders due to calcium/phosphorus imbalance including the disease known as krafft have been demonstrated (see Chapter 8 and Durand and Kchouk, 1958). In general, in the extensive areas over which camels graze it is probably not practicable to feed phosphorus supplements. Cures can be effected by rotational use of an area as in salt bush where imbalances do not occur.

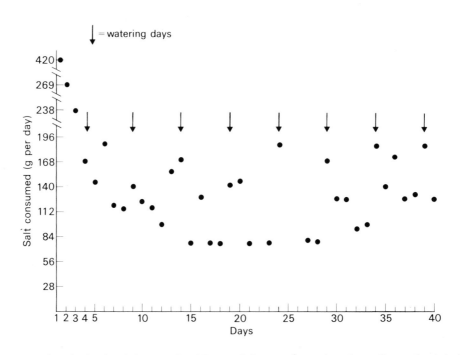

fig. 7.2 Daily consumption of salt when fed to camels *ad lib* on a 5 day watering regime after a diet previously including 30 g salt per day (*Source*: **Peck, E. F.** (1938). The relationship of salt starvation to contagious necrosis and lameness in camels. *Vet. Rec.*, **50**, 409–410.)

Table 7.9 The mineral content of West African plants browsed by camels. (*Source:* **Le Houérou, H. N.** (1980). Chemical composition and nutritive value of browse in tropical West Africa. In: Le Houérou, H. N. (ed.) *International symposium on browse in Africa. 5th–12th April, 1980, Addis Ababa.* International Livestock Centre for Africa: Addis Ababa, Ethiopia.)

Family and species	Mineral composition in per cent of dry matter					
	Total Ash	Silica	Phosphorus	Calcium	Magnesium	Potassium
All families	10·9	2·2	0·15	1·68	0·60	1·47
Capparidaceae	14·0	5·3	0·15	1·70	0·60	1·50
Boscia						
senegalensis	7·6	1·8	0·11	0·50	0·35	1·20
Cadaba farinosa	18·2	0·7	0·12	1·70	1·10	2·70
Capparis thoningii	10·9		0·04	1·83		
Maerua crassifolia	17·8	1·2	0·14	3·30	1·20	2·00
Combretaceae	6·5	0·97	0·39	1·02	0·28	0·95
Combretum						
aculeatum	9·6	2·2	0·23	1·90	0·30	1·20
Combretum						
micranthum	5·8	1·0	0·90	0·70	0·30	0·60
Guiera						
senegalensis	6·2	1·4	0·20	0·75	0·28	1·00
Leguminosae	6·8	0·9	0·25	1·29	0·33	1·35
Bauhinia						
rufescens	6·8	0·5	0·19	1·50	0·28	1·00
Piliostigma						
reticulata	5·1	0·2	0·18	0·56	0·13	1·45
Acacia laeta	8·9	0·6	0·12	2·60	0·30	1·10
Acacia raddiana	6·4	0·9	0·20	1·62	0·30	1·40
Prosopis						
africana	2·9		0·29	0·22		
Rhamnaceae						
Ziziphus						
mauritiana	8·6	0·7	0·16	2·00	0·30	1·10
Salvadoraceae						
Salvadora persica	29·1	1·3	0·10	7·00	6·20	1·60
Zygophyllaceae						
Balanites						
aegyptiaca	13·4	1·2	0·11	1·70	0·72	2·65

The syndrome would recur where repeated use of imbalanced feeds forms a necessary part of the nomadic cycle.

Feeding behaviour and nutritional requirements on open range

Camels on natural range will browse and graze at any time of the day or night. During very hot weather they tend to avoid feeding during the heat of the day and to adopt positions which reduce heat gain and thus conserve energy. Even when not under extreme climatic stress, camels tend to feed more actively at certain times of the day than at others, for example just before and after sunset (Acland, 1932).

The nature and sparseness of the food available to camels make rapid feeding rates and, therefore, high levels of dry matter intake difficult to achieve. In addition, although camels can resist thorns to some extent (Fig. 7.3), they are not completely immune to them and on very thorny species such as *Balanites aegyptiaca* (on which the thorns may be up to 70 mm in length) and some types of *Ziziphus* spp. feeding is a slow business. Some of the extremes in feeding behaviour noted in Mauritania

are shown in Table 7.10 where it can be seen that it is not only the number of bites taken which have an effect on food intake but also the size of the bite. Evidently a slow feeding rate can be compensated to some extent where mouthfuls are large or where the dry matter content of the fodder is high. Conversely where the bite size (the amount taken in dry matter at each bite) is small, rapid feeding rates are required if nutritional requirements are to be met. Table 7.11, complementary to Table 7.10, shows the variations in feeding behaviour and intake throughout the day for individual animals grazing on the same type of fodder or within the same area. From the data in Tables 7.10 and 7.11 it is clear that the intake of dry matter and hence of nutrients is very variable. The highest rate of intake (1 254 g per hour) would allow a camel to have a maximum intake of 2·5 kg per 100 kg (12·5 kg for a 500 kg castrate) in a feeding period occupying 10 hours. The lowest rates of less than 100 g per hour would make it impossible for the camel to fulfil either appetite or nutritional requirements. These results from one area support other data on daily food intake, which apparently is very variable (Table 7.12). It is clear from these results that very little is known or understood about what governs the feeding habits of camels.

From the available evidence, then, there are very great differences in feed intake and thus in the time required for feeding among camels. In addition to time for feeding, camels need an approximately equivalent time to ruminate. Camels feeding solely

fig. 7.3 Camel browsing in Australia

Table 7.12 Some estimates of total daily feed intake of camels

Country/area	Total food intake kg per day	Source
West Africa	30 – 50	Leroux, 1960
	19	Gauthier-Pilters, 1969
Somalia	40 – 55	Silberman, 1959
India	27 – 36	Yasin and Abdul Wahid, 1957
Iran	15 – 20	Khatami, 1970

Table 7.10 Feeding and intake rates of camels under varying conditions of feed and temperature. (*Source*: **Gauthier-Pilters, H.** (1969). *Observations sur l'écologie du dromedaire en Moyenne Mauritanie. Bull IFAN*, **31A**, 1259–1380.)

Fodder type	Animal type	Time of day (h)	Temperature °C	Number of bites per hour	Average weight per bite (g DM)	Total dry matter intake (g per hour)
Acacia raddiana (branch tips)	Dry female	12–13	38·5	140	1·00	140
Balanites aegyptiaca	Lactating female	13–14	40·8	260	2·00	520
Salsola (salt bush)	Castrate	10–11	38·6	124	0·76	94
Nucularia (salt bush)	Castrate	8–9	42·4	550	1·76	968
Maerua	Castrate	16–17	41·3	440	1·26	528
Capparis	Castrate	13–14	38·5	360	1·35	486
Ziziphus lotus	Castrate	21–22	34·0	500	1·10	550
Aristida pungens (dry stems)	Male	18–19	41·6	240	2·85	684
Panicum (fresh growth)	Castrate	19–20	30·5	760	1·65	1 254

Table 7.11 Variations in feeding and intake rates of individual camels throughout the day (*Source*: as for Table 7.10.)

	Time of day (hours)	Number of bites per hour	Average weight per bite (g DM)	Dry matter intake (g per hour)
Female camel on grass (*Aristida pungens*)				
	8–9	395	0·99	393
	9–10	412	1·24	511
	10–11	370	1·38	511
	Mean per hour	392	1·20	472
Castrate on dry salt bush (*Salsola foetida*)				
	10–11	124	0·76	94
	11–12	129	1·29	166
	12–13	200	1·35	170
	15–16	155	1·22	189
	Mean per hour	152	1·23	180

on *Balanites aegyptiaca* at an intake of 520 g DM per hour (Table 7.10) would acquire 3·17 MJ of energy (Table 7.5 on p. 107). A 500 kg camel would need 17 hours of feeding time to achieve the maintenance level given in Table 7.6 on p. 108 while a camel of MPW 307 kg would need almost 11½ hours. On *Salsola* spp. at an intake of 94 g DM per hour it is obvious that energy would be grossly deficient; owners probably accept some weight loss at this time to enable a salt cure to be effected. On good quality grass at an intake of 1 250 g DM per hour energy requirements could be satisfied in about 10 hours. In general these figures seem to give feeding times which are rather longer than has actually been recorded in practice but not unreasonably so. For example, it has been estimated that on good grazing of *gizu* type vegetation only 4 hours feeding is required, while 6-8 hours are required on medium quality feed and 10 or more on poor feed (Villachon, 1962). Gauthier-Pilters (1969) estimated 10-12 hours as the time spent in feeding. Acland (1932) was of the opinion that 'tree grazing' was better than all except the most valuable grasses but longer feeding times needed to be allowed.

The amount of time camels spend feeding will vary very much, depending on conditions. The indications are that theoretical energy requirements for maintenance can be obtained for much of the time off natural feed – and this is obvious from traditional practice. There is further scope for a better understanding of both the nutritional requirements of camels and of their feeding habits.

Supplementary feeding for special conditions

Although mainly subjective knowledge is available

fig. 7.4 Working camel being given supplementary rations of green berseem in Egypt

Table 7.13 Supplementary rations for camels with notes on nutritive value (weights in kg)

	Sudan riding camels[1]	South Yemen riding camels[2]	Somalia military camels[3]	India heavy working camels[4]	India heavy working camels[5]	Tunisia plough camels[6]	Iran 'Beef' camels[7]
Grain (sorghum)	6·8						
Grain (barley)						3·0	2·5
Pulse (*Phaseolus* spp.)							
Cotton seed		2·3	1·8	2·3	2·7		
Oilseed concentrate		2·3					
Bran			0·9				
Hay			4·5				
Chopped millet straw		11·3					
Barley straw				11·3		5·0	
Phaseolus spp. haulms					9·1		
Green cactus						10·0	
Nutritive value energy MJ/day	50·7	59·0	27·4	54·4	58·2	39·7	
DCP g/day	469	1 440	488	900	1 512	440	
Source	Acland (1932)	Leese (1927)	Peck (1938)	Yasin and Abdul Wahid (1957)	Leese (1927)	Burgemeister (1975)	Khatami (1970)

1 barely adequate energy for 450 kg camel: excess protein
2 no natural fodder available: barely adequate energy: grossly excessive protein
3 plus several hours range grazing: low energy: excess protein
4 energy sufficient for maintenance: grossly excessive protein: additional high energy supplement needed
5 according to Leese a little supplementary grazing is required: with grazing probably adequate energy: grossly excessive protein
6 very low in energy: excess protein: requires considerable time on range grazing
7 plus straw, sugar beet pulp and molasses: gives daily liveweight gain of 1·4 kg for males and 0·9 kg for females

concerning camels on natural feed a great deal of work has been done on supplementary feeding. Rations for work have been formulated over a relatively long period, for different purposes and over a wide geographic area. In general, supplementary rations make best use of locally grown crops and attempt to provide adequate energy for various requirements (Table 7.13). Where necessary, additional requirements for differing times of grazing on poor, fair or good quality feed are often indicated in the original references. Figure 7.4 shows green berseem being used as a supplementary feed for a camel doing pack work.

The main problem is the apparent excess of protein supplied with supplementary feeds. The camel's ability to recycle urea (Chapter 5) really only manifests itself in animals with high protein requirements, although the ability to recycle urea with decreasing nitrogen content also occurs in cattle and sheep (Payne, 1965). Schmidt-Nielsen's original work on this aspect of protein metabolism was carried out on a young growing female with a high protein demand which had been on a low protein diet comprised mainly of dry dates for more than 6 weeks. In formulating rations for growing stock or for milking animals, in spite of the urea recycling mechanism, nitrogen for metabolism is still required. Part of this requirement could, if necessary, be fed in the form of non-protein nitrogen such as urea, leaving conversion into the required aminoacids to the rumen fauna.

Water

The remarkable ability of the camel to conserve water should not obscure the fact that, in common with other domestic mammals, it does need to drink. On occasions it can go for weeks, occasionally months (Chapter 9) without access to free water. This ability is advantageous for range management but milking cows, working camels and animals on dry feed have requirements which need to be fulfilled at regular intervals. Normally, other things being equal, most camels will return freely to water under all but the very hottest temperatures every 4 to 5 days (Table 9.11 on p. 149). This period can be extended either naturally, or artifically by controlling herding, while

feeding conditions permit, e.g. the availability of plants with a high moisture content. The watering interval can then be extended in order to make more range available for feeding.

Working camels generally need to be watered every day if possible or at least once in every 2 days. When it is necessary to extend this interval for special reasons, camels should be accustomed gradually to the longer period.

Further reading

Acland, P. B. E. (1932). Notes on the camel in the eastern Sudan. *Sudan Notes Rec.*, **15**, 119–149.

Ayoub, M. H., Awad, Y. L. and Bayyazeed, L. A. (1960). Chlorides in serum of Egyptian farm animals. *Indian J. Vet. Sci.*, **30**, 34–37.

Bhattacharjee, R. C. and Banerjee, S. (1962). Biochemical studies on Indian camel (*Camelus dromedarius*). 2. Inorganic constituents of serum. *J. Sci. Indust. Res.*, **21C**, 106–107.

Burgemeister, R. E. (1975). *Elevage de chameaux en Afrique du Nord*. Office Allemand de la Coperation Technique: Eschborn, West Germany.

Durand, M. and Kchouk, M. (1958). *Le 'krafft', une osteopathie dystrophique du dromedaire*. *Arch. Inst. Pasteur Tunis*, **35**, 107–152.

Field, C. R. (1979). *Ecology and management of camels, sheep and goats in Northern Kenya*. UNESCO: Nairobi, Kenya.

Gauthier-Pilters, H. (1969). *Observations sur l'écologie du dromadaire en Moyenne Mauritanie*. *Bull. IFAN*, **31A**, 1259–1380.

Ghosal, A. K. and Dwaraknath, P. K. (1976). Plasma carotene and vitamin A levels in cows, sheep and camels of the Thar desert. *Indian Vet. J.*, **58**, 640–642.

Hansen, H. and Schmidt-Nielsen, K. (1957). On the stomach of the camel with special reference to the structure of its mucous membrane. *Acta anat.*, **31**, 353–375.

Hintz, H. F., Schryver, H. F. and Halbert, M. (1973). A note on the comparison of digestion by New World camels, sheep and ponies. *Anim. Prod.*, **16**, 303–305.

Khan, M. K. U. and Appanna, T. C. (1967). Carotene and vitamin A in camel milk. *J. Nutr. Diet.*, India, **4**, 17-20.

Khatami, K. (1970). *A new promising approach to the solution of the meat and protein problems in the arid and semi-arid countries of the world.* Ministry of Agriculture: Teheran, Iran.

Leese, A. S. (1927). *A treaties on the one-humped camel in health and disease.* Haynes & Son: Stamford, Lincs, UK.

Le Houérou, H. N. (1980). *Chemical composition and nutritive value of browse in tropical West Africa.* In: Le Houérou, H. N. (ed.) International Symposium on Browse in Africa, 5th-12th April 1980, Addis Ababa. International Livestock Centre for Africa: Addis Ababa, Ethiopia.

Leitch, I. (1940). *The feeding of camels.* Imp. Bur. Anim. Nut. Tech. Commun. No. 13. Imperial Bureau of Animal Nutrition: Aberdeen, UK.

Leonard, A. G. (1894). *The camel: its uses and management.* Longmans Green: London.

Leroux, Ch. (1960). *Aspects de la régulation thermique des animaux du désert.* Thèse, ENV Lyon No. 27. Ecole Nationale Vétérinaire: Lyon, France.

MAFF (1973). *Energy allowances and feeding systems for ruminants.* Ministry of Agriculture Tech. Bull. No. 33. Her Majesty's Stationery Office: London.

Maloiy, G. M. O. (1972). Comparative studies on digestion and fermentation rate in the free-stomach of the one-humped camel. *Res. vet. Sci.*, **13**, 476-481.

Moty, I. A., Mulla, A. el and Zaafer, S. A. (1968). Copper, iron and zinc in the serum of Egyptian farm animals. *Sudan Agric. J.*, **31**, 146-151.

Ohri, S. P. and Joshi, B. K. (1961). Composition of colostrum of camel. *Indian Vet. J.*, **38**, 604-607.

Payne, W. J. A. (1965). Specific problems of semi-arid environments. *Qual. Plant. Mat. Veg.* **12**, 269-294.

Peck, E. F. (1938). The relationship of salt starvation to contagious necrosis and lameness in camels. *Vet. Rec.*, **50**, 409-410.

Schmidt-Nielsen, B., Schmidt-Nielsen, K., Houpt, T. R. and Jarnum, S. A. (1957). Urea excretion in the camel. *Am. J. Physiol.*, **188**, 477-484.

Silberman, L. (1959). *Les nomades du plateau Somali. Rev. int. Sci. soc.*, **11**, 582-598.

Toofanian, F. and Aliakbari, S. (1977). Studies on the digestion of carbohydrates in the camel *Camelus dromedarius. Trop. Anim. Hlth Prod.*, **10**, 75-81.

Villachon, M. A. (1962) *Aliments et alimentation du dromadaire au Tassili N Ajjer (Sahara Central).* Thèse, ENV Alfort No. 31. Ecole Nationale Vétérinaire: Maisons Alfort, France.

Williams, V. J. (1963). Rumen function in the camel. *Nature*, **197**, 1221.

Yasin, S. A. and Abdul Wahid (1957). Pakistan camels - a preliminary survey. *Agric. Pakistan,* **8**, 289-295.

Part 3: Management for health and productivity

8 Diseases and parasites

*"The only person who knows how to
care for a camel is the person who has
reared it"*

Arab saying quoted by Cauvet (1925).

Temperature, respiration and pulse in the healthy camel

Physiologically the camel is peculiar among
domestic animals (see Chapter 5). Its ability to
allow its body temperature to rise and fall is quite
exceptional. Temperature, therefore, used as an
indication of the state of health of a camel must be
used with caution. Under Saharan summer conditions a rise of 6·2 °C in the rectal temperature –
from 34·5°C to 40·7°C – has been recorded in an
11-hour period from 0800 hours to 1900 hours.
Temperature ranges are much wider in dehydrated
camels than in camels watered daily (Fig. 8.1).

In a similar fashion the respiration rate varies
considerably in the healthy camel in response to
heat load and the need to conserve or lose water. A
typical morning rate in a Saharan summer may be
about 8 respirations a minute in a range of 6–11
rising to about 16 in the afternoon in a range of
8–18.

Pulse rate, which can be determined most easily
from the artery under the tail or, when the camel is
in its normal sitting position, from the tibial artery,
exhibits similar variations. It can normally be expected to be in the range of 32–44 per minute in
the morning, rising to 36–45 per minute during the
hottest part of the day.

Signs of illness and ill-health

The signs of illness and ill-health in the camel are,
in general, those common to other animals. These
may, however, be masked owing to the normal
variations in physiological functions as outlined
above. A staring skin, usually symptomatic of ill
health, may be difficult to notice in the camel but
an animal not chewing its cud should be considered
to be ill, as should an animal which refuses to eat.
Even vocal expressions of pain in the camel may be
mistaken for the normal vocalisations with which it
accompanies almost every change of position or
pace.

Specific disease- or parasite-related symptoms
are generally easier to recognise. Thus discharges
from the eyes, nose and excessive salivation
(although the latter is normal during rutting in
males and in both males and females after eating
salt) may indicate disease. Changes in the size and
consistency of dung pellets may be indicative of
disease but may equally be due to changes in diet
or to a change of handler. Urine containing minor
amounts of blood is not uncommon in camels and
need not necessarily indicate ill-health.

In general terms, much more commonsense and
experience is needed to diagnose camel illness from

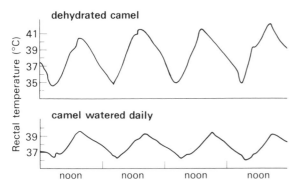

fig. 8.1 Daily variations in body temperature of dehydrated
camels and in those watered daily (*Source:* **Schmidt-
Nielsen, K.** (1964). *Desert animals: physiological problems
of heat and water.* Oxford University Press: Oxford UK.)

external symptoms than with other species of domestic stock. Any changes from what is considered normal for an individual animal remarked by its owner or handler should be considered to be indicative of a likely disease or health problem. Traditional owners recognise many of the common camel diseases and their diagnoses can often give an early lead. Table 8.1 lists vernacular names of many diseases in the areas in which they are known, omitting only the names for trypanosomiasis which are given in Table 8.4 on p. 123.

Virus diseases

Camel pox

Camel pox is caused by a variole virus related to those of other poxes. It is the most serious and widespread virus disease of camels. The virus has recently been isolated in Iran, in Kenya and in Egypt among other places. In Egypt the specific causal organism of the disease in camels has been shown to be *Orthopoxvirus* which differs in some properties from the related vaccinia and cowpox viruses (Tantawi, El-Dahaby and Famhy, 1978).

The symptoms are the classic ones of pox with papules, vesicles, pustules and crust formation appearing successively. Lesions are usually confined to the head but in serious cases may become generalised. Young animals from 6 months to 2 years are most seriously affected and death sometimes occurs. Recovered camels are immune for life and young animals suckling immune mothers acquire a passive immunity. The disease generally occurs, and is most serious, during the rainy season – and it is at this time that deaths are likely to occur. A crude form of vaccination is carried out by some camel owners but the disease is generally benign and runs its course in about 3 weeks. Where topical treatment is required

Table 8.1 Vernacular names of the common camel diseases

Disease	Vernacular names in					
	India	Somalia	Mahgreb[1]	Arabia	French	Ethiopia
Camel pox	thaddi chechak mata	afrur	djidri			
Contagious skin necrosis	jhooling jhoolak	dallahan		gub latia	necrose cutanée	douala maha
Haemorrhagic septicaemia		kud	el ghedda		pasteurellose	
Blackquarter	(as for anthrax)	kud	oulsis		charbon symto- matique	
Anthrax	sool, zehmat morhi, sut, sujhan, garhi	kud	khudad		charbon bacteridien	
Mange	kharish, pan, garr, kujli	addo		djarab	gale	
Ticks	chichri	shillin			tique	

[1]Mahgreb = Tunisia, Algeria, Morocco

because of the severity of lesions or the value of a particular camel then a proprietary antiseptic can be used.

Rabies

Confirmed rabies in camels has been reported from India and from Tunisia (Leese, 1927).

The most common symptom is nervousness, shown by unusual interest in what is going on, and a disinclination to feed. There may be abnormal aggressiveness towards the handler but this is not always apparent. The eyes may be glazed, the head carried abnormally high and there may be some saliva from the mouth. Spitting and ejection of saliva is a common cameline reaction to handling and it is probable that this represents the greatest danger of infection to man as the saliva is infective several days before clinical symptoms appear.

Paralysis appears early in camels, they may bite themselves and strain. Death occurs about a week after the onset of symptoms. Camels suspected of having rabies should be isolated and treated with care. Once diagnosis is positive the animal should be destroyed and the carcass burnt.

It is possible to confuse rabies with a variety of other effects including: natural nervousness after attack by a wild animal or snake bite; heavy rut in males; trypanosomiasis when it affects the brain.

Foot-and-mouth disease (FMD)

Camels appear to be completely immune to foot-and-mouth disease. There are no confirmed records of either natural or experimental infection. In a recent outbreak of FMD in cattle in Ethiopia with which camels were intimately associated no camels were infected and no antibodies of A,O or C types could be demonstrated in camel sera (Richard, 1976). Camels in Kenya pasturing on the same area as cattle, which showed 94 per cent of antibodies in spite of being vaccinated every 6 months, and wildlife showed no A, O, SAT 1 or SAT 2 antibodies (Paling, Jessett and Heath, 1979). Whether camels can be involved as carriers of the virus remains to be demonstrated.

Rinderpest

In contrast to FMD the antibodies of rinderpest have been demonstrated in camels in Kenya (Taylor, 1968), in Chad (Provost, Maurice and Borredon, 1968) and in Ethiopia (Richard, 1976) and clinical cases have been described from West Africa and India but without experimental confirmation. In Ethiopia, 14 per cent of 684 serum samples showed antibodies. The general conclusion is that the camel may be susceptible to subclinical infections but is unlikely to be a carrier unless the virus is much modified. If it is shown that the camel can act as a carrier it might well have repercussions on the establishment of disease-free zones for livestock and meat exports.

Other viruses

Bluetongue antibody has recently been isolated from 26 out of 32 camel sera in Botswana (Simpson, 1979). It is not clear, in this case either, whether the camel is a potential reservoir for the disease. Two other viruses of possible importance as zoonoses have been isolated in Chad: influenza virus type B, of which there was a low incidence; and para influenza (*Myxovirus parainfluenza III*) of which apparently the incidence was 100 per cent (Bares, 1968). Para influenza was also demonstrated in 81 per cent of camels in a Tunisian sample (Burgemeister, 1975) as well as a number of other viruses. What significance the influenza virus has is not known, but it is obviously very widespread as a level of 80 per cent antibody response has recently been obtained in Oman (Hedger, Bennett and Gray, 1980). In Kenya, Rift Valley fever antibodies have been found in camels but not antibodies of malignant catarrh, the primary host of which is the wildebeest but which can be an important disease of cattle.

Bacterial diseases

Bacterial diseases in camels, as in other domestic animals, vary in importance and distribution. Much research undoubtedly remains to be done but a preliminary indication of the distribution and importance of the main diseases is given in Table 8.2.

Contagious necrosis of the skin

This is perhaps the most important bacterial disease of camels and is very widespread (Rutter

Table 8.2 Distribution and importance of bacterial diseases in camels

Disease	India	Egypt/ Sudan	Kenya/ Somalia	North Africa	West Africa	Eritrea Ethiopia	West Asia/ Arabia
				Area			
Skin necrosis	+++	+++	+++	+	++	+++	++
Anthrax	+(+)	+	+	+(+)	+	+	
Brucellosis		++	+	++	++	+	
Blackquarter	+		+	++	+		
Pasteurellosis (Haemorrhagic septicaemia)	++	++	++	+++	+		+
Plague				+			
Salmonellosis	+	+	++	+			+
Tuberculosis	+	+	+	+			
Pulmonary streptothricosis		++					

and Mack, 1963). The principal bacteria involved are *Streptothrix* spp. but they are often associated with other genera. The disease is contagious and usually occurs in outbreaks affecting several animals at once. The most common site is on the back or hump with the base of the neck also being affected fairly frequently.

The disease first appears as a swelling under the skin and later develops into an ulcer of raw flesh. The ulcer gradually spreads and generally shows no tendency to heal spontaneously. Treatment requires strict hygiene; all pus should be removed from the affected areas and the area then thoroughly cleaned. With the availability of antibiotics cure is much easier and more rapid than formerly but considerable economic loss can still be caused by camels being unable to work during the period they are infected. A lack, or an insufficiency, of salt in the diet may be a predisposing factor to this disease (see Chapter 7 (Peck, 1939)). Damage by thorn scrub is known to be a predisposing factor in cattle and is probably so in camels.

Other pyogenic organisms implicated in general abcess formation are very common and it is often difficult to isolate a specific causal agent. *Streptococcus agalactiae*, *Corynebacterium* spp., *Staphylococcus* spp., *Lactobacillus* and *Actinomyces* spp. (a genus of fungi) may be involved. In cases where outbreaks are severe or regular it might be worth while preparing autovaccines from

the particular organism or mixture of organisms.

In Ethiopia a chronic suppurative disease known as *mala* (Somali for pus) leading to the formation of internal as well as external abcesses is apparently more important than contagious necrosis of the skin. The abcesses are normally ganglionic and usually found on the lower neck or on the rump. The causal organisms are *Corynebacterium pseudotuberculosis* and a Type B *Streptococcus* (Domenech, Guidot and Richard, 1977).

Other bacteria

The occurrence and seriousness of other bacterial diseases vary greatly from one area to another. A **haemorrhagic septicaemia** due to *Pasteurella* spp. is widespread, the usual pulmonary symptoms being observed. Immediate treatment with antibiotics may be effective but as with most bacterial diseases vaccination is more certain than cure, at least under field conditions.

Anthrax caused by *Bacillus anthracis* is apparently also fairly common in camels although it is not always distinguished from blackquarter. Formerly enormous losses were attributed to anthrax in Algeria and in India and more recently losses have been reported from Kenya and Ethiopia (Bremaud, 1969; Richard, 1975). The major symptom of anthrax is usually rapid death. At death a black tarry blood exudes from the natural orifices. Preliminary signs include oedematous swellings, occasional apoplexia and diarrhoea. **Blackquarter** or **black leg** (*Clostridium chauvei*) is often mistaken for anthrax and needs to be differentially diagnosed from it. Crepitation of the lesions is a common occurrence in blackquarter.

Infections with *Brucella* spp. appear to be fairly low in camels, even where the disease is common in other domestic stock. For instance, in determining levels of infection in Chad using the serum agglutination test only 1·8 per cent of camels were positive compared with 5·3 per cent of sheep and goats, 18·5 per cent of cattle and 27·7 per cent of equines (Bares, 1968). In Sudan, serum tests gave positive results in 1·75–5·75 per cent of cases. The complement fixation test can also be used for diagnosis and is more reliable in chronic or recent infections. In Africa the causal agent appears generally to be *B. melitensis* but *B. suis* may also be involved while in Asia it is *B. abortus*. *Salmonella* spp. may also occasionally cause problems including enteritis, sterility and abortion. While this is a widespread infection the most recent serious outbreak has been in Somalia (Cheyne, Pegram and Cartwright, 1977). However, by far the commonest cause of abortion in camels is due to infections by trypanosomes.

The sensitivity of camels to **contagious bovine pleuropneumonia** and their possible role as carriers or reservoirs of the disease are as much the subject of discussion as their role in rinderpest. Complement fixation tests in Chad showed positive results in less than 9 per cent of animals (8 per cent for rinderpest) but it was not clear whether the bacterium was in fact *Mycoplasma mycoides* - the causal organism of contagious bovine pleuropneumonia - or a related mycoplasma and none of the animals showed clinical symptoms of the disease (Bares, 1968).

Tuberculosis is rare in camels except in special circumstances; the causal organism is identical with that of cattle. The disease has been shown to occur only in camels which live in close proximity to cattle, and in Egypt, for example, it is not found in nomadic camels although it occurs in camels owned by the cultivators along the Nile and, formerly, in camels imported from Syria and Arabia (Mason, 1917).

Other bacterial diseases including leptospirosis, glanders, epizootic lymphangitis, paratuberculosis (Johne's disease), tetanus, plague and the rickettsias appear to be of very minor importance.

Diseases caused by Protozoa

Trypanosomiasis

Trypanosomiasis is by far the most important protozoan disease of camels and is probably the most important health problem of all. Unlike the trypanosomal diseases of other domestic animals its principal vector is not the tsetse fly. In fact, the tsetse is very seldom the vector and it is normally transmitted mechanically by other species of biting fly.

Table 8.3 Principal characteristics of camel trypanosomiasis

	Acute form	Sub-acute form	Chronic form
Duration	3–6 months	2 years (starting 4–6 months after infection)	up to 4 years (starting about 1 year after infection)
Parasites found in blood	2–3 times a month	1–2 times a month	1–2 times a year
Main symptoms	death may be rapid (11 days to 11 weeks) emaciation very rapid (not necessarily in young animals)	intermittent fever emaciation rapid (not necessarily in young animals)	intermittent fever emaciation prolonged

The chronic form of the disease is far more common than the acute; Table 8.3 outlines the principal characteristics of both forms. The acute form more commonly affects the adults. Real immunity is never acquired although pre-immunity is fairly common. Young do not acquire immunity through their dams. An infection level of 20 per cent in areas where the disease occurs is not uncommon and up to 70 per cent is not unknown. Deaths may reach 3 per cent (Rutter, 1967). Declining milk production, abortion and chronic poor condition are the classic symptoms of the disease in the camel.

The widespread nature of the disease and its importance is perhaps best illustrated by reference to the large number of local names by which it is known. The commonest vernacular name is *surra* which, although originating in Asia, is the word most used to express the presence of camel trypanosomiasis among English-speaking people associated with livestock. In parts of Africa where a South African influence has been present it is also known as *nagana*. Other local names and their areas of usage are given in Table 8.4 while Fig. 8.2 shows the importance by countries. The disease was diagnosed in South Africa early in the twentieth century in camels imported from Somalia (Theiler, 1905) and in Australia in camels in quarantine in 1907 (Seddon, 1952). It may in fact have been present in Australian camels imported from India as early as 1866.

The causal organism is normally *Trypanosoma evansi* or *T. brucei*. A number of trypanosomes originally given separate specific status have now

Table 8.4 Vernacular names, with areas of origin, for camel trypanosomiasis

Area	Name	Notes
Syria, Algeria, Egypt	*debab*	From the Arabic for fly. In Egypt and Sudan recovered animals are referred to as *bentic el debab* (preserved from the fly). In Algeria an infected animal is known as *madbub*.
Egypt	*zoubib, djaffa*	
Libya (Cyrenaecia)	*slal*	
Sudan	*gufar*	Probably from the Sudanese Arabic for a tabanid. A variation of this word is used in Chad.
Somalia (southern part)	*chindhi* (acute) *duken, salof* (chronic)	
Mauritania	*tabourit*	An infected camel is called *m'bori* and a tolerant one is known as *zaguer*.
Senegal		Tolerant camels known as *ouolof* because resistance is acquired on this part of the lower Senegal river.
Mali (Tuareg of Niger river)	*tahaga*	
Mali (Songhrai)	*n'diomdé*	
Nigeria (Hausa)	*tioutangoussoum*	
India	*surra, tibersa, sar, sargiya, phata, phitguja, kana hogi.*	
Kenya	*gandi*	
Eritrea	*alleh, gudho*	

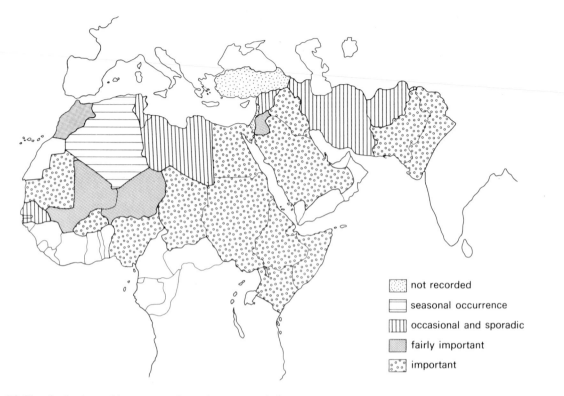

not recorded

seasonal occurrence

occasional and sporadic

fairly important

important

fig. 8.2 The distribution and importance of camel trypanosomiasis

been submerged in *T. evansi*, some of these having names of a regional character such as *T. berbera*, *T. marocanum* and *T. soudanense*. Spontaneous infection by *T. congolense* can occur in the Sudan but *T. vivax* has so far not been demonstrated in camels.

Trypanosomiasis due to *T. evansi* does not require the presence of tsetse flies (*Glossina* spp.) to ensure its maintenance. It is unique among trypanosome diseases in this respect; this also accounts for its widespread distribution in areas far removed from tsetse infestation. It is only where the tsetse fly is present that natural infections of organisms other than *T. evansi* occur, for example in Somalia (where *Glossina* spp. occur) and in Kenya where infection may be due to *T. brucei*. There is probably *T. brucei* in Nigeria and perhaps in Upper Volta.

Biting flies of the family Tabanidae are the most important agents in transmission. In Chad, 11 species of this family are involved from four genera including *Atylotus* (2 species), *Ancala* (3 species), *Tabanus* (5 species) and *Haematopota coronata* (Gruvel and Balis, 1965). Elsewhere *Chrysops* are implicated and in India horn flies of the genus *Lyperosia* are involved. In northern Somalia (former British Somaliland) *Pangonia* spp. is a vector (Peck, 1936) and Pangonidae and Hippoboscidae are probably also agents of transmission in Kenya. Muscidae (houseflies) are also actively involved in transmission, not only the biting fly *Stomoxis* spp. but in addition non-biting flies which lap blood including *Musca* spp. *Eumarus* spp. and *Bdellopharynx* spp. In some areas mosquitoes and ticks also can be responsible for transmission. Most of these insects are, of course, more prevalent in the rains and around wet and swampy places, including watering points. The

Table 8.5 A comparison of diagnostic methods for the identification of camel trypanosomiasis

Method	Country and approximate date of first use	Efficiency	Notes
Physical symptoms		varies	differentiation from the wasting diseases on post mortem
Blood smears		fair	parasites present in peripheral blood at any given moment in only 45–60 per cent of cases
Animal inoculation		twice as good as blood smears	
Formol gel	Algeria, 1923	90 per cent accuracy in adults	gives some false positive results, particularly in young animals
Complement fixation test	USA, 1924	good	no practical value because of difficulty of preparing suitable antigen
Mercury (II) chloride	Sudan, 1927	varies, generally good	
Thymol turbidity	Egypt, 1960	more accurate than mercury	can be used on haemolysed blood
Indirect haemogglutination	1964		not yet used for camels but applicable to *Trypanosoma evansi*.
Indirect fluorescent antibody test (IFAT)			
Micro-scale enzyme-linked immunosorbed assay (micro ELISA) IgM	being developed in Sudan	generally better than indirect methods	

parasites remain alive on the flies' mouthparts for only a short period but can live in the gut for varying lengths of time up to 40 hours.

Trypanosomiasis in camels is usually chronic, involving recurrent fever, anaemia and death. Animals may survive up to 3–4 years. Oedema is a fairly constant symptom and additional complications involving the respiratory, gastro-intestinal and nervous systems may also be present. Nervous symptoms may be confused with rabies. In acute cases persistent fever is present and parasites can almost always be demonstrated in the blood.

Clinical symptoms are often sufficient to give a fair idea that infection is present but a certain diagnosis of trypanosomiasis is only fully satisfactory if the parasites can be demonstrated in peripheral blood. With camel trypanosomiasis, unfortunately, this technique may identify less than 50 per cent of infected animals and it is usual, therefore, to use other tests either alone or in conjunction with microscopic diagnosis (Table 8.5). Such tests have been developed over the last 60 years, while research is still going on to find improved tests (Pegram and Scott, 1976; Luckins *et al.*, 1979; Mahmoud and Gray, 1980). Much of the early and current research work is located in Sudan. A comparison of the advantages of the mercury(II) chloride test over that of formol gel (Bennett and Kenny, 1928) while considerably dated, serves to illustrate the emphasis which is still sought in trypanosome diagnosis. The mercury(II) chloride test has the following advantages.

1 It can be used in small amounts and remain reliable.
2 Detects infections a shorter time after initial infection than formal gel and even before trypanosomes appear in the blood serum.
3 The test is easily and rapidly carried out.
4 The results are easy to assess.

Treatment and cure of camel trypanosomiasis due to *T. evansi* or *T. brucei* infections used to be a long and tedious business, complicated by uncertainty as to whether a cure had been effected. Arsenic and antimony, either alone or in combination, and tartar emetic were used in curative treat- ment. To administer tartar emetic involves 17 or 18 injections on alternate days over a period of 35 days, each injection varying from 50 ml to 200 ml of a 1 per cent aqueous solution administered intravenously. Some veterinarians even recommended 25 treatments over a period of 49 days!

The introduction of suramin in 1920 marked the start of trypanosome treatment using modern drug therapy. Much of the early work was carried out in Sudan in conjunction with the development of diagnostic methods (Knowles, 1925; 1927). Some of the subsequently developed treatments are shown in Table 8.6.

Drugs used with success against the common

Table 8.6 Drugs and methods for treatment and control of camel trypanosomiasis

Drug	Dosage	Method	Efficiency	Common name and notes
Arsenicals, antimonials		long and complicated	30–70 per cent	narrow safety margins
Suramin	10 g aqueous solution	intravenous	very good	'Naganol' 'Bayer 205' 'Antrypol'; if used as prophylactic can lead to resistance.
Suramin + stibophen	4 g + 40 ml	intravenous	100 per cent	stibophen = 'antimosan'
Stilbamidine isethionate	5 mg per kg	intravenous		unsafe at this dose and unreliable at lower rates
Pentamidine isethionate		intravenous		ineffective at safe dose rates
Dimidium bromide	2 mg per kg		ineffective	'Phenanthridium 897' and '1555'
Quinapyramine	2 g aqueous solution (10 mg per kg)	subcutaneous/ intramuscular	approaches 100 per cent	'Antrycide'; higher rates are toxic
Diminazene aceturate	5 mg per kg aqueous solution	subcutaneous/ intramuscular	very good in combinations	'Berenil'; highly toxic at 7 mg per kg
Isometamidium	1 mg per kg in 2 per cent aqueous solution	intravenous	not as effective at this dose against *Trypanosoma evansi* as other products	'Samorin'; can also be used subcutaneously and intramuscularly; higher doses more effective but very poorly tolerated

trypanosomes of other domestic animals (*T. congolense, T. vivax*) are not always very efficient against the camel trypanosome. For example isometemidium ('Samorin'), in addition to being poorly tolerated by the camel, has a very low success rate against *T. evansi* and treatment has to be relatively prolonged (Balis and Richard, ·1977). As with all trypanocides strict control of dosage should be enforced as resistant strains can build up very quickly. Successful treatment can often be achieved by combining two or more different drugs or by using a drug unrelated to one to which resistance has developed. For example, quinapyramine sulphate (antrycide prosalt) will clear suramin-resistant trypanosomes.

Some drugs used as curatives have prophylactic properties in addition but the period of protection is usually of short duration, seldom exceeding 3, or at the most 4 months. In general great care should be exercised in using anti-trypanosome drugs prophylactically unless the regime can be strictly controlled. Short term prophylaxis can be useful for camels migrating through an area of known high risk.

Camel trypanosomiasis is kept alive by wild hosts and by insect vectors. Both of these are very numerous and eradication is almost certainly an impossible dream. Spontaneous recovery may occur but the camel itself may then act as a reservoir of infection. Whether spontaneous recovery confers immunity against further attack is not clear – camels cured by drugs are certainly not immune. Some pre-immunity giving protection for a limited period probably occurs but most so-called immunity is the result of careful management. This involves seasonal movement of camel herds away from fly-infested areas; regular movement of camps to avoid hatching of dung-breeding flies (e.g. *Lyperosia* spp. and *Stomoxys* spp); travelling at night in known *Tabanus* spp. zones; watering in tight groups in *Tabanus* spp. areas and during the hottest part of the day in hot weather and the coldest part in cool whether. All the foregoing measures are adopted by traditional owners. 'Official' camels may be protected by smudge fires, insect repellants, sacking on the bellies and close coralling with some form of protection for the outermost animals. Pure management factors, apart from nomadism and transhumance are, however, of only limited effect.

Other protozoal diseases

There is very little evidence that flagellate Protozoa, other than trypanosomes are pathogenic to camels.

Coccidiosis due, for example, to *Eimeria* spp. or *Globidium* spp. is probably universally present although in Chad, oocysts of the latter were demonstrated in only about 7 per cent of camel faeces sampled (Gruvel and Graber, 1965). Up to 1 260 oocysts per gram of faeces were found. Gastro-enteritis and emaciation in such cases may be due to other causes such as intestinal worms or trypanosome infections, with aggravation by the coccidia. If the last is suspected of pathogenicity it can be treated with sulphonamides.

Anaplasma spp. organisms were incriminated in camel deaths in Kufra oasis in southern Libya in the 1930s, the vector being a *Hyalomma* spp. tick (Monteverde, 1937) but it does not appear to have been recorded elsewhere. In the Kufra case 40 per cent of the red blood cells of clinically healthy camels showed anaplasma-like inclusions. In India 13 per cent of a sample of camels, also clinically healthy, had sera positive to *Toxoplasma* spp. (Sharma and Gautam, 1974) although spontaneous infection elsewhere has not been shown and experimental infection cannot always be achieved. Sarco-sporidiosis, due to *Sarcocystis* spp. was shown to infect camels without any ill effects as early as 1910 and more recently an infection level of 4·5 per cent has been demonstrated in Sudan (Ginawi and Shomein, 1977). The parasites, which have no apparent effect on the camel, encyst in skeletal, oesophageal and cardiac muscle. They may be of importance as a zoonose and could result in economic loss due to condemnation of carcasses.

Diseases of reproduction

Trypanosomiasis is the main disease affecting fertility in female camels and results in general debility as well as abortions. *Pasteurella* spp. and *Salmonella* spp. are also causal organisms of abortion in camels and are usually more involved in this problem than *Brucella* spp. (Richard, 1975).

Infections of the female reproductive organs often follow difficult parturitions or retention of the placenta and may cause pyometra resulting in subsequent lowered fertility or infertility. Degeneration of the ovaries due to cysts occurs in a small number of camels. There is evidence that this type of cyst formation is associated with excessive production of follicle-stimulating hormone (FSH) in the case of multiple small cysts and to a lack of leuteinising hormone (LH) in the case of large cysts. Early embryonic mortality appears to be much more prevalent in camels than in other domestic animals and results in an apparent lowered fertility rate.

In male camels filarial infestations may lead to enlargement of the testicles and cirrhosis of the epididymis.

No references to venereal diseases in camels, such as *Trichomonas* spp., *Vibrio* spp. or infectious epididymitis and cervicovaginitis appear to exist. However, these diseases occur in other domestic animals which are often associated with camels and it is possible that accidental transmission by man may occur.

Miscellaneous other diseases

Arthritic diseases are of common and widespread occurrence in camels. They have been recorded from Somalia where under the Somali name *barrak* the disease is manifested by an inability to kneel down, stiffness and lameness (Rabagliati, 1923). Arthritis is also a major problem in the few camels in Botswana (Simpson, personal communication).

In North Africa bone dystrophia occurs over much of the region where it is known under the local name of *krafft* (Durand and Kchouk, 1958). This is characterised in extreme cases by spontaneous fractures. The cause is due to an imbalance in calcium/phosphorus ratios resulting in a phosphorus deficiency. The same disease is described by Burgemeister (1975) who also reports a bone malfunction in new-born camels in which the hocks are completely misformed and which may well be due to the same cause. The disease affects 15 per cent of new-born camels; those affected are usually killed by their owners at birth.

Degeneration of the arteries known as spontaneous atherosclerosis has recently been recorded in Iranian camels (Ezzi and Zakarian, 1979).

Leese (1927) and Curasson (1947) remain the major sources of information for other medical and surgical problems affecting the camel.

Internal parasites

Internal and external parasites are perhaps the most important cause of economic loss in camels with the exception of trypanosomiasis. No doubt in recognition of this much recent research on camels has been concentrated in this field, both in the identification of species and in their control. A large part of this work has been done by the French not only in their former colonies – where the camel is, of course, often the principal domestic animal – but also in Ethiopia. A quick review of the literature reveals the existence of more than 60 parasites directly injurious to camels. Many of these are of minor or academic interest only, being either new host records or specific to this particular host. This and the next section will concentrate, therefore, on the main groups and their control, mentioning specific parasites only where they are of special importance or of general interest.

Flukes (trematodes)

In general it might be considered that the habitat and management system of camels would not be conducive to a high incidence of liver flukes. In fact, although they seldom reach a high level of individual infestation, they appear to be present in a fair proportion of animals. Camels can become infested at watering points and particularly where they are associated part of the year with irrigation schemes. Thus in Saudi Arabia camels from the east of the country on the Persian Gulf show a higher percentage infestation than camels from other areas. But in Saudi Arabia camels imported from Sudan for slaughter showed a higher level still with 14 per cent being infested (Magzoub and Kasim, 1978). Many Sudanese camels, particularly those found close to the Nile and its major tributaries, are regularly associated with irrigation schemes. In such situations not only flukes of the genus *Fasciola* are likely to be present but also

Schistosoma spp. which is associated with bilharzia. Although camels are not apparently affected by bilharzia their possible role in its transmission to humans and other animals might be of importance.

Tapeworms (cestodes)

Intestinal tapeworms are also almost universally present in camels (Altaif, 1974; Bouvier, 1976) although they have not been investigated as thoroughly as roundworms. From the general health point of view, and especially where camel meat is an important component of the human diet, the main problems are associated with the larval forms of certain worms. Inspection of meat for human consumption should pay particular attention to the presence of the larval stages of *Echinococcus polymorphus* and of *Taenia marginata*. The former occur as hydatid cysts and the latter as encysted cysticerci. Hydatid cysts occur mainly in the lungs (where they are certainly most obvious) but also in the liver, heart and spleen. Cysticerci occur in the heart, on the tongue and throughout the muscle tissue. Very heavy infestation rates of hydatid cysts are quite common; at Kano in northern Nigeria almost 60 per cent of more than 3 400 camels slaughtered in a 4 month period were infested (Dada, 1978) and there is 64 per cent infestation in Iran (Mobedi, Madadi and Arfaa, 1970). In Lebanon and Syria levels of infestation may reach 100 per cent (Dailey and Sweatman, 1965). In Kenya hydatids are common in Turkana camels but not in Rendille and Gabbra animals; this may result from cultural and hygienic differences between these tribes. In Sudan many camels inspected at slaughter had hydatid cysts. Other results from Sudan indicate that infestation levels may not be generally very high but camels still play the main role in the epizootiology of echinococcosis, the primary chain being camel – dog – camel with infestation of man following eating of camel meat (El-Badawi, Eisa, Slepner and Saad, 1979).

Treatment against intestinal tapeworms can be carried out with anthelmintics specific for these parasites. Control of the encysted stages is more complicated, requiring control of grazing management and education of the human population -

part of the life cycle may be undergone in the alternative human host and eggs are voided in the faeces.

Roundworms (nematodes)

While nematode infestations are generally thought of as intestinal or occasionally pulmonary, roundworms are by no means confined to these sites. In addition there are nodule-forming roundworms, e.g. *Onchocerca armillata* recently discovered in the camel and *O. fasciata* which has been known for a long time, and blood parasites of the filaria group, e.g. *Dipetalonema evansi*. Other roundworms, for example *Thelazia leesei* which appears in the mucus of the eyes, infest other sites.

It is nonetheless the gastro-intestinal roundworms which are economically the most important, especially those of the genera *Trichuris, Nematodirus, Strongyloides* and *Haemonchus*. Clinical symptoms of gastro-enteritis are diverse and include diarrhoea and constipation, general debility and inappetence. Heavy infestations, particularly of *Haemonchus* spp., may predispose the animal to *Pasteurella* spp. Positive diagnosis is usually on the basis of faecal egg counts from which the necessity and intensity of treatment can be decided. A slide agglutination test gives satisfactory results for filaria (Michael and Saleh, 1977). Nematode infestation in some degree is almost universal, for example, in southern Ethiopia where 92 per cent of camels were shown to be carrying parasites (Richard, 1975), and in India where heavy infestation levels have been demonstrated (Lodha, Raisinghani and Karwasra, 1977).

Treatment of roundworm infestation should depend on the levels of infestation and the species involved. Where, however, a wide range of worms is present it may be necessary to use a broad spectrum dewormer at fairly heavy dose rates. For example, tetramisole ('Nilverm') is very effective against *Trichostrongylus* spp. larvae at low dosage rates but is much less effective against *Haemonchus* spp. even at relatively high dosages. Nitroxynil is not only effective against *Haemonchus* spp. but also, when the method of treatment is by subcutaneous injection, against the larvae of the camel nasal fly, *Cephalopina titillator*, and against liver flukes (Delavenay, 1978). Some comparative trials

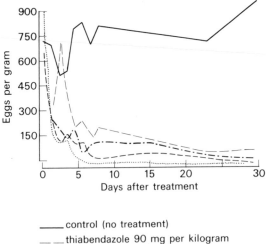

control (no treatment)
thiabendazole 90 mg per kilogram
tetramisole ('Nilverm') 3 per cent drench 0·5 ml per kilogram
morantel tartrate 4 per cent ('Banminth') 1 ml per kilogram
methyridine 90 per cent injectable ('Promintic') 0·22 ml per kilogram

fig. 8.3 Effects of various anthelmintics on overall roundworm egg counts in camel faeces (*Source*: **Lodha, K. R. Raisinghani, P. M. and Karwasra, R. S.** (1977). Chemotherapeutic trials of some anthelmintics against helminth parasites in camels. *Indian J. Anim. Sci.*, **47,** 677-682.)

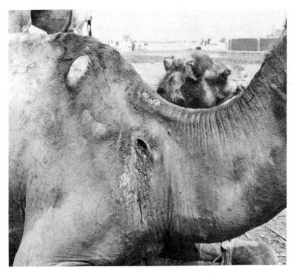

fig. 8.4 Suppurating wound in the neck of a camel aggravated by fly irritation. (Niono, Mali)

on the effects of various drugs have been carried out (Lodha, Raisinghani and Karwasi, 1977). These show (Fig. 8.3) generally good but variable results. Some drugs very effective in other domestic animals are not so efficient in camels; this is true also for drugs against trypanosomiasis. Further research into control of internal parasites would obviously be worthwhile.

External parasites

Insects

The role of insects as carriers of camel disease has already been outlined on p. 127. In particular, insects of the order Diptera are important as irritants and in myiasis (the general effects of flies on organisms). They aggravate many small wounds (see, for example, Fig. 8.4) by their biting and licking actions and since they lay their eggs in these sites, through the depredations of their larvae.

The larvae of the camel nasal fly *Cephalopina titillator* are important parasites of the nasal and frontal sinuses of the camel. They occur almost universally in camels in Ethiopia, in Sudan and in Arabia and probably everywhere the camel is found. In some areas they are important only seasonally (Abul-Hab and Al-Abbas, 1977). Very severe infestations lead to perforation of the sinuses and compression of the meninges resulting very often in nervous disorders. Treatment, as already mentioned, can be effected in conjunction with that for *Haemonchus* spp. by subcutaneous injections of nitroxynil. The larvae of the beetle *Ergaster faber* are occasionally also found in the nasal cavities in addition to those of the common sheep nasal fly *Oestrus ovis*. The role of tabanids and other biting flies in simple disturbance, and in anaemia in severe cases, is of minor importance compared with their role as vectors of trypanosomiasis.

The flea, *Vermipsylla alakurt*, is specific to camels and occasionally achieves pest status.

Mites and ticks

Camel mange is often quoted as the second most important cause of loss in camels after trypanosomiasis. The causal organism is a sub-species of the common sarcoptic mange mite and is known as *Sarcoptes scabiei cameli*. An indication of its wide geographical range is given by the local names by which it is known: mange in English; *la gale* in French; *al gharab* in Arabic; *addo* in Somali; *khuyli, lharish, paun* and others in India. Curiously it does not appear to be very common in southern Ethiopia but it is in the north. Mange is very contagious between camels and is transmissible to humans although it is doubtful if it can maintain itself on the latter. Diagnosis is easy microscopically – although the mite is just visible to the naked eye – and there is no danger of confusion with other mange-causing mites as sarcoptic mange is the only mange disease of camels. Treatment with modern acaricides is relatively simple and efficient: lindane, where it can still be obtained, assures complete recovery after two applications at 0·05 per cent strength at intervals of 8 days (Lodha, 1966).

Ticks, mainly of the genera *Rhipicephalus, Amblyomma* and *Hyalomma* are mainly important for the physical irritation they cause. While there is some indication they might be involved in the transmission of trypanosomiasis there are no reports of the normal tick-borne diseases being prevalent in camels. In Kenya they have been known to cause blindness by affecting the cornea and it is suspected that toxins produced by ticks may be the cause of death in calves (Field, personal communication).

Other external parasites

Leeches have been reported as pests in India (Leese, 1927) and also in Kenya (Field, personal communication). Ringworm, caused by *Trychophyton dankaliense* affects both camels and humans in northern Somalia and the Ogaden area (Peck, 1938).

Mineral and vitamin deficiencies and plant poisoning

Apparently the only common deficiencies are a lack of common salt and calcium/phosphorus imbalance (Chapter 7). The deficiency of salt is well recognised by camel-owning peoples, particularly in the circum-Saharan countries, who regularly take their animals to the salt cure – grazing areas where the grasses are said to be salty or where the camels obtain salt from the earth itself by licking (Chapter 9). When the salt cure is not practised or is not available, as much as 140 g of salt per day are needed to avoid deficiencies arising.

There is some evidence from the Niger Republic of a relationship between low vitamin levels and intensity of attack by gastro-intestinal parasites. This refers particularly to vitamins A and B. The latter, of course, should not cause any problems in camels but supplementation with vitamin A may be worthwhile if suspected or known deficiencies exist.

Plant poisoning This is occasionally a problem in camels grazing new areas or where new plants have been introduced. Studies carried out on plants indicated as poisonous, or as causing illness in camels, are as likely to show no toxic constituents. This does not, of course, mean that they do not affect camel metabolism in some, as yet, unexplained way. Camel owners, as other traditional livestock owners, are often able to achieve quite good correlations between cause and effect. One such case may be that of *Diplotaxa harra* in North Africa which, owners are convinced, results in a stiffness of the hindquarters 4 to 6 months after the camel has eaten it. In Kenya during the dry season *Capparis tomentosa*, one of the few green plants remaining at that time, is also suspected of contributing to metabolic problems.

Further reading

Abul-Hab, J. and Al-Abbass, N. N. (1977). Seasonal occurrence of the domestic camel bot fly *Cephalopina titillator* (Diptera, Oestridae) in Central Iraq. *Bull. Biol. Res. Centre (Baghdad).* 8, 97–104.

Altaif, K. I. (1974). Helminths in camels in Iraq. *Trop. Anim. Hlth Prod.,* 6, 55–57.

Balis, J. and Richard, D. (1977). *Action trypanocide du chlorohydrate de chlorure* d'isométamidium sur Trypanosome evansi *et essai de traitement de la trypanosomiase du dromadaire*. Rev. Elev. Méd. vét. Pays trop., **30**, 369-372.

Bares, J. F. (1968). *Contribution à l'étude de la pathologie infectueuse du dromadaire au Tchad.* Thèse, ENV Toulouse: Toulouse, France.

Bennett, S. C. J. and Kenny, P. A. C. (1928). Mercuric chloride as a diagnostic agent for trypanosomiasis in camels. J. Comp. Path. Therap., **41**, 341-353.

Bouvier, C. (1976). *Etude des parasites gastro-intestinaux du dromadaire dans la region de Dire-Dawa (Sud-est Ethiopie) et essais therapeutiques.* Thèse, ENV Alfort: Maisons Alfort, France.

Bremaud, O. (1969). *Notes sur l'élevage camelin dans les districts du nord de la République de Kenya.* Institut d'Elevage at de Médecine Vétérinaire des Pays Tropicaux: Maisons Alfort, France.

Burgemeister, R. E. (1975). *Elevage de chameaux en Afrique du Nord.* Office Allemand de la Cooperation Technique: Eschborn, West Germany.

Cauvet, G. (1925). *Le chameau.* Baillière: Paris, France.

Cheyne, I. A., Pegram, R. G. and Cartwright, C. F. (1977). An outbreak of salmonellosis in camels in northeast Somalia. Trop: Anim. Hlth Prod., **9**, 238-240.

Curasson, G. (1947). *Le chameau et ses maladies.* Vigot Frères: Paris, France.

Dada, B. J. O. (1978). Incidence of hydatid disease in camels slaughtered at Kano abbatoir. Trop. Anim. Hlth Prod., **10**, 204.

Dailey, M. D. and Sweatman, G. K. (1965). The taxonomy of *Echinococcus granulosus* in donkey and dromedary in Lebanon and Syria. Ann. Trop. Med. Parasit., **59**, 463-477.

Delavenay, R. P. (1978). *Emploi du nitroxynil chez le dromadaire.* Rev. Elev. Méd. vét. Pays trop., **31**, 171-177.

Domenech, J., Guidot, G. and Richard, D. (1977). *Les maladies pyogènes du dromadaire en Ethiopie. Symptomatologie-Etiologie.* Rev. Elev. Méd. vét. Pays trop., **30**, 251-258.

Durand, M. and Kchouk, M. (1958). Le 'krafft', une osteopathie dystrophique du dromadaire. Arch. Inst. Pasteur, Tunis, **35**, 107-152.

El-Badawi, El-K. S., Eisa, A. M., Slepenev, N. K. and Saad, M. B. A. (1979). Hydatidosis of domestic animals in the central region of the Sudan. Bull. Anim. Hlth Prod. Afr., **27**, 249-251.

Ezzi, A. and Zakarian, B. (1979). A survey on spontaneous atherosclerosis of camels (*Camelus dromedarius*) in Iran. Trop. Anim. Hlth Prod., **11**, 102-105.

Ginawi, M. A. and Shomein, A. M. (1977). Prevalence of sarcosporidiosis in sheep, goats and camels in the Sudan. Sudan J. Vet. Sci. Anim. Husb., **18**, 92-97.

Gruvel, J. and Balis, J. (1965). *La trypanosomiase à Trypanosoma evansi chez le dromadaire au Tchad et ses principaux vecteurs.* Rev. Elev. Méd. vét. Pays trop., **18**, 435-439.

Gruvel, J. and Graber, M. (1965). *Quelques résultats d'enquêtes récentes sur la globidiose du dromadaire au Tchad. Note préliminaire.* Rev. Elev. Méd. vét. Pays trop., **18**, 423-428.

Hedger, R. S., Bennett, I. T. R. and Gray, D. F. (1980). Some virus diseases of domestic animals in the Sultanate of Oman. Trop. Anim. Hlth Prod., **12**, 107-114.

Knowles, R. H. (1925). Treatment of camels affected with *Trypanosoma sudanense* with 'Bayer 205' and further observations on the formol gel test. J. Comp. Path. Therap. 38, 42-48.

Knowles, R. H. (1927). Trypanosomiasis of camels in the Anglo-Egyptian Sudan: diagnosis, chemotherapy, immunity. J. Comp. Path. Therap., **40**, 59-71 and **40**, 118-143.

Leese, A. S. (1927). *A treatise on the one-humped camel in health and disease.* Haynes & Son: Stamford, Lincs, UK.

Lodha, K. R. (1966). Studies on sarcoptic mange in camels (*Camelus dromedarius*). Vet. Rec., **79**, 41-43.

Lodha, K. R., Raisinghani, P. M. and Karwasra, R. S. (1977). Chemotherapeutic trials of some anthelmintics against helminth parasites in camels. Indian J. Anim. Sci., **47**, 677-682.

Luckins, A. G., Boid, R., Rao, P., Mahmoud, M. M., El Malik, K. H. and Gray, A. R. (1979). Serodiagnosis of infection with *Trypano-*

soma evansi in the Sudan. *Trop. Anim. Hlth Prod.*, **11**, 1-12.

Magzoub, M. and Kasim, A. A. (1978). The prevalence of fascioliasis in Saudi Arabia. *Trop. Anim. Hlth Prod.*, **10**, 205-206.

Mahmoud, M. M. and Gray, A. R. (1980). Trypanosomiasis due to *Trypanosoma evansi* (Steel, 1885) Balbiana, 1888. A review of recent research. *Trop. Anim. Hlth Prod.*, **12**, 35-49.

Mason, F. E. (1917). Tuberculosis in camels. *Agric. J. Egypt.*, **7**, 1-11.

Michael, S. A. and Saleh, S. M. (1977). The slide agglutination test for the diagnosis of filariasis in camels. *Trop. Anim. Hlth Prod.*, **9**, 241-244.

Mobedi, I., Madadi, H. and Arfaa, F. (1970). Camel (*Camelus dromedarius*) as intermediate host of *Echinococcus granulosis* in Iran. *J. Parasit.*, **56**, 1255.

Monteverde, G. (1937). *Anaplasmosi nei cammeli in Cirenaica, Clin. vet., Milano*, **60**, 73-76.

Paling, R. W., Jessett, D. M. and Heath, B. R. (1979). The occurrence of infectious diseases in mixed farming of domesticated wild herbivores and domestic herbivores including camels in Kenya. I. Viral diseases: A serological survey with special reference to foot and mouth disease. *J. Wildl. Dis.* **15**, 351-358.

Peck, E. F. (1936). *Annual Report of the Veterinary and Agricultural Department for 1935*. Hargeisa: British Somaliland Protectorate.

Peck, E. F. (1938). Notes relating to the camel. *Vet. Rec.*, **50**, 1052-1054.

Peck, E. F. (1939). Salt intake in relation to cutaneous necrosis and arthritis of one-humped camels (*Camelus dromedarius*) in British Somaliland. *Vet. Rec.*, **51**, 1355-1360.

Pegram, R. G. and Scott, J. M. (1976). The prevalence and diagnosis of *Trypanosoma evansi* infection in camels in southern Ethiopia. *Trop. Anim. Hlth Prod.*, **8**, 20-27.

Provost, A., Maurice, Y. and Borredon, C. (1968). *Note sur la peste bovine expérimentale du dromadaire. Rev. Elev. Méd. vét. Pays trop.*, **21**, 293-296.

Rabagliati, D. S. (1923). Poly-arthritis in camels. *J. Comp. Path. Therap.*, **36**, 90-96.

Richard, D. (1975). *Etude de la pathologie du dromadaire dans le sous-province de Borana (Ethiopie)*. Thèse, ENV Alfort: Maisons Alfort, France.

Richard, D. (1976). The diseases of the dromedary (*Camelus dromedarius*) in Ethiopia. *Ethiopian Vet. Bull.*, **21**, 46-47.

Rutter, T. E. G. (1967). Diseases of camels: Protozoal diseases. *Vet. Bull.*, **37**, 611-618.

Rutter, T. E. G and Mack, R. (1963). Diseases of camels: Bacterial and fungal diseases. *Vet. Bull.*, **33**, 119-124.

Seddon, H. R. (1952). *Diseases of domestic animals in Australia*. Service Publications (Division of Veterinary Hygiene) No. 8. Department of Health: Canberra, Australia.

Sharma, S. P. and Gautam, O. P. (1974). A note on the prevalence of toxoplasma antibodies among camels and pigs in Hissar. *Indian J. Anim. Sci.*, **44**, 214-216.

Simpson, V. R. (1979). Bluetongue antibody in Botswana's domestic and game animals. *Trop. Anim. Hlth Prod.*, **11**, 43-49.

Tantawi, H. H., El-Dahaby, H. and Fahmy, L. S. (1978). Pox virus strains from camels. *Acta virologica*, **22**, 451-457.

Taylor, W. P. (1968). The susceptibility of the one-humped camel to infection with rinderpest virus. *Bull. Epiz. Dis. Afr.*, **16**, 405-510.

Theiler, A. (1905). *Transvaal Agric. J.*, **3**, 717-721 (quoted by Rutter, 1967).

9 Husbandry and management

"The camel has its own way of protesting against unreasonable treatment. It dies with a surprising simpleness and ease. It is the camel's way of going on strike."

Cauvet, 1925.

Ecology and the camel's role

The camel, as we have established, is essentially an animal of the desert and the near desert. The classic picture of the desert as being an endless tract of sand or of bare rock is as true as it is untrue. At different times and in different areas most deserts will produce some vegetation, which can be eaten by wildlife such as the addax and the oryx, occasionally, if conditions are relatively very good, by sheep and goats, and more often if anything grows at all, by camels.

So the second point about camels which may be consequent upon the first is that they are highly mobile. In an original wild state they were thus migratory, moving from one patch of ephemeral vegetation to another over very considerable distances. After domestication, if camels were to retain their ability to live in deserts they had to remain migratory and this migration imposed upon the camel herders the necessity of nomadism.

Throughout the zones in which camels are the only or principal kind of domestic livestock, nomadism is the only or principal way of human life; transhumance often demands equally as much movement but allows a return to a fixed base. In the desert and near desert (Fig. 9.1) permanent bases are possible only in the oases which are few and far between but where permanent water is assured. Crop production on a very limited scale is attempted at oases and often consists only of growing dates.

When camel owners have to move with the herd they are obliged to move their families and all their personal belongings. They need to be able to move quickly from one area to another in search of pasture, or to maintain contact with other groups

of the family or tribe. They become almost totally dependent upon the herd for all the necessities of life. Dependence is not quite total, as on occasions there are opportunities for other activities – economic, including transport and perhaps even war, in the service of, let us say, a political power, or subsistence such as the hunting or gathering of wild fruits or seeds.

In the overall nomadic economy camels fulfil three roles: transport of effects; transport of personnel; and provision of subsistence, mainly milk. There are some additional products such as meat,

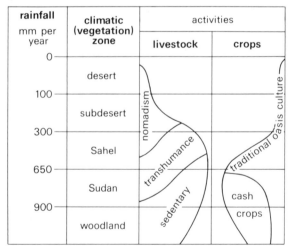

fig. 9.1 Livestock and crop production systems as a function of rainfall in Africa (*Source:* **Matlock, W. G. and Cockrun, E. L.** (1974). *A framework for evaluating longterm strategies for the development of the Sahel-Sudan Region.* Centre for Policy Alternatives, Massachusetts Institute of Technology: Cambridge, Mass., USA)

occasionally skins and hair and, exceptionally, blood. In Chapter 3 two types of camel were described on a functional basis: pack and personnel transport or riding camels. This is less a traditional notion of the camel's functions than a developed one. The vast majority of camels, not only those of the Somalis which, in any case, already amount to a third of the total, are maintained to assure milk for human food, and are managed under a traditional system.

Thus management for transport and riding, management in the modern sense that is, occurred in only a few areas and involved only a few camels (usually military) and persisted for only a short time, a few years or a few decades at most. There are some exceptions, in Tunisia for example, where camels still are part of regular military and police units; and where they are used traditionally for harness and draught animals. In the Nile delta and riverine areas of India and Pakistan, imported camels are managed for work. Another exception is in southern Arabia where the true Mehari is bred.

In very simple terms traditional management for subsistence milk production is achieved in two basic ways:
1 Manipulation of the sex and age structure of the herd.
2 Manipulation, within the limits imposed by time, space, rainfall, etc. of the feeding regime – the daily, seasonal, annual or longer-term grazing cycle.

Herd structures

Herd structures in the majority of subsistence societies result from a large variety of factors, some intrinsic to the herd, most extrinsic to it.

Intrinsic factors affecting herd structure
Intrinsic factors include the levels attained by the production parameters common to all animal species: age at sexual maturity; age at first calving; fertility levels and gestation period resulting in the reproductive rate or number of young born per breeding female; nutritional levels affecting growth and perhaps sexual maturity; death rates. In early-maturing species with short gestation periods, which may give birth to more than one young at a

time, growth in animal numbers can be very rapid and the possibilities of manipulation by the imposition of extrinsic factors are correspondingly great. The camel matures late, has a long gestation period, high embryonic mortality and high levels of calf deaths (Chapter 6). It has, thus, a slow intrinsic growth rate and presents little opportunity for manipulation of herd demography to achieve increased milk production, except in the long term.

Some of the intrinsic factors affecting herd demography in different species of domestic animals are shown in Table 9.1 and, based in part of these data, Fig. 9.2 shows some projected herd and flock growth rates. This figure should be considered only as indicating the relative rapidity of potential growth rates. The dip for camels in the figure is based on the assumption that culling of breeding females starts only at the twentieth year.

Extrinsic factors affecting herd structure
Herd composition in domestic livestock is rarely left to the simple demographic processes outlined above. Management of the structure of a livestock population is carried out to fulfil the manager's requirements. Allan (1965) and Brown (1971), respectively, have developed the concepts of the human carrying capacity of a given area under various management systems, and the subsistence requirements of a family being provided in terms of a number of livestock units producing milk, meat, blood, etc. The potential of camels for producing subsistence food requirements is dealt with in Chapter 10.

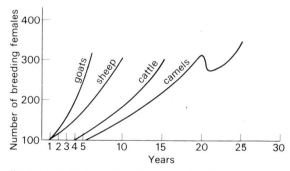

fig. 9.2 Growth in number of breeding females from a base of 100 in various species of domestic animals (based on data in Table 9.1).

Table 9.1 Some parameters affecting herd structures in various species of domestic animals. (*Sources*: Goats and sheep on data from three semi-arid areas, Kenya, Sudan, Mali (**Wilson R. T.** (1980). Population and production parameters of sheep under traditional management in semi-arid areas of Africa. *Trop. Anim. Hlth Prod.*, **12**, 243–250. **Wilson, R. T.** (1982). *Productivity of indigenous goats in the traditional livestock systems of semi-arid Africa.* Proc III Int. Conf. Goat Prod. Dis., 10–15 Jan 1982, Tucson, Arizona, USA, p. 314. Cattle and camel generalised data from several areas, birth rates probably slightly optimistic.)

Parameter	Animal species			
	Goats	Sheep	Cattle	Camels
Age at first parturition (months)	15	15	48	60
No. of young per parturition	1·4	1·05	1·0	1·0
Interval between births (months)	9	0	20	24
No. of young per female per year	1·8	1·4	0·6/0·7	0·5
Death rate to 1 year (%)	35	35	30	50
Subsequent death rate (%)	10	10	7	5

The camel-owner's requirements The family's requirements for milk, the opportunities of using camels for transport, of selling them for meat, and of the labour available to maintain the herd, i.e. to ensure its grazing and watering, will affect and determine the composition of the herd. Another factor which affects the composition of the herd is the possibility of spreading the risk or the load of milk production. In slightly better endowed areas this means the possibility of providing milk from other livestock such as goats or sheep or perhaps even cattle. It depends on the availability of grazing, the distance that has to be travelled to water, the depth from which water has to be drawn and the method of extraction of the water.

The land The carrying capacity of the whole area of land utilised by the camels of the group and of competitive groups and the stocking rate on the land also affect herd structure. Carrying capacity varies from year to year over a particular area and is outside the effective control of the camel owner. Stocking rates, where land is communally owned or grazed is also, in effect, outside the control of a single herd owner who therefore, rarely takes it into consideration.

Herd size Herd composition is to some extent governed by herd size and herd size is to a certain extent a function of family size and development. At first subsistence requirements may be for a man and his wife only but the family is likely to develop faster than the herd, quickly passing the limits of the herd potential. To avoid this occurrence delayed marriage and birth control are two strategies that can be adopted. Herding contracts where payment is in kind or partly in kind is another. A system of stock friends, including long-term loans of productive animals under various arrangements, is a method of adjusting herd composition, as is warfare and theft. The latter is ritualised in some areas (Sweet, 1965).

Labour As herd and family development progresses the requirements for, and the ability to provide, labour also change. Camel herding is labour intensive for only a fraction of the total time, mainly at watering but also at milking. Watering is heavy work and can rarely be done by women: two men or at least a man and a strong boy are required. Male animals, if they are not productive in terms of transport or growing for meat, may have to be disposed of to reduce these labour requirements. Milking can be done, physically, by women but they are often forbidden to do so and even further limitations on labour availability may be imposed by additional requirements, as in the case of the Gabbra of Kenya, that camels should be milked only by uncircumcised boys or by men in a state of sexual abstinence (Torry, 1971).

Some empirical examples

Since many of the factors, both intrinsic and extrinsic governing herd structure are known and many camel-owning societies have a large vocabulary describing sex and age groups (Tables

9.2 and 9.3) the establishment of structures should be a relatively easy task. It is not even necessary to establish this by physical examination of the teeth (p. 63). However, the structure of camel herds in traditionally managed units remains largely unknown.

Southern Darfur in western Sudan Camels here are approaching the limits of the ecological conditions favourable to them and they are in either constant or seasonal contact with

Table 9.2 Terminology of the age-groups of camels in various countries

Age (years)	India (Leese, 1927)	Arabic Arabia (Leese, 1927)	Arabic Algeria (Leese, 1927)	Arabic Sudan (Wilson 1978a)	Tuareg (Wilson, unpublished) male	Tuareg (Wilson, unpublished) female
Less than 1				wad kemish		awara
1–2	kotela	howar	bel el bun	mafrud	amougay	tamougayte
2–3	muzat	libni	haguh	wad lebun	aglam	taglamte
3–4	trihan, tahak	hej		hiqq	assaka	tassakayte
4–5	chatr	djida	djeda	jadi'	assak-naridjan	tallamte
5–6	doak	theni	theni	tani	arridjan	tabazouzte
6–7	chowga	roba	baa	raba'		
7–8	chiga	sedess	sedess	sadis		
8–9	nesh	sheg en naba, wafyat, muftar	graa			
9+	armosh		djemel			

Table 9.3 Camel terminology in various countries by position in herd or by function

Position or Function	Somalia (Bozzi & Triulzi 1953)	Sudan (Acland, 1932)	Tuareg (Wilson unpublished)
Breeding bull	bargab	fahl, jemel 'arudh	amaly
First calf female	ugup		
Subsequent calf female	urur		
Barren female	aber		'agir
Castrate	coron		arzouzal
Riding camel	recub	makhlufa, rakub	
Pack camel	gadit, rarosc	hamla, sheil	

agriculturalists. In spite of some recent changes in long distance transport – the development of lorries and the arrival of the railway in the early 1960s – camels still assure the bulk of grain transport from village to primary market when grain surpluses are considerable. The introduction of groundnuts as a cash crop has also increased the requirement for transport. These requirements create a justification and an economic incentive to maintain baggage camels. Males are used almost exclusively and it is unusual to castrate camels in this area. A generalised herd structure based on observations and questioning of owners in more than 20 herds and involving almost 1 100 animals is shown in Table 9.4. Management of these herds (which are probably not entirely representative of the total Sudan camel population) involved production of milk and provision of transport. Animals for meat are only available after the end of a useful working life: females are killed locally, males are less often killed locally and more often exported – to Libya or Egypt from this area.

Milk from these herds is an important source of subsistence but can easily be supplemented by grain which is paid for out of income from the transport function. The total number of females in the herd is only slightly over 50 per cent and breeding females of four years and upwards total just over 25 per cent of the whole herd. These herd structures were established after a year of good rainfall which probably affected the short-term structure in two ways: it allowed calves of the previous year to attain a higher than normal rate of survival and also enabled a high percentage of calves to be born in the year of study. These are, however, minor factors and in a series of normal years (if such a series can be considered a possibility) breeding females would probably account for no more than 30 per cent of the herd. This allows little possibility of rapid herd expansion after a natural catastrophe, for example, drought or disease, and is a type of structure which is viable only where alternative sources of income or alternative outlets for excess labour are available.

Somali camels The Somali, whether in Somalia, in Ethiopia or in Kenya are almost entirely dependent on milk, this dependence being reflected in the herd structure and in the way it is manipulated. A premium is placed on milking females. The total environment of the Somali, with two possible breeding seasons (see p. 97 and Fig. 6.8), their high mobility, and their management of males for breeding enables them to achieve a considerable success in this respect. Somali herds in Kenya may have more than 80 per cent of females with breeding females accounting for 66–89 per cent of these or 53–71 per cent of the total herd (Bremaud, 1969). In Somalia itself herd

Table 9.4 Population structure of mixed milk/transport herd in western Sudan (*Source*: **Wilson, R. T.** (1978a). Studies on the livestock of southern Darfur, Sudan. V. Notes on camels. *Trop. Anim. Hlth Prod.*, **10**, 19–25.)

Age group (traditional terminology)	Probable absolute age (years)	Percentage of total animals
wad kemish	<1	15
mafrud	1–2	13
wad lebun and *hiqq*	2–4	23
jadi', tani, raba', sadis	4+	49

Table 9.5 Camel herd structure in Somalia (*Source*: **Swift, J. J.** (1979). *The economics of traditional nomadic pastoralism: The Tuareg of the Adrar n Iforas* (*Mali*). Thesis, University of Sussex: Brighton, UK.)

	Percentage of total animals (n = 69704)	
Age	**Males**	**Females**
Less than 4 years	11	25
Over 4 years	15	49
All animals	26	74

structure is similar but without quite the same emphasis on females; the data in Table 9.5 are an analysis of herd structure from almost 70 000 camels from various Somali sources.

The Somali, with very few exceptions do not use camels for riding and rarely use them for baggage except for moving camp. The former British administration imported riding and baggage camels to the most populous camel country in the world from India, Sudan and Arabia. To the Somali male camels are, therefore, of relatively little importance. The number of male animals in the herd is reduced in two ways and at two points in the camel's life cycle. A percentage of male calves are slaughtered at birth or within a few weeks of it (Bozzi and Triulzi, 1953). This allows more milk for female calves and for family consumption. This is a simple and classic management ploy in societies wholly or almost wholly dependent on milk for their own food. The Afar in Ethiopia adopt this strategy to varying degrees in camels, depending, for example, on the opportunities for salt transport. They own few cattle, but in sheep and goats slaughter of males at birth is almost universal and flocks are comprised of up to 98 per cent female animals (Wilson, 1975). Males not slaughtered at birth in Somali camel herds are allowed to grow until they are about 4 years old. At this age the majority are castrated and become fat; a few are slaughtered for meat for family use but most are now sold to provide the few cash needs of the Somali. Males of possible breeding value are not castrated. Somali camel management involves considerable control of breeding and males of 5 years are allowed to serve a few cows. The progeny of these animals are judged by Somali standards – possible milk production, colour, etc. – and some further services by 6-year-old bulls may be allowed. In general bulls are not allowed free access to the breeding females until they are 8 years old.

This type of herd structure involving a minimum of 50 per cent breeding females is very suitable for assuring a more or less continuous supply of milk and normally allows a rapid recovery of herd numbers after a drought or an outbreak of disease. It does have the disadvantage of inducing complete dependence on the camel herd and its milk and in the event of a really severe catastrophe there is little

opportunity of an alternative source of food or income.

Tuareg camels In a small sample of less than 300 animals belonging to the Tuareg of northern Mali the herd structure was very similar to that of Somalia with 78 per cent total females and 57 per cent breeding females (Swift, 1979). The herds examined had only 2 per cent of mature males and it was thought that, as the survey was undertaken in the winter when the opportunities for caravan work are greatest (and the work is less exhausting) a number of mature, male pack camels would be missing from the household herds. Thus, it appears that the Tuareg, in this area at least, have a dual-purpose economy tending towards the Sudanese type and that total breeding females would be between 40 and 50 per cent. In fact a computer model based on these herds showed a stable herd structure at 50 years which contained 72 per cent female and 47·5 per cent breeding females.

Kenya Two camel-owning groups in Kenya also have intermediate types of herd structure. For the Rendille it was estimated that total females accounted for 60 to 70 per cent of all animals (Spencer, 1973), which would imply 40–50 per cent breeding females. The Rendille keep few other livestock but in time of shortage or of surplus labour they are able to obtain the basic necessities of life by undertaking herding and other tasks for the cattle-owning Samburu who occupy the same area. The growth of Rendille camel herds is apparently very slow and this has affected the Rendille human population, their own growth being related to some extent to that of the herds. The opportunities of interaction with the Samburu allow some manipulation of both camel and human populations.

Also in Kenya the Gabbra have a dual- to triple-purpose camel economy. Their herds are comprised of some 56 per cent females (Bremaud, 1969) which implies about 33–40 per cent breeding females. The Gabbra use camels for milk, occasionally for blood, for meat and for transport. The last two functions require a fairly high percentage of mature males, mostly castrates, in the herd.

Families own about 25 head (Torry, 1971); the ideal structure of these are shown in Table 9.6; the values are extrapolated to percentages because of the small size of the herd.

Ratios of breeding animals

In domestic animals in which the breeding season is closed, either naturally or artificially, more bulls are normally required than in herds in which the breeding season is open, i.e. extends throughout the year. Both male and female camels are more or less seasonal or closed breeders. The possible disadvantage of this on the requirement for bulls is offset to some extent by the apparent difficulties camels often have in natural mating (Chapter 6) and the use to which this is put by camel owners as, for example, the Somali quoted on p. 138. In practice, with some degree of control over mating, one mature bull appears to be capable of assuring adequate coverage of around 50 females in a single breeding season. At one end of the scale it has been said (Leese, 1927) that a bull in good condition and well looked after will serve up to 70 females. In Kordofan, in Sudan, it has been estimated that one bull is capable of covering 30 females but, as the same author quotes three bulls for 150 females (Asad, 1970), an actual ratio of 1:50 appears more correct.In Somalia herds comprised of up to 100 camels have at least one mature male (Lewis, 1961) which, based on the herd structure above implies a breeding male to female ratio of 1:50–60.

In multi-male herds the strongest and dominant male serves most of the females (Chapter 6). It is probable that herds are constituted during the breeding season in order to assure that this male does not tire himself out fighting other males to the detriment of his primary function.

In some areas adult males not required for breeding are castrated, for example in Somalia and in Somali-influenced Kenya camel-owning tribes. In others, there are considerable restrictions on castrating camels. In parts of Sudan, for example, male camels may be separated from the breeding herds, along with younger animals of both sexes, during the breeding season.

Traditional management systems: some examples

A considerable number of studies on camel-owning peoples has been carried out. For the most part these have been undertaken by social anthropologists who, at least until recently, have not always been concerned with the management aspects but rather with the attitudes of people to their livestock and the effects of the livestock on social interactions. Without mentioning the very large volume of travel literature, some studies of this nature which contain varying amounts of camel management information are Musil (1928), Gulliver (1955), Lewis (1961), Nicolaisen (1963), Asad (1970), Spencer (1973) and Cole (1975).

Table 9.6 'Ideal' structure of Gabbra camel herds. (*Source*: **Torry, W. I.** (1971). *Animal husbandry and social organisation among the Gabbra, with notes on the Rendille tribe.* Range Management Division, Ministry of Agriculture: Nairobi, Kenya.)

Males		Females	
Class of stock	Percentage of total herd	Class of stock	Percentage of total herd
Breeding bulls	2	Breeding cows in milk	25
Pack animals	10	Breeding cows dry	10
Meat animals	7		
Young 1–4 years	14	Young 1–4 years	16
Calves	8	Calves	8
Total	51	Total	59

Many camels are managed under a nomadic system although it is probably more true to say that in the late twentieth century the trend has been, and continues, towards a transhumant system. An analysis of various migration patterns in Africa and Asia, classifying them into vertical and horizontal types, based on library materials has been carried out (Johnson, 1969). Vertical patterns involve seasonal movements from winter grazing on lowlands to summer grazing on mountains. Horizontal patterns involve spatial movements at similar altitudes to take advantage of favourable grazing or water at different seasons. Most systems involving camels are of the horizontal type.

Seasonal movements based on transhumance almost invariably involve the splitting of the herds into different management groups and this maybe one of the reasons for the lack of any detailed knowledge of herd structures. There are two reasons for this: the necessity of ensuring a supply of milk for the family members who stay behind, usually the old, the very young and most of the women and girls; and the necessity of assuring the greatest possible mobility for the transhumant part of the herd. The main herd is made up of mature males (including breeding bulls), dry cows, all the young stock between 1 and 4 years old and a few lactating cows with older calves to assure a milk supply for the herders who are the youths and young men of the group. One or two experienced older men usually go along as leaders. The household herd consists of lactating cows and young calves, a breeding bull if the main herd is away during the breeding season and one or two pack camels if these are required for transport of water or other items.

Winter grazing in the Sahara

In most livestock production systems in dry areas it is water which provides the main check on animal numbers. Very often there is a total lack of water. Other limiting factors are the time taken to lift water out of the ground into troughs or the distance animals have to travel to find it. When the dry season is in the winter with comparatively low temperatures the problem is much less acute with camels than with other classes of stock, in fact a problem may not arise. Over much of the Sahara, at least away from the central core, the water economy of the camel is supported, by a peculiar vegetational phenomenon. In Sudan and Chad this is known as *gizu* while in much of the western half of the Sahara it is known as *acheb*. Similar phenomena occur in southern Arabia (see Philby, 1922, for example), in the Kalahari in south-west Africa and undoubtedly in other desert areas with hot summers and cool winters. The derivation of the world *gizu* is not clear but probably has to do with the fact that camels grazing this vegetation are completely independent of water for long periods, up to several months on occasions. *Acheb* is the north-west African vernacular for the sedge *Cyperus conglomeratus* which is the common factor of the winter grazing in that area. The *gizu* has been described by Wilson (1978b).

The *gizu* occurs only in certain years. The exact conditions for its growth have yet to be determined. It is, however, an important element in the management of Saharan camels. The Kababish of northern Kordofan (who own something of the order of 400 000 camels) base much of their annual management cycle on *gizu* and travel up to 600 km in each direction to take advantage of it. In *gizu* years the main herds are away from the household ones for several months, the camels are fat and content and conception rates are high. Years without *gizu* are miserable by contrast. A summary of the cycle of the main herds in *gizu* years is given in Table 9.7. While the Kababish are the principal beneficiaries and main users of the *gizu* it plays an important part in camel management practices for all camel-owning groups in Sudan west of the Nile and for large numbers of camels in Chad. Some attempt to indicate the importance of this is shown in Fig. 9.3. In total perhaps 1·5 million camels, one-tenth of the world population, are affected by the *gizu*. Perhaps as many as a further one million animals take advantage of *acheb* in the western part of the Sahara.

The main species of both *gizu* and *acheb* are similar. They belong to various families but all have in common a high percentage of water in their total mass especially in those parts which are eaten (Table 9.8). It should also be noted that the plants as analysed (and probably as eaten) had appreciable quantities of sand attached to them. This

Table 9.7 The annual migration cycle of the main herds of Kababish using *gizu* winter grazing in northern Sudan (*Source*: **Asad, T.** (1964). Seasonal movements of the Kababish Arabs of Northern Kordofan. *Sudan Notes Rec.*, **45**, 45–58.)

Season	Climate	Period	Movements
Sayf	hot/dry	Feb-June	return from NW in early summer to dry season well centres; move S or SW in late summer to exploit early pastures in central Kordofan and Darfur
Kharif	cold/wet	July-Sept	rapid move N to exploit pasture in area of principal settlements (Dar Kababish)
Darad	warm/dry	October	separation from household herds and slow move NW
Shita	cold/dry	Nov-Jan (Mar)	move farther NW to exploit winter grazing in desert.

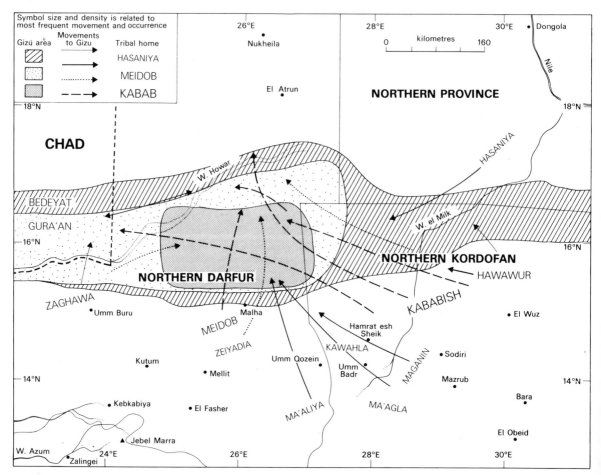

fig. 9.3 Location and tribal use of *gizu* winter grazing in northern Sudan (*Source*: **Wilson, R. T.** (1978). The *gizu* winter grazing in the south Libyan desert. *J. Arid. Env.*, **1**, 325–342.)

might add considerably to estimates (Chapter 7) of dry matter consumed and has also been implicated in deaths of camels (Mason, 1920). It is the high percentage water content of the plants coupled with the low temperature which make camels independent of free water for long periods. This has been known for ages, of course, by the traditional owners. It was noted subjectively some 60 years ago by an administrative officer (Davies, 1957) in north Kordofan who remarked on a large herd of camels on 11 May 1917 which had just returned from the *gizu*. The camels were having the first drink of free water since some time in the previous October. It

has been shown more clearly in recent years (Gauthier-Pilters, 1961; 1965; 1969) just how independent of water camels can be on this type of grazing. Depending on appetite, they are still capable of obtaining 24 litres of water from plants alone at the end of April in southern Algeria (Fig. 9.4).

The salt cure from soil, water or vegetation

It has been shown in Chapter 7 that salt is an essential part of the camels' diet. Under natural grazing, salt is often lacking for much of the year. Traditional grazing practices, in addition to having to

Table 9.8 Some principal winter grazing plants of the Sahara with percentage water content and appetability

Family and plant	Average moisture content (per cent)	Appetability
Chenopodiaceae		
Cornacula monocantha		very high, very drought resistant
Salsola foetida	63–81	low
Leguminosae		
Indigofera hochstetteri	73	high
Indigofera bracteolata	66	high
Zygophyllaceae		
Fagonia indica	50	medium, excellent nutritive value
Tribulus (several species)		high
Neuradaceae		
Neurada procumbers (*gizu* only)		very high
Nucularia perrini (*acheb* only)	80	very high
Cruciferae		
Farsetia (several species)		very high
Morettia philaeania		very high but average feeding value
Graminae		
Aristida (several species)	55–65	depends on species but usually high
Panicum turgidum	40	high except when very dry
Trianthema pentandra	80	high
Cyperaceae		
Cyperus conglomeratus (+ others)		high after seeding

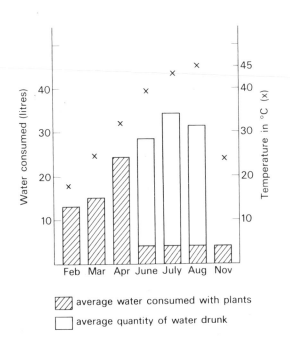

average water consumed with plants

average quantity of water drunk

take into account seasonal variations in forage quality and quantity have also to allow for the need for salt. Some areas are naturally better provided with salt than others, in the form of saline wells, salt earths or of salty plants (halophytes).

The Tuareg of northern Mali and southern Algeria are well aware of the need for salt and their annual grazing cycle makes full use of salt water wells (Jousselin, 1950). In the relatively favoured upland area of the Adras n Iforas there are opportunities for a fairly varied annual grazing/browsing cycle. At two specific periods in the year, usually just before and just after the rains, animals are taken to Tessabit where the earth is known to be particularly salty (Table 9.9). While these two salt cures provide many of the mineral requirements of

fig. 9.4 Daily water consumption by camels from plants and from drinking in southern Algeria. (*Source*: **Gauthier-Pilters**, H. (1969). *Observations sur l'ecologie du dromedaire en Moyenne Mauritanie*. Bull. IFAN, **31A**, 1259-1380.)

Table 9.9 Seasonal grazing pattern in the Adrar n Iforas in northern Mali (*Source:* **Jousselin, M.** (1950). *Notes sur quelques pâturages camelin et la cure de sel dans l'Adrar des Iforas et la region de Tombouctou. Rev. Elev. Méd. vét. Pays trop.*, **4**, 209-211.)

Period	Climatic condition	Type of grazing and main species
May/mid-July	Hot humid	dry pasture: *Tephrosia polystachia*, *Blepharis edulis* early green browse green pasture:
end-July/mid-August	Relatively wet	*Panicum turgidum* green pasture
August/October	Wet – hot humid	becoming dry: *Tribulus terrestris*, *Tephrosia polystachya*, *Trianthema pentandra*; *Convolvulus fatmensis*, *Blepharis edulis*
	salt cure	
end-Oct/mid-Nov	Hot – cooler drier	dry pasture, browse
late Nov/mid-March	Cool dry	dry pasture, browse *acheb* mainly *Shouwia thebaica*
late March/early May	Hot dry	*acheb* in north, mainly *Cornulaca monocantha*
	salt cure	
		browse mainly in dry wadi beds.

camels, in themselves they are not sufficient to cover the total needs for the whole year. When the demands of the grazing cycle are such that the animals must be away from salt earth or salty well areas supplementary minerals have to be supplied. In the Adrar n Iforas this is usually in the form of Tessabit earth specially transported for the purpose. About 2 kg of earth for every seven camels is provided at intervals of 15 – 20 days.

In the region to the north of Timbuctoo conditions are much less favourable and the annual cycle tends to provide a less varied diet (Table 9.10). The salt cure is still practised wherever possible but more emphasis has to be placed on salt supplementation. Timbuctoo is the centre of the caravan trade in salt from the mines of Taoudeni which is 700 km away. Some pack camels are retained by the Tuareg for salt transport (p. 139). This is a very profitable business, salt being worth five times as much at Timbuctoo as at Taoudeni. For every camel load of four slabs (each of 30 kg) of salt the owners keep one for their own camels and use the others for trade. In 1971 a young camel could be bought for 2½ slabs of salt (Swift, 1979) which

gives some idea of the economics of salt trading and its value in the eyes of camel owners.

In Tunisia the problem of the salt cure does not arise: the problem is rather to get the camels off the salt pastures and away from the salt water wells (Burgemeister, 1975). Camels spend 8 – 9 months in the halophytic pastures of the *sebkha* grazing or browsing such plants as *Anthrocnemum indicum*, *Suaeda mollis*, *Halocnemum strobilaceum*, *Salsola tetranda* (all Chenopodiaceae), the grass *Aeluropus litoralis* and the rush *Juncus maritimus*. Well water used for drinking contains up to 3 500 mg/litre of salts. In the spring, for 3 – 4 months, herds migrate (Fig. 9.5) to the *hamada* - rocky desert areas in the south. Here the grazing is fresh from the rains and includes species associated elsewhere with *acheb*: *Fagonia microphylla*, *Zygophyllum alba* (Zygophyllaceae), *Anthemis pedunculata*, *Artemesia campestris*, *Atractylis serratuloides* (Compositae) and the grasses *Lyzeum spartum* and *Aristida plumosa*. The shrub *Tamarix gallica*, one of the favourite plants of the camel, is found in both types of vegetation. Water in wells in the *hamada* contains as little as 500 mg per litre of salts.

Table 9.10 Seasonal grazing pattern in the Timbuctoo area in northern Mali. (*Source*: as for Table 9.9.)

Period	Climatic conditions	Type of grazing and main species
May/mid-July	Hot dry – humid	very dry pasture: *Cenchrus biflorus* and *C. ciliaris*
late July/mid-Sept	Relatively wet – hot dry	green pasture turning dry: *C. biflorus* and *C. ciliaris*
late Sept/Nov	Hot dry – cool	move north to *acheb*: *Cyperus conglomeratus*, *Tephrosia purpurea*; browse: *Leptadenia spartaca*
mid-Nov/early March	Cool dry	*acheb*: *Indigofera spp.* dry pasture: *Blepharis edulis*, *Aristida pungens*
salt cure		
mid-March/early May	Hot dry	*acheb*: *Cornulaca monocantha*

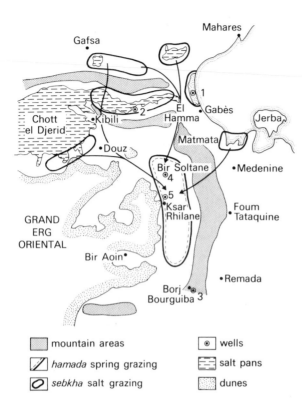

fig. 9.5 Transhumance patterns of camel herds in Tunisia (*Source*: **Burgemeister, R. E.** (1975). *Elevage de chameaux en Afrique du Nord*. Office Allemand de la Cooperation Technique: Eschborn, West Germany.)

Legend:
- mountain areas
- *hamada* spring grazing
- *sebkha* salt grazing
- wells
- salt pans
- dunes

Map labels: Gafsa, Mahares, Chott el Djerid, Kibili, Douz, El Hamma, Gabès, Jerba, Matmata, Bir Soltane, Medenine, Ksar Rhilane, Foum Tataquine, GRAND ERG ORIENTAL, Bir Aoin, Remada, Borj Bourguiba

Effects of political changes on traditional systems

For more than a hundred years nomadic and transhumant groups have been subject to political (and military) pressure of a kind which they could hardly have known in earlier times. First the colonial powers and later the politically independent states have attempted with more or less success to impose restrictions on nomadic movements across so-called national frontiers; in terms of habitat or land-use these are usually completely artificial frontiers. During the same period pressures from the same sources have been exerted to prevent factional warfare and stock raiding. The restrictions on free movement and the imposition of a kind of peace have both acted together in the long run against the best interests of the pastoralists. Restrictions on movement have reduced the previously very efficient use of vast areas of sparse grazing thus putting more pressure on limited areas which, in turn, has reduced animal and vegetative productivity. The restriction of warfare and raiding has resulted in an increae in the human population with concomitant attempts to increase animal population. This has been successful to some extent and has put yet further pressure on the available fodder resources. The end result is reduced animal output. The slow reproduction rate of camels, the long generation time and the pre-existing lack of epidemic diseases have militated to some extent against a very rapid expansion in the camel population of the kind which has occurred in cattle in recent history (see, for example, Wilson, 1977; 1979).

The following quotation summaries the foregoing.

Having lived . . . . . . in nomad camps we have been able to convince ourselves just how much these people live in perfect harmony with their environment, and better for the fact that they have learnt to preserve their traditional way of life. Their standard of living is generally better than that of the sedentaries, their health is better, their food (which is unequally distributed among the sedentaries) is shared among all. Resistance to climate and fatigue is better. The life force among many tribes, and in particular the true nomads . . . . is absolutely intact in spite of all the changes (abolition of slavery, reduction in the caravan trade, disintegration of traditional ruling groups, loss of prestige, etc.) that have occurred to them since the arrival of the French. As [a French officer] has underlined, our error was the belief that the nomadic way of life was capable of a progressive evolution without its breaking down. The nomads, in acquiring the qualities of sedentaries, must, automatically, lose those of their own which enabled both them and their herds to survive in the desert environment.

(Gauthier-Pilters, 1969)

Traditional husbandry, carrying capacity and stocking rate

In an arid environment subject to low but highly fluctuating rainfall from one year to another and subject to restrictions and variations in water availability, the establishment of long-term carrying capacity is, to say the least, problematical. Additional complications arise in calculating carrying capacity depending on the way it is expressed. Carrying capacity may be expressed as production units: forage units, (UF) total digestible nutrients (TDN), dry matter production; or consumption units: livestock units, domestic herbivore biomass (DHB) metabolic weight biomass.

Similar problems arise in the establishment of stocking rate when use is seasonal and where numbers, type and class of stock vary from year to year. Seasonal use is not always at the same time of the year in spite of the stylised patterns established in the previous section.

Carrying capacity and stocking rate as well as being independent of each other are also interdependent and under traditional systems of husbandry are rarely if ever in balance. In the early stages of a drought, fodder production is low but livestock biomasses are high: the available fodder is quickly eaten off, starvation results and animals die or at best fail to reproduce. Stocking rate is reduced. In years of good rainfall after such a series of events fodder production is increased, there are few mouths to eat it and few feet to trample it: seed is set, woody growth flourishes. Carrying capacity increases. These conditions can be simulated by means of exclosures on natural rangeland; the results are often spectacular (Fig. 9.6).

Carrying capacity

Carrying capacity, it is generally agreed, increases

fig. 9.6 The results of 5 years of protection from livestock in Sudan. The photograph shows improved carrying capacity from low stocking rate in the background and almost zero carrying capacity from overstocking in the foreground

with rainfall. For an increase in rainfall there will be an increase in fodder production although the relation may not be linear over a very wide range. Some progress has been made recently in estimating carrying capacity for the arid and semi-arid areas around the Sahara (Le Houérou and Hoste, 1977). These estimates could probably be applied to other areas with similar climates. One of the main factors to note is that for a given quantity of rainfall, carrying capacity, in terms of vegetation production, is less in areas of summer rainfall than it is in areas of winter rainfall. This is due mainly to the effects of greater evapotranspiration in the higher temperatures prevailing in summer rainfall areas.

Several series of equations have been established based on fodder units, livestock units, and so on but carrying capacity expressed in terms of consumable dry matter (CDM) is more easily understood in terms of stocking rate. In relation to total dry matter production (for purpose of comparison) CDM averages about 40 per cent. The equations for CDM in the Sahelian zone of summer rainfall are:

$$y = 42\cdot17 + 1\cdot03x \quad \text{for a linear regression}$$
$$y = 1\cdot057x^{1\cdot001} \quad \text{for a power curve}$$

where y equals production of CDM in kg per hectare per year and x is annual rainfall. For the Mediterranean basin with winter rainfall the equations for CDM are:

$$y = 2\cdot17x - 103\cdot72$$
$$y = 0\cdot972x^{1\cdot09}$$

From these equations Fig. 9.7 has been drawn to show annual fodder production for a given amount of rainfall. Some words of caution need to be added. The figure shows the variation in fodder production for a given amount of rainfall. Fodder production includes the field layer only, browse having been ignored so that production figures will be conservative for most areas. Where average figures for any area are based on long-term rainfall it should be borne in mind that variations in annual rainfall within that area will affect production in that year. Attempts to match stocking rate to carrying capacity should thus be based on expected minimum rainfall figures rather than on average

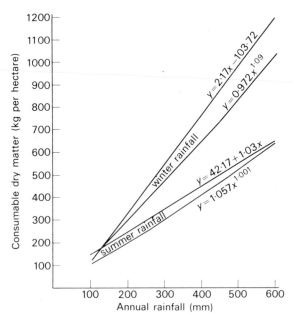

fig. 9.7 Carrying capacity expressed as production of consumable dry matter (CDM) for given level of rainfall in summer (Sahel) and winter (Mediterranean) rainfall areas (*Source*: **Le Houérou, H. N.** and **Hoste, G. H.** (1977). Rangeland production and annual rainfall relations in the Mediterranean Basin and in the African Sahel – Sudanian Zone. *J. Range Mgmt*, **30**, 181 – 189.)

figures if long-term carrying capacity is not to be reduced. Where rainfall varies by a factor of ten, as it often does in arid areas, it is obviously difficult to arrive at a reasonable assessment of carrying capacity.

While vegetation is the principal factor in carrying capacity the availability of water may limit it in some areas, where, for instance, there is only one well with a limited output capable of providing water for only a certain number of animals.

Stocking rate

As for carrying capacity the stocking rate can be expressed in a number of ways – sheep units (equivalent to one ewe and lamb), livestock units (a mythical and very variable beast), domestic herbivore biomass (DHB) or the metabolic weight of DHB. All require to some extent a knowledge of

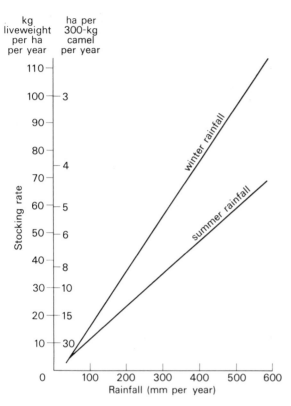

fig. 9.8 Maximum stocking rate in kg liveweight of camels per hectare and number of hectares per camel per year for given rainfall in winter and summer rainfall areas

little is known of the appetite and consumption of dry matter of camels. However, consumption per 100 kg body weight generally decreases with increasing size and we can assume that in the camel it is of the order of 2·5 kg per 100 kg liveweight which for a herd with a MPW of 300 kg is equivalent to 7·5 kg per head per day or 2 750 kg per head per year. From these figures it is thus possible to calculate a maximum stocking rate based on either rainfall or production of CDM (Fig. 9.8). Stocking with mixed species, where this is possible, usually improves efficiency of utilisation and allows higher overall stocking rates than can be achieved with only a single species of animal.

Stocking rate is difficult to calculate where use is seasonal or discontinuous but there are additional complications even when the exact number of animals and the total occupation time of the area are known. It is highly probable that the whole of an area which can be utilised from, for example a fixed water point such as a well, is not used every year. Camels can obtain much of their water from plants but their water consumption is related to temperature as well. When their free water requirements are low they can go several days without drinking. Variations in the frequency of drinking in a single area where camels were allowed to roam freely are shown in Table 9.11. It is

Table 9.11 Frequency with which free-ranging camels come to water in two different years in north-west Sahara. (*Source*: **Gauthier-Pilters, H.** (1972). *Observations sur la consommation d'eau du dromedaire en été dans la région de Beni-Abbas (Sahara nord-occidental). Bull. IFAN,* **34A**, 219–259.)

Number of days before returning to water	Percentage of all camels returning after time specified in	
	1955	1969
3	0	24
4	30	37
5	40	10
6	20	10
7–8	10	6

actual weights although for convenience standard conversions are often used, most of which are generally unsatisfactory. For example, a tropical livestock unit (TLU) is considered to be an animal equivalent to one adult cow (*Bos indicus*) weighing 250 kg liveweight. Calculations can then be made on the basis of herd structures and the average weight of all animals in the herd (called MPW in Tables 2.1 and 2.2). Some common conversion factors are: camels and horses, 1·0; cattle 0·7; donkeys, 0·5; sheep and goats, 0·2. Reference to the footnotes in Table 2.1 or Table 2.2 on pp. 19 and 20 will immediately show the errors in these figures.

Stocking rate is probably better calculated, where carrying capacity is expressed in kg CDM, as liveweight DHB. As we have seen in Chapter 7 very

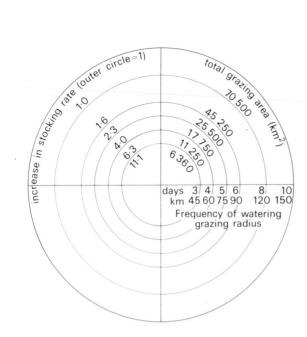

fig. 9.9 Effects of frequency of watering on available foraging area and on stocking rate when distance covered is 30 km per day and number of animals remains constant

apparent that in the years when camels drink more frequently they cannot range as far away from the water point. The immediate area of the well in thirsty years will obviously be considerably overstocked. Some repercussions of this are shown in Fig. 9.9 assuming a fixed number of camels uses the water point and can graze over a distance of 30 km a day.

In summary the determination of carrying capacity and the calculations of stocking rates in camel carrying country are subject to many errors and variables. In practice it has so far been impossible to determine with any accuracy either the one or the other over the long term.

An aspect of modern management: the pack camel

Selection

Camels under 6 years of age, before they are quite full grown, are unfit for heavy work. If it is necessary to use younger animals it is necessary to adjust loads accordingly. Traditional owners often use younger animals without their apparently coming to any great harm but they are not loaded as heavily as mature animals.

The general points of pack camels as given on p. 40 should be borne in mind when selection is made. Camels with high withers are supposed to be less good weight carriers than ones with normal withers (Acland, 1932). An outsize hump is a disadvantage as it adds to the difficulty of fitting the saddle. A large hump means that the animal is fat certainly but this is not synonymous with fit and ready to work, and may well imply that the animal has not worked for some time and will need to be treated gently at first. Burn marks, particularly if heavy or repeated, on the legs and round the joints mean that the animal has been subjected to traditional cures for stiffness and lameness, probably arthritis, and should lead to rejection of the animal. In areas where the nose ring is used as a means of control, scars of old ring marks probably mean that rings have been torn out and might indicate an animal difficult to control. Check for blindness by moving the hand across the eyes and for recent saddle sores or bruising. Ensure that the camel is a free and easy walker and can stand and couch easily and smoothly. Examine the elbows and hocks for signs of rubbing, the fetlock for brushing and the condition of the feet. Remember that a camel recently watered will look in better condition and will act in a generally more sprightly way than one which has not been watered for some time. Do not pick the best out of a bad lot – he is probably only mediocre in better company.

Castration

Camels used for transport are better castrated. Where camels are required for work castration should not be carried out too early as this results in stunted growth and loss of potential weight-carrying ability due to less development of bone and muscle. Leese (1927) recommends that it should not be done until mature body size and weight have been achieved at 8 years. Castration at 3 years leads to really stunted development and the longer it can be delayed through 4, 5 or 6 to even 8 years the better. Castration of pack camels reduces the tendency to fight, particularly during the rutting season, this prevents injury and the possibility of having to take animals out of work. The effects of the rut can be overcome by giving camels constant hard work but if this cannot be guaranteed, castration is an advantage. Objections to camel castration may be encountered in certain Muslim countries and it is not traditional practice to castrate in Pakistan, Afghanistan, Iran, the Middle East, Arabia, Sudan or Egypt.

Castration should be carried out in the coolest season of the year and only on camels in good condition otherwise the results can be 'very fatal' (Leese, 1927). Young camels can be castrated by the Burdizzo but the open method is more usual. Traditional methods include macerating the cord between two sticks, are generally crude, not to say cruel, are often only partially effective and are not to be recommended.

Daily routine under load
Camels, like other working animals, need to be in good condition to perform at their best. Camels straight off natural fodder which have not been worked for a long period cannot be expected to give 100 per cent performance immediately. They need to be exercised and worked up gradually to full loads and distances. The following points are important (Acland, 1932).

1   When long distances have to be covered it is better to pack the camel over 5 days and give 2 days complete rest than to accomplish the objective in 7 days marching.
2   Do not trek during the heat of the day. Make two stages, a longer one in the morning than in the evening.
3   Start as early as possible, say 0300 hours, stop for 30 minutes before sunrise to allow the camels to forage but without unloading. Stop trekking in general about 2 hours after sunrise, possibly 3 hours in cool weather.
4   The afternoon session should be completed before sunset to allow the camels to graze, which they do better in the evening.
5   Seven hours a day is generally sufficient: good baggage camels will cover 30 km in this time and the very best up to 40 km.
6   Where there is an absolute necessity to cover

long distances in a short time three stages will be necessary: early morning, late afternoon and night. This might total 10 hours of march and will necessitate extra grain feeding which should be given in the evening.

Travel in style
To get the best performance from baggage camels you must ensure that you yourself travel in style! Your own personal train in addition to the thoroughbred racer on which you ride should be comprised of:
Camel No. 1: Cook plus main cook boxes (175 kg);
Camel No. 2: Camp servant plus cold box (for lunch), chair, table and bedstead (125 kg);
Camel No. 3: Bed roll, encased in cowskin to prevent damage, balanced by bath, lamps, spare clothes, etc. (100 kg);
Camel No. 4: Tent, in two half loads each wrapped in its own cowskin (80 kg);
Camel No. 5: Two 50-litre galvanised iron water tanks (140 kg);
Camel No. 6: Grain for other camels (220 kg).
For loading all these you will need 75 metres of best quality rope, not including that for tying and leading the camels. Of course you will, in addition, require a man to look after the camels.

Further reading

Acland, P. B. E. (1932). Notes on the camel in the eastern Sudan. *Sudan Notes Rec.*, **15**, 110–149.

Allan, W. (1965). *The African husbandman.* Oliver and Boyd: Edinburgh, UK.

Asad, T. (1970). *The Kababish Arabs: Power, authority and the lineage in a nomadic tribe.* C. Hurst. and Co.: London.

Bozzi, L. and Triulzi, G. A. (1953). *Osservazioni sugli animali domestici allevati in Somalia. Riv. Agric. subtrop. trop.*, **47**, 266–294.

Bremaud, O. (1969). *Notes sur l'élevage camelin dans les districts du nord de la République du Kenya.* Institut d'Elevage et de Médecine Vétérinaire des Pays Tropicaux: Maisons Alfort, France.

Brown, L. H. (1971). The biology of pastoral man

as a factor in conservation. *Biol. Conserv.*, **3**, 93-100.

Burgemeister, R. E. (1975). *Elevage de chameaux en Afrique du Nord*. Office Allemand de la Coopération Technique: Eschborn, West Germany.

Cauvet, G. (1925). *Le chameau*. Baillière: Paris, France.

Cole, D. P. (1975). *Nomads of the nomads: The Al Murrah Bedouin of the Empty Quarter*. Aldine Publishing Company: Chicago, USA.

Davies, R. (1957). *The camel's back: Service in the rural Sudan*. John Murray: London.

Gauthier-Pilters, H. (1961). *Observations sur l'écologie du dromadaire dans le Sahara nord-occidental. Mammalia*, **25**, 195-280.

Gauthier-Pilters, H. (1965). *Observations sur l'écologie du dromadaire dans l'ouest du Sahara. Bull. IFAN* **27A**, 1534-1608.

Gauthier-Pilters, H. (1969). *Observations sur l'écologie du dromadaire en Moyenne Mauritanie. Bull. IFAN*, **31A**, 1259-1380.

Gulliver, P. H. (1955). *The family herds: A study of two pastoral tribes in East Africa, the Jie and the Turkana*. Routledge and Kegan Paul: London.

Johnson, D. L. (1969). *The nature of nomadism: A comparative study of pastoral migrations in south-western Asia and northern Africa*. Department of Geography Research Paper No. 188. University of Chicago: Chicago, USA.

Jousselin, M. (1950) *Notes sur quelques pâturages camelins et la cure de sel dans l'Adras des Iforas et la région de Tombouctou. Rev. Elev. Méd. vét. Pays trop.*, **4**, 209-211.

Leese, A. S. (1927). *A treatise on the one-humped camel in health and disease*. Haynes & Son: Stamford, Lincs, UK.

Le Houérou, H. N. and Hoste, C. H. (1977). Rangeland production and annual rainfall relations in the Mediterranean Basin and in the African Sahelo-Sudanian zone. *J. Range Mgmt.*, **30**, 181-189.

Lewis, I. M. (1961). *A pastoral democracy: A study of pastoralism and politics among the northern Somali of the Horn of Africa*. Oxford University Press: Oxford, UK.

Mason, F. E. (1920). Mortality in camels by ingestion of sand. *Agric. J. Egypt.*, No. 9.

Musil, A. (1928). *The manners and customs of the Rwala Bedouins*. New York, USA.

Nicolaisen, J. (1963). *Ecology and culture of the pastoral Tuareg*. National Museum: Copenhagen, Denmark.

Philby, H. St. J. (1922). *The heart of Arabia: A record of travel and exploration*. Constable: London.

Spencer, P. (1973). *Nomads in alliance: Symbiosis and growth among the Rendille and Samburu of Kenya*. Oxford University Press: Oxford, UK.

Sweet, L. (1965). Camel raiding of North Arabian Bedouin: a mechanism of ecological adaptation. *Amer. Anthr.*, **67**, 1132-1150.

Swift, J. J. (1979). *The economics of traditional nomadic pastoralism: The Twareg of the Adrar n Iforas (Mali)*. Thesis, University of Sussex: Brighton, UK.

Torry, W. I. (1971). *Animal husbandry and social organisation among the Gabbra, with notes on the Rendille tribe*. Range Management Division, Ministry of Agriculture: Nairobi, Kenya.

Wilson, R. T. (1975). Comparative data on two populations of sheep and goats in Sudan and Ethiopia. *Sudan J. Vet. Sci. Anim. Husb.*, **16**, 1-11.

Wilson, R. T. (1977). Temporal changes in livestock numbers and patterns of transhumance in Southern Darfur, Sudan. *J. Dev. Areas*, **11**, 493-508.

Wilson, R. T. (1978a). Studies on the livestock of Southern Darfur, Sudan. V. Notes on camels. *Trop. Anim. Hlth Prod.*, **8**, 221-232.

Wilson, R. T. (1978b). The *gizu*: winter grazing in the South Libyan desert. *J. Arid. Env.*, **1**, 325-342.

Wilson, R. T. (1979). The incidence and control of livestock diseases in Darfur, Anglo-Egyptian Sudan, during the period of the Condominium, 1916-1956. *Intl. J. Afr. Hist. Stud.*, **12**, 162-182.

10 Productivity

"A camel has no real price. The buying and selling of camels merely represents a rough equivalent of their value, and it goes on because people need things, not because it represents the true value of camels. One can drink camel's milk, use its hair, make it carry a load – and even eat it. And with the blessing of God it multiplies under your hands."

Kababish shaykh to Talal Asad, 1964

Herd and individual growth

Both herd and individual growth are the base of productivity in any species, a fact which is sometimes overlooked.

Herd growth

Herd growth is one of the aspects of camel biology which has been neglected. Models of camel herds developed under computer simulation indicate herd growth rates of between 1·5 and 7·5 per cent per year (Dahl and Hjort, 1976; Swift, 1979a). Based on FAO camel population data given in Table 2.5 on p. 25 the annual growth over the 28-year period 1950–1978 of the camel population in Africa has been about 2·0 per cent while for Asia it is less than 0·3 per cent although there are considerable fluctuations in the rate for the latter continent. The model of Swift (1979a) shows an annual growth rate of 1·4 per cent which allows for an annual offtake of 6·5 per cent. These figures would appear to be reasonable working estimates.

Individual growth

Growth in the womb undoubtedly follows the normal mammalian pattern with foetal length increasing at a more or less constant rate throughout the period of gestation but with very low gains in weight until about two-thirds of the way through the period. From about the eighth month gain in weight becomes very rapid and, if the normal pattern is followed, will increase from about 7 kg to an average birth weight between 30 and 35 kg. Actual birth weights range from an average of 25·8 kg for 33 calves in Tunisia (Burgemeister, 1975) to 37·3 kg for 134 calves in India (Bhargava, Sharma and Singh, 1965). Male calves weigh slightly heavier than females.

Early growth rates depend very much on management and the competition for milk from the human family. In Kenya in a dry year Gabbra and Rendille calves gained 222 g per day to 6 months and in a wet year showed little improvement at 255 g. In the same area where camels were kept under project conditions and the calves were allowed all or almost all of the milk, gains were as high as 655 g per day (Field, 1979). In Tunisia calves average 520 g gain per day to 7 weeks (Burgemeister, 1975), a slightly lower gain of 500 g to 3 months being obtained for dromedaries in Turkestan (Blagověščenskiĭ, 1963). In Turkestan the calves of Bactrian camels averaged about 10 g per day more than dromedaries, as did Bactrian/dromedary hybrids. The reciprocal and less normal cross (dromedary × Bactrian) averaged 27 g per day better than the purebred dromedary.

Subsequent growth also depends very much on management, environment and the general climatic and vegetational conditions during the period of growth. According to Field (1979) there is a marked growth check at weaning. Some comparative growth rates are shown in Fig. 10.1. Mature weights are not reached until about 8 years of age in males, probably about 6 years of age in females or slightly older if calving is delayed. The small camels of the Afar and of parts of Somalia may weigh as little as 350 kg, but most breeds at maturity weigh 450–550 kg while the very heavy

153

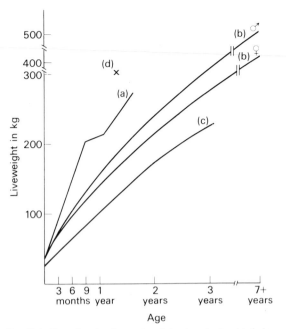

fig. 10.1 Growth rate of camels: a) best project animals in Kenya, b) males and females in western Sudan, c) Tunisia, and d) Turkestan (*Sources*: a) **Field, C. R.** (1979). *Ecology and management of camels, sheep and goats in northern Kenya.* UNESCO: Nairobi, Kenya; b) **Wilson, R. T.** (1978). Studies on the livestock of Southern Darfur, Sudan, V. Notes on camels. *Trop. Anim. Hlth Prod.*, **10**, 19-25; c) **Burgemeister, R. E.** (1975). *Elevage de chameaux en Afrique du Nord.* Office Allemand de la Cooperation Technique: Eschborn, West Germany; d) **Lakoza, T.** (1962). A valuable source for production of meat, milk and wool, (trans.) *Konnevodstro*, No. 12, 2-5. (in Russian abstracted in Animal Breeding Abstracts)

camels of India weigh up to 660 kg when mature and in good condition.

Weight estimation

An indication of weight may be required to determine stocking rates or for calculating feed requirements. Approximate weights are needed for veterinary purposes especially for estimating dosage rates of the antitrypanosome drugs which are toxic or poisonous. Even under conditions where normal facilities are available camels are difficult animals to weigh, and on open rangeland the problems are often insuperable.

Two formulae for estimating weight have been calculated. One is rather complicated involving measurements of chest girth, taken immediately behind the breast pad (T), the abdominal girth taken over the highest part of the hump (A) and the shoulder height (H). All these measurements are taken in metres and give the weight in kg when the following formula is applied:

$$P = 53\,TAH$$

As an example a camel of chest girth 1·90 m, of abdominal girth 2·00 m and shoulder height 2·05 m would weigh:

$$P = 53 \times 1{\cdot}90 \times 2{\cdot}40 \times 2{\cdot}05$$
$$= 495 \text{ kg}$$

The measurements were taken after 2 days of starvation and thus gave a net weight; if taken without starvation then 40 kg should be added to the weight calculated from the formula. An accuracy to within 25 kg is claimed (Boué, 1949).

A second formula based on linear regression of girth alone (taken in front of the breast pad) is probably simpler to use. Although not as reliable as such formulae calculated for cattle, it gives results accurate enough to be used with reasonable confidence (Wilson, 1978a). The best results are obtained when the measurement is taken with the camel in the couched position. The formula is:

$$y = 5{\cdot}071x - 457$$

where y is weight in kg and x is chest girth in cm. As an example for a camel of 190 cm chest girth:

$$y = (5{\cdot}071 \times 190) - 457$$
$$= 506{\cdot}5 \text{ kg}$$

Milk production

Lactation length and yield

Estimates of lactation length vary from 9 to 18 months (although there are reports of camels in Kenya still milking after 22 months) and total lactation yields from about 800 litres to 3 600 litres. These figures translate into daily yields of between 2·8 and 11·0 litres. Undoubtedly, milk yields fall between the extremes quoted but most authorities are extremely vague as to the method of estimation.

Table 10.1 Data on milk production in the camel

Country or area	Nutritional conditions	Mean daily yield[1] (kg)	Lactation length (days)	Lactation yield[1] (kg)	Sources
Pakistan	good	(10·0 – 6·6)	270 – 540	2 700 – 3 600	Leupold, 1968
Pakistan	desert	(6·3)	270	1 700	Institut für tropische veterinärmedizin, 1973
Pakistan	good	(6·7 – 5·7)	480 – 540	2 720 – 3 630	Yasin and Abdul Wahid, 1957
Pakistan	desert	(5·8 – 4·2)	270	1 135 – 1 560	Yasin and Abdul Wahid, 1957
Indian (Bikaneri)		4·5 – 1·8	213 – 547	(958 – 985)	Sharma and Bhargava, 1963
Russian (Turkestan)		(9·1 – 7·0)	213 – 547	7 500 – 5 000	Various Russian sources
Sahara		5·1 – 2·8	(365)	1 022 – 1 865	Capot-Rey, 1962
Southern Sahara		10·0			Nicolaisen, 1963
Eritrea		5 – 6			Mason and Maule, 1960
Ethiopia	good	6·7	365	2 442	Knoess, 1977
Kenya	(poor)	(5·8 – 4·0)	329 – 469	1 897	Field, 1979
Kenya		4·5	(365)	1 660	Spencer, 1973

[1]bracketed figures are calculated

Yields obviously depend on the number of times an animal is milked - some camel-owning people milk six times a day, some only once every 2 – 3 days - the food it obtains, the climate and the frequency of watering. Where camels are grazed on *gizu* (Chapter 9) both the camels and the herdsmen can survive without water; the herdsmen can obtain all their own liquid requirements from milk.

In Ethiopia, camels grazed on irrigated pastures of *Panicum maximum* or on lucerne gave high yields over long periods; one animal was reported to be producing 9 kg per day after 14 months of lactation (Knoess, 1977). In Kenya production from three camels has been estimated at 21 litres per day in the second week after calving falling to 4·8 litres per day in the sixteenth week. Lactation there normally lasts 47 – 67 weeks, the end of lactation occurring between 4 and 8 weeks after the next conception (Field, 1979). Some general data on milk yields are given in Table 10.1.

Composition

There are varied reports on the composition of camel milk as well as on total milk yields. That it is very white and unlikely to contain carotene (the precursor of vitamin A) is universally agreed. The vitamin C content at 2·3 – 5·6 mg per 100 ml is generally held to be fairly high (Kon, 1972), vitamin A varies from 3·36 to 7·14 mg per 100 ml (Khan and Appanna, 1967) while B complex vitamins are comparable in levels to those of the milk of other domestic animals. The aminoacid content appears in general to be similar to that of other domestic species with which it can be compared (Table 10.2). What little information is available on mineral composition indicates a low calcium level but reasonable levels of phosphorus and iron.

A summary of the composition of camels' milk is given in Table 10.3. In general terms it does not differ from the milk of other domestic species (as can be seen from Table 10.4) except for that of sheep and buffalo in which the percentage of fat is considerably higher. Camel milk fat contains less butanoic (butyric) acid than that of the cow and the buffalo and also has a low content of steam-volatile

Table 10.2 Aminoacid composition of the milk of some domestic animals. (*Source:* **Hoeller, H. and Hassan, Y. M.** (1965). The aminoacid composition of camel milk casein. *Sudan J. Vet. Sci. Anim. Husb.* **6**, 60–63 (ref. 1); **Harvey, D.** (1970). *Tables of the aminoacids in feeds and feeding stuffs.* Commonwealth Agricultural Bureaux: Farnham Royal, UK (ref. 2).

Aminoacid	Camel	Cow (g per 16 g N)	Goat	Notes (camel compared with others)
Alanine	3·1–3·4	3·5–4·8	3·6	camel significantly lower in ref. 1
Arginine	3·2–4·6	2·9–4·2	2·1	camel significantly lower in ref. 1 but higher in ref. 2
Aspartic acid	6·2–7·7	6·2–7·8	7·4	
Glutamic acid	15·4–23·5	15·8–23·2	20·3	
Glycine	0·6–1·6	0·8–2·1	2·1	camel significantly lower in ref. 1
Histidine	2·5	3·0	5·0	camel significantly lower in ref. 1
Isoleucine Leucine	18·0–21·0	8·1–17·4	14·4	camel slightly higher in ref. 2
Lysine	7·6	8·1	8·2	
Methionine	3·5	3·2	3·5	
Phenylalanine	5·7	5·4	6·0	
Proline	13·3	10·1–11·8	14·6	camel significantly higher in ref. 1
Serine	5·9	6·6	5·2	camel significantly lower in ref. 1
Threonine	6·3	4·3	5·7	camel significantly higher in ref. 1
Tyrosine	5·8	5·8	4·8	
Valine	7·4	7·5	5·7	

Table 10.3 Composition of camels milk principal constituents as percentages.

Constituents

Moisture	Fat	Lactose	Protein	Ash	Source
87·6	5·4	3·3	3·0	0·7	Barthe, 1905 (mean of 7 samples)
86·3	2·9	5·8	3·7	0·6	Leese, 1927
87·0	2·9	5·4	3·9	0·8	Davies, 1939
87·6	3·4–4·4		8·3		Purchase, 1943
	3·8	3·9	3·5		El-Bahay, 1964
87·2	4·2	4·1	3·7	0·8	Institut für Tropische Veterinärmedizin, 1973
87·0	3·3	5·1	3·9	0·7	Dahl and Hjort, 1976
87·2	4·2	4·5	3·5	0·8	Knoess, 1977 (mean of 3 samples)
	3·2–7·0				various Russian sources

Table 10.4 Gross composition of milk of various animal species (ranges, from various sources).

Species	Percentage composition					
	Moisture	Solids – not fat	Fat	Lactose	Protein	Ash
Camel	86·3 – 87·6	7·0 – 10·7	2·9 – 5·4	3·3 – 5·8	3·0 – 3·9	0·6 – 0·8
Cow (*Bos taurus*)	86·2 – 87·6	8·7 – 9·4	3·7 – 4·4	4·8 – 4·9	3·2 – 3·8	0·7
Cow (*B. indicus*)	86·1	8·5	5·4	4·6	3·2	0·7
Buffalo	83·1	9·0 – 10·5	7·4(-15·0)	4·9	3·8	0·8
Goat	87·1 – 88·2	7·8 – 8·8	4·0 – 4·5	3·6 – 4·2	2·9 – 3·7	0·8
Sheep	79·5 – 82·0	11·6 – 12·0	6·9 – 8·5	4·3 – 4·7	5·6 – 6·7	0·9 – 1·0
Horse	90·1 – 90·2	8·6 – 8·9	1·0 – 1·2	6·3 – 6·9	2·0 – 2·7	0·3 – 0·4
Pig	82·8	12·1	5·1 – 6·7	3·7	7·1 – 7·3	1·0 – 1·1
Human	88·0 – 88·4	8·3 – 8·9	3·3 – 4·7	6·8 – 6·9	1·1 – 1·3	0·2 – 0·3

fatty acids, probably on account of the dry food which constitutes its normal diet (Dhingra, 1934). Sour camels' milk cream does not have a butanoic (butyric) acid smell (Purchase, 1943), probably also indicating a low content of this fatty acid.

Butter, cheese and other milk products

Traditional societies apparently have problems in converting camels' milk to butter or cheese and it is often stated that conversion is not possible. This is not so. It is also said that camels' milk sours very quickly although this may be deliberate policy on the part of the owners. Sour milk keeps much longer and is pleasant to drink once the taste has been acquired. Once the utensils into which the milk is drawn or in which it is stored have acquired the right bacteria, little effort is needed to make it. Some Bedu (Musil, 1928) and Somali (Mares, 1954) do, however, store milk in the form of curds. Since the camel has a longer lactation than other domestic animals and is probably less seasonal in its milk production a fairly constant milk supply is assured. In this care the need for storage is to some extent obviated.

Most attempts at butter production have been made in the USSR and there are several accounts of success in this respect. Various products other than butter and cheese are made traditionally in India, a recent review of the literature being give by Rao, Gupta and Dastur (1970).

Difficulty may be experienced in churning to butter and the yield is fairly low. Leese (1927) quotes a yield of 57 g from 1·6 kg of milk after four hours churning. In Kenya, however, in one series of trials no difficulty was experienced. The cream separated easily and was kept for 43 hours at a temperature between 28·3 and 32·2 °C (Purchase, 1943). There was no butanoic (butyric) acid smell when the cream soured naturally, but it smelled rather like native beer. Butter was easy to make with the 'break' occurring at 10 to 33 minutes. The butter was very white and waxy and a certain amount was lost with the buttermilk as it broke in very fine grains.

Cheese was difficult to make under natural conditions but success was achieved by using 50 – 70 times the normal amount of rennet. The curd was light and friable. Three cheeses were made eventually from naturally soured milk and preserved in fat from the Blackhead Somali, the local fat-rumped sheep. These cheese were ripened for two months at 5 – 10°C when they developed a good green venation due to *Penicillium rocquerforti* which had previously established itself in the ripening chamber. The cheese was granular, friable and white and had a fully developed flavour with some slight bitterness.

In the Kenya experiments ghee (clarified butter) could be obtained without undue trouble either from the butter or directly from washed cream.

The yield was only about 2 per cent by either method and when used for cooking a slight flavour was imparted to bland foods. The ghee melted at 43·5–44·7 °C and solidified at 34–35 °C (compare with that of the cow which melts at 28–38 °C and solidifies at 19–30 °C); when solid it was very white and in liquid form a pale olive colour. It was almost free of butanoic (butyric) acid esters and had a higher unsaturated fatty acid content than ghee made from cows' milk.

Colostrum is seldom used by traditional owners. It should normally be reserved for the young animal but this is not always done by camel-owning peoples (see Chapter 7).

Nutritive value of camel milk

To obtain a nutritive value available to a human family certain assumptions need to be made. These are: 50 per cent of the herd is comprised of breeding females and each cow calves once every 2 years (which might be slightly optimistic but will serve as a reference). Twenty-five animals out of every 100, therefore, are producing milk at any one time and probably are producing of the order of 2 kg of milk, surplus to calf requirements. Camel's milk contains per kilo about 2 930·8 kJ of energy and about 35 g of protein. The average annual availability of energy and protein from milk for all animals in the herd is thus 534 863·7 kJ and 6·4 kg. At a daily human adult requirement of 11 723 kJ energy and 60 g protein a total of eight animals is required to provide energy while only 3·4 animals would be required to provide protein. These are the number of animals required if total nutritional requirements are fulfilled from milk.

Meat

General data, carcass weights and dressing percentages

There is often some resistance to the consumption of camel meat, particularly in developing countries in which camel meat might contribute an important fraction of total protein availability. It is probable that preferences for cattle meat over camel are of the same order as preferences for sheep over goat. The taste difference is psychological rather than real. Meat from similar cuts, of animals of similar age, is of similar taste. Camel meat may be sweeter, it may be coarser, but few people would remark the difference. Taste, of course, is very subjective and owes much to individual preference.

As with other facets of camels production, hard data on aspects of its value as a meat animal are hard to find. Yet with a total of more than 12 million camels in Africa alone and almost 3 million elsewhere in the world its meat production potential is not inconsiderable. In Africa such countries as Sudan, Somalia and Ethiopia must consume or export (or both) large numbers of camels, yet virtually no statistics are available on trade. Some countries with low camel populations have relatively high consumption rates of camel meat. In 1974, for example, a total of 64 000 camels were imported into Egypt for slaughter, the national herd at that time being estimated at 109 000 head (Alim, 1976). In Kano, in northern Nigeria, 3 410 adult camels were slaughtered in the 4-month period September–December 1977; Nigeria's estimated camel population is 17 000 head. In the 1960s between 600 and 1 000 camels a month were believed to be smuggled from Kenya to Somalia and more than 69 000 camels were slaughtered at Archer's Post in northen Kenya over a period of a few years (Bremaud, 1969). While camels were being smuggled into Somalia at one end they were apparently being legally exported at the other – 174 head in 1950, 3 613 in 1959, 21 954 in 1972 and 34 223 in 1975 (Swift, 1979b).

The most serious problem relating to meat production concerns the lack of coordinated data. We have lots of estimates of liveweights from various areas: these have been given in Chapter 3 and on p. 154 and need not be repeated here. There are also estimates of dressing percentage: these generally seem to be rather high – for example in the range of 54–57 per cent – when compared with other domestic animals, or even in comparison with game animals. Only one source (Congiu, 1953) provides data relating to liveweight, carcass weight and dressing percentage. Actual carcass weight data are almost completely lacking. Faulkner (1978) refers to an average carcass weight of 300 kg for over 1 000 animals in Qatar. It is not clear whether the figure is the average carcass weights of

fig. 10.2 Somali (Benadir) camels in Garissa district of northern Kenya; the man is 190 cm tall

for Somali camels by Congiu (1953). For camels with an average carcass weight of 270 kg he found a great variation in the weight of humps, 3–93 kg, with a mean of 18 kg and liver weights averaging 12 kg. Camel meat contains about 22 per cent protein but only about 1 per cent fat (Nasr, El-Bahay and Moursy, 1965), almost all fat being stored in the hump (Chapter 5). Camel fat is considered a delicacy by some: Musil (1928) says that it can be stored for 3 years as suet, while the Gabbra of Kenya are said to castrate their camels purely to get the hump to develop, the fat of one castrate being enough for one family for a year. It is probable that most estimates of the contribution of hump fat to total carcass weight are on the high side. Thus while estimates of 5–10 per cent are normally quoted it is considered that less than 5 per cent is a more realistic figue for the average of all animals slaughtered. In addition, bones in the average carcass will be equivalent to about 20 per cent of total carcass weight.

all camels slaughtered or of specially selected ones. If the former, these must surely have been very good animals as even at a dressing percentage of 57 per cent they would have gone to 520 kg liveweight and at a perhaps more reasonable 50 per cent they would have weighed 600 kg. The Iranian male camels with carcass weights quoted at 300–400 kg (Khatami, 1970) must have been truly enormous, but were probably either fed in feedlots or on sugar beet tops (see Chapter 7). The best Kenyan camels yield 290 kg carcasses (Bremaud, 1969) a fact which can be appreciated from the appearance of the castrate in Fig. 10.2.

In an attempt to provide at least some hard data on the potential of camels for meat production some studies were conducted in Sudan in 1977. A summary of the results (Wilson, 1978a) is given in Table 10.5 and 10.6.

These data for dressing percentages are clearly not as optimistic as most other sources. The figure for females of 47·7 per cent does compare rather well with the only other data available which have been used to make similar calculations. This refers to 23 females slaughtered at Wajir in Kenya and in which the dressing percentage was 48·2 per cent.

Data supplementary to Table 10.6 is provided

Nutritive value of camel meat

A possible offtake of 6 per cent (p. 153) seems realistic for a camel herd in which males are retained to mature ages for pack and transport purposes. An average carcass weight of 210 kg would yield 10 kg fat, 160 kg meat and 40 kg bones. Each carcass would thus yield 35·2 kg protein (at 22 per cent of the meat only) and 997 312·5 kJ energy (at 36·8 kJ per gram for fat and 17·9 kJ per gram for meat protein). Total energy and protein from a herd of 100 animals would thus be 5 983 917 kJ energy and 211·2 kg protein, equivalent to an output per animal of 59 817·7 kJ and 2·11 kg protein. In theory, one camel will provide 5 days energy requirements for one adult but 35 days' protein requirements. They are thus a good source of protein but less good in terms of energy.

Blood

The use of camel's blood as a food seems to be confined to East Africa. The Turkana, Rendille and Gabbra are the only people who systematically bleed their camels, although camels are apparently occasionally bled by some Boran and Somali clans.

Table 10.5 Liveweight, carcass weight and dressing percentage of Darfur camels (*Source*: **Wilson, R. T.** (1978a). Studies on the livestock of Southern Darfur. V. Notes on camels. *Trop. Anim. Hlth Prod.*, **10**, 19–25.)

	Males	Females	Total
Number of animals	21	39	60
Liveweight (kg)			
mean	447·9	414·4	426·2
± SD	84·10	50·83	65·74
range	305·5–581·0	307·5–522·5	305·5–581·0
Carcass weight (kg)			
mean	231·3	196·3	208·5
± SD	49·18	24·94	38·78
range	144·0–310·0	141·0–248·0	141·0–310·0
Dressing percentage			
mean	51·4	47·4	48·8
± SD	2·88	3·25	3·65
range	46·2–55·6	41·3–53·5	41·3–55·6

Table 10.6 Weights and percentages (of empty liveweight) of carcass and body organs of male and female camels combined (*Source*: as for Table 10.5.)

Body part	Weight (kg)			As percentage of liveweight		
	mean	±SD	range	mean	±SD	range
Forequarter	120·2	22·21	79·0–183·5	34·0	1·51	31·42–38·15
Hindquarter	84·5	14·53	59·5–124·5	24·7	1·38	20·98–28·53
Hump	4·0	4·30	0·0–20·0	1·1	1·04	0·00–4·45
Total: carcass weight	208·5	38·78	141·0–310·0	60·7	2·09	55·75–65·11
Heart + lungs	8·4	1·13	6·5–10·5	2·5	0·33	1·78–3·36
Liver	7·5	1·45	4·5–11·0	2·2	0·41	1·47–3·45
Head (skinned)	12·1	1·81	8·0–16·5	3·6	0·32	2·80–4·49
Feet	14·6	2·25	10·5–19·5	4·3	0·37	3·31–5·16
Hide	34·8	6·11	22·5–47·0	10·2	0·81	8·50–11·76

The use of blood is, of course, forbidden by Islam (*Koran*, Sura 5 Verse 4) along with the meat of dead animals and that of swine.

Data on yields are sparse. Pratt and Gwynne (1977) mention 5·5 litres with animals being bled twice a month and Morgan (1972) quotes 5 litres once a month. The Rendille and Gabbra usually bleed (by way of the facial vein) only in dry conditions when milk is scarce although warriors sometimes take about 2 litres of blood during the rains. It is probable that not more than 10 per cent of any camel herd can be used for regular bleeding and the average herd yield will therefore be between 6 and 12 litres, equivalent to approximately 0·5–1·0 kg of protein and 8 583–17 166 kJ per animal per year. Blood from one camel therefore,

Table 10.7 Production of energy and protein from each camel in a herd

Item	Quantity per animal per year (kg)	Energy (kJ)	Protein (g)
Milk	182·5	534 864	6 400
Meat and fat	160 + 10	59 838	2 110
Blood	9	12 874	750
Total		607 460	9 260

will provide only 1 – 1·5 days' energy requirement for an adult man but between 8 and 16 days' protein requirements.

Value of camels as human food

From the data presented above, it is possible to attempt at least a rough calculation of the ability of the camel to supply human dietary requirements. A summary is shown in Table 10.7. Each camel in a herd (that is every animal irrespective of its sex, production status, size) will thus provide the energy requirement of one adult human (at 11 723 kJ per day) for 52 days and the protein (60 g per day) requirement for 154 days. According to these calculations a family dependent entirely on camels for their food would require 7 camels per human adult equivalent per year for energy but only 2·4 camels for protein. This, of course, assumes that herd composition, offtake and productivity are as outlined above. Economically, and probably ecologically, a family might do better to sell protein (meat and fat) and buy energy (grain) to fulfil its annual food needs.

Hides, wool and hair

Hides

In spite of its large size and weight the hide of the camel appears to be of little commercial value. In Darfur wet hides weighed between 22·5 and 47·0 kg, equivalent to between 8·5 and 11·8 per cent of empty liveweight (Wilson, 1978a). Perhaps partly due to the method of slaughter which involves flaying along the back line, no attempt was made to sell hides and these were collected by the poorer women of the town.

With the exception of Faulkner (1978), who writes that the camel hide is especially valued for its large size and the quality of the leather obtained (being used for, among other things, the making of car seat covers!) all other authorities are unanimous in condemning camel hides. Thus, Leese (1927) says that hides do not make good leather and Lewis (1955) indicates that it is possible to make only six pairs of sandals from one hide. Among the Kababish of Sudan no mention is made of hides by Asad (1964), and the quotation at the heading of this chapter conspicuously lacks any reference to them – although it remarks on the use of camel hair.

Camel hides are, of course, used for the manufacture of tourist items in Egypt and the Middle East generally – an eloquent enough expression, perhaps, of the real value of this commodity in the eyes of camel-owning peoples. The last word may well be left to the Kababish – they prefer the long arduous hunt of the Scimitar-horned Oryx for the quality of its skin in rope-making rather than use the material readily to hand.

Wool and hair

Wool or hair often adds considerably to the subsistence economy of camel-owning societies; it is used for the manufacture of tent cloths, blankets and cloaks. Hair growth tends to be unevenly distributed over the body, being often confined to the shoulders and hump in the dromedary (Fig. 10.3).

In contrast to the wool of the Bactrian camel and of the South American camelids, that of the Arabian camel has been little commercialised.

Hand shears can be used to clip the dromedary but the commonest method for traditional usage, at least in Africa and the Middle East, is to shave the wool with the ubiquitous double-edged knife. Yields, in comparison to the reported 4·5 kg of the Bactrian camel (Kulaeva, 1964) are low, although there is mention of 5·4 kg from the colder regions of India (Singh, 1966).

In North Africa it has been said that young

fig. 10.3 Typical hair growth of a 3 year old Kababish camel in a Darfur market

animals yield 3 kg of raw wool while older animals yield only 2 kg (Burgemeister, 1975). However, in this region wool clipping is not universally practised and is rarely done on a regular basis. In Kenya the absence of seasonal variations in temperature result in very little wool growth.

A more normal, perhaps more realistic, estimate of yield should be of the order of 1·0 – 1·4 kg (Nanda, 1957; Leupold, 1968).

Work

The main form of work output of the camel is probably in its role of riding animal, at least at the present day. In terms of economic output the principal contribution of the camel is as a baggage animal although in certain areas important, and now often

fig. 10.4 Camels of the Egyptian camel corps

increasing, additions to low technology systems are made in the form of draught for wheeled transport and agricultural implements, and as a provider of industrial power. In general it is only males, entire or castrated, that are used for work, although females are occasionally involved.

Riding animals

Since the domestication of the dromedary it has played an important role as a saddle animal for personnel transport. The light riding camels of the Bedu, and the Anafi and Bishari strains of eastern Sudan are justly famous for their speed and endurance. In addition to use as an individual riding animal, camels have been used as cavalry or for mounted infantry in both traditional and modern warfare. Napoleon was the first modern general to use a camel corps, in Egypt from 1799 to 1801. They were also used – but without great success – by the British Army in the Nile campaign of 1884–1885 and their use has continued well into this century (Fig. 10.4). The French have used them as mounts both for native troops and for the Foreign Legion.

In Sudan, the Camel Corps (which was used well into the 1940s) consisted of 400 soldiers mounted on Bishari camels. These animals, whose natural pace has been described as an amble of between 7 and 8 km per hour (Boustead, 1934) carried on active service the soldier, 4-days' rations of water and 3-weeks' ration of food (both for the soldier), personal belongings (cooking gear, blankets, overcoat), 200 rounds of ammunition and 8-days' grain for the camel – a total load of about 180 kg. With this load they were expected to travel up to 650 km to the general area of operations and then average anything up to 65 km per night for five nights in seek and destroy missions.

Various paces have been described (see also Chapter 4). For example, Leese (1927) specifies the walk, 4 km per hour; the jog, 9·5–13 km per hour (this being the usual pace for a riding camel); the fast run, 14·5–19 km per hour; and the canter, seldom used as it is tiring to both camel and rider. Gillespie (1962) records a trot, 8 km per hour and a fast run of 16–32 km per hour. The former author gives an average day's travel as 65–80 km which can be maintained for a period of up to 2 weeks: longer distances impose penalties in the number of days they can be maintained, for example, 112 km for each of 2 days and 144 km for 1 day only. In all cases proper rest periods of a minimum of 7 days are required before further demands are made. In Sudan the 1 400 km distance from Khartoum – El Obeid – El Fasher used to be covered in 9 days using relays of camels to deliver mail, a service which was recognised by the postage stamp itself being a camel carrying the mail (Fig. 10.5). There are many other local tales of outstanding feats and of long distances covered in record time.

The Kababish (Fig. 10.6) and the Moors (Fig. 10.7) of the African Sahelian zone, and most camel-owning societies elsewhere, continue to use the camel for the transport of their womenfolk. In this case the camel and/or the woman are highly valued and the camel is almost invariably led by a man.

fig. 10.5 A postage stamp recognising the role of the camel as the principal means of mail delivery

fig. 10.6 A Kababish riding camel returning northwards to its rainy season grazing area in May 1977

fig. 10.7 A Moorish lady on her way to market in northern Mali.

Control of riding animals is usually achieved by means of a halter and neck rope supplemented by use of a light stick and the feet. Saddles are of various designs depending on the regions, the development of these being touched upon in Chapter 1. Some existing types are illustrated in Fig. 10.8. See also Fig. 2.7 for a two-man saddle in which the second rider faces the rear. Adequate padding should be – but often is not – provided to protect the hide and hump. The most comfortable riding posture is very quickly discovered, usually involving some varient where the rider's legs are crossed over the camel's neck.

Pack or baggage animals

Baggage and pack camels are more sturdily built and heavier than riding types. They normally move at a slow even pace of 2–3 km per hour. In certain circumstances they may need to move faster, as for instance the baggage animals of the Camel Corps in Sudan, which moved with the column.

When the camel was commonly used as a military or police animal regulations usually contained provisions for maximum loads. For example, in Sudan during the 1920s the maximum, load allowed was about 165 kg but regulations could not always be obeyed (p. 163). Sudan Camel Corps' animals on campaign – and remember these were the Bishari riding variety – carried total loads of 180 kg (Boustead, 1934), and an official exploration party in the northern Sudan deserts at about this time had its camels loaded at about 220 kg and carried most of this weight for 1 000 km or more. The British army allowed maximum loads of 200 kg and recently official loads in India were restricted to 180 kg. A French instruction of 1902 for Algeria, specified loads of 120 kg or a maximum of 150 kg if the total burden consisted of two indivisible loads. The Italians in Somalia also made use of the camel for military transport.

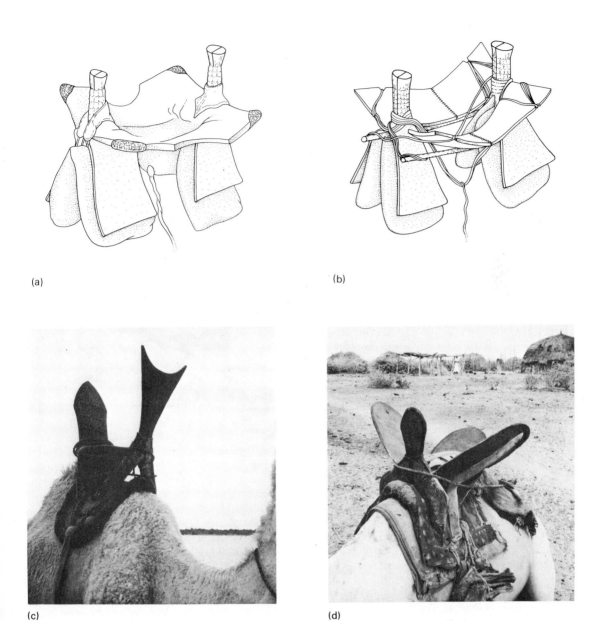

(a)

(b)

(c)

(d)

fig. 10.8 Riding saddles: a) *makhlufa* and b) *kur* from Sudan – note the wooden bar under b) considerably adding to the strength and the fact that in neither case are the pads attached to the saddle; c) Tuareg and d) Moor saddles in the same village in Mali

Traditional owners are, or have been, for the most part illiterate and lack access to any form of weighing equipment. Possibly they work on the well-known principle that it is only the final straw that breaks the camel's back. In fact, it is probable that it is volume rather than weight which is limiting. Thus various weights, some probably in excess of the camel's own body weight, have been quoted – 545 kg (for short distances) and 410 kg in India (Nanda, 1957). In Sudan it is not unusual to see camels carrying four sacks (each nominally containing 100 kg) of grain for long distances. Depending on the bulk density of the load, most camels still used for transport probably regularly carry in excess of 300 kg and carrying this load are expected to achieve distances of 20–25 km per day over extended periods. The distribution of weight, the ease with which individual parts of the total load can be manipulated by the driver, the nature of the terrain and climatic conditions all affect total work output. Even so, spectacular results can still be achieved: during the rainy season of 1973 camel trains were observed reprovisioning Buram from Nyala in Southern Darfur in the far west of Sudan. Conditions were appalling with shade temperatures – although, of course, no shade existed on the march – of around 38–40 °C and long stretches of water up to 1·5 m deep (Fig. 10.9). Camels carried three 100 kg sacks of sugar and, festooned like Christmas trees with various other bits of baggage, accomplished the 160 km journey in 5 or 6 days.

In Ethiopia camels perform an important function in the transport of salt from the Danakil Depression to the Tigre Highlands. The loading rate of these animals is low – 90 kg on average – but the animals cover the 160 km journey in 4 days and gain an altitude of about 2 800 m in the process (Wilson, 1976). In Mali camels carrying salt from the northern desert to Timbuctoo are loaded with 4–6 blocks of 35 kg each.

Baggage camels may be led individually or in short columns. Control is achieved in a variety of ways but most usually by means of a simple halter or nose peg. When in column the head rope of a camel is usually attached to the tail of the one preceding it. In open country, where no timetable is adhered to, camels are often driven slowly and

fig. 10.9 Camels in heavy going (1·2 m of water) in Darfur, July 1973.

allowed to forage on the way. It would probably be less tiring on the camel to be allowed to cover the same distance at a decent pace and spend the time saved browsing at will – standing or slow progress with heavy loads is very tiring. (For an experienced camel transport officer's view of this, see p. 151) Pack saddles are of infinite variety, as are the methods of attaching them (Fig. 10.10) The *hawia* is perhaps the commonest basic type and is used widely throughout India and in Sudan. A skilled camelman can attach his load to this saddle with a long rope and have the whole unit balance on the back of the camel without the use of girths, breast pieces or cruppers. Nets are occasionally used where the load is comprised mainly of a large number of small items.

Some indication of the relative contribution of the camel to the total transport demand in a traditional network is given in Table 10.8. These data were collected in an area which until recently had been considered to be south of the normal limit for the distribution of the camel. If we assume the

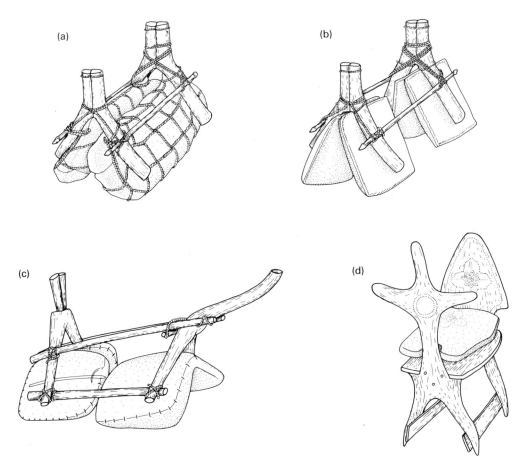

fig. 10.10 Pack saddles: a) and b) *hawia* from Sudan, the former with grass mats, the latter with leather pads, c) a dual purpose pack/riding saddle, the *téda-daza* - note the exaggerated pommel, and d) a hybrid saddle for the tourist trade with a Tuareg fore and body of dual pack/riding type with separate supports (*Sources*: a) and b) **Acland P. B. E.** (1932). Notes on the camel in the eastern Sudan. *Sudan Notes Rec.* **15**, 119 - 149; c) and d) from **Monod, Th.** (1967). **Notes sur le harnachement chamelier**. Bull. IFAN **29B** 234 - 306.)

average load of a camel as 250 kg and that of a donkey as being 50 kg then, in terms of pack animals only, it can be seen that camels in the transport pool of this area carry six times as much burden as donkeys.

Draught and industrial uses

Although one supposedly authoritative source (FAO, 1972) states that camels are seldom harnessed except for drawing water in Mauritania and Niger, camels have always played a considerable role in many areas, and continue to do so, in agricultural and industrial operations. They have been used throughout history, sometimes for the most bizzare events and in the most unlikly places. A few examples in time and space will serve to illustrate this point. As early as 283 BC they were used to draw coaches for the coronation of Ptolemy

Table 10.8 The role of animals in transport in western Darfur, expressed as number of journeys and load types (*Source*: **Wilson, R. T.** (1978). Studies on the livestock of Southern Darfur, Sudan. VI. Notes on equines. *Trop. Anim. Hlth Prod.* **10**, 183–189.)

Load	Types of animal				
	pack donkey	cross-bred donkey	syrian donkey	horse	camel
Rider only	405	15	32	262	194
Rider + Pack	351	12	4	1	72
Pack only	199		2	1	229
Total observations	955	67	38	264	495

II and in Rome, in 42 BC, chariot races with camels formed part of the spectacle. Nearer our own time Samuel White Baker, on his appointment to the governorship of Equatoria (now in the south of Sudan) transported boilers, each weighing 400 kg, on gun carriages drawn by two camels. In Algeria in 1917 the French army moved 80 mm field guns (in one case for a journey of 9 days) across the northern Sahara with the help of camels. Some data from areas where the camel is not native are even more instructive: in South Africa a single camel in a 2-wheeled cart pulled a load of 750 kg and in Australia six or more camels were harnessed in a fan (one in the shafts, two in the swing and three in the lead) to 4-wheeled waggons. In the Australian case, where females were also commonly used, a team of 13 or 14 camels could pull a load of 8 tonnes at a speed of about 2·5 km per hour on good going.

For agricultural production the camel is perhaps most commonly used as a plough animal: singly, paired, or paired with a variety of other animals – oxen, mules, donkeys (Fig. 10.11). Leese (1927) even notes the case of a woman and a camel pulling a plough in Baluchistan with a man driving. In the west of Sudan a boy mounts the camel while a man guides the plough. In this case, as can be seen from Fig. 10.12, the draught is taken from the hump of the camel by means of two traces attached to a swingletree behind the camel. In other areas where single camels are used, for example in North Africa, they are driven from behind by means of reins and the draught is taken from the

neck and shoulders. Ingenuity needs to be used where mixed teams of animals are widely different in height. I have seen a camel and donkey in traces together where the draught from the camel was taken from the neck to a swingletree under the belly, that from the donkey from a breast band to a swingletree behind the donkey, the two then being connected to a balk in the normal way.

fig. 10.11 Camel and bullock harnessed together for ploughing in Egypt.

fig. 10.12 Ploughing alluvial land for millet under *Acacia albida* trees in the valley of the Wadi 'Azum in Darfur

Ploughing in Ethiopia, a single camel was said to out-perform a pair of oxen and could plough 1 ha in 20 hours. In Sudan a camel drawing a mouldboard plough turning a furrow 15 cm deep and 25 cm wide ploughed a hectare, not including time for rest stops, in just over 11 hours. A comparison of the draught power of various species of domestic animals is given in Table 10.9 from which it can be seen that for comparable weights the camel is relatively efficient.

For non-agricultural purposes camels are most commonly used for lifting water and also are often used for the milling of oil from sesame seeds, for example in Iran, the Yemen, in Tunisia and in Sudan. In Sudan power output for oil milling is greater than for ploughing (see Table 10.9). The mortar is made from the hollowed out trunk of a tree, usually *Acacia albida*, while the pestle, made from *Acacia tortilis*, is attached to a beam yoked to the camel, the whole system of attachment and operation is illustrated in Fig. 10.13.

Fighting camels
Camels are used as spectacles in fighting in Pakistan (Yasin and Abdul Wahid, 1957). Specially trained bulls are taught to fight. The method appears to be an extension of the normal rutting behaviour involving the neck.

Further reading

Acland, P. B. E. (1932). Notes on the camel in the eastern Sudan. *Sudan Notes Rec.*, **15**, 119–149.
Alim, K. A. (1976). The livestock and meat industry in Egypt. *Wld Rev. Anim. Prod.*, **12**, 59–68.
Asad, T. (1964). Seasonal movements of the

Table 10.9 Normal draught power of some species of domestic animals. Where appropriate draught and power have been calculated for single animals (*Sources*: 1 **Hopfen, H. J.** (1969). *Farm implements for arid and tropical regions*. Agric. Dev. Paper, No. 91. FAO: Rome; 2 author's records.)

Animal	Average weight (kg)	Approximate draught (kg)	Average speeds (m per second)	Power developed (kgm per second)	(hp)
Light horses[1]	400–700	60–80	1·0	75	1·00
Bullocks[1]	500–900	60–80	0·6–0·8	56	0·75
Buffaloes[1]	400–900	50–80	0·8–0·9	55	0·75
Cows[1]	400–600	50–60	0·7	35	0·45
Mules[1]	350–500	50–60	0·9–1·0	52	0·70
Donkeys[1]	200–300	30–40	0·7	25	0·35
Camels (ploughing)[2]	450–500	75	1·0	75	1·00
Camels (oil milling)[2]	450–500	90	1·0	90	1·20
Oxen (Ethiopia)[2]	400	55	0·6	33	0·44
Oxen (Mali)[2]	350–450	55	0·76	42	0·56
Donkeys (Mali)[2]	110–130	35	0·7	24	0·32

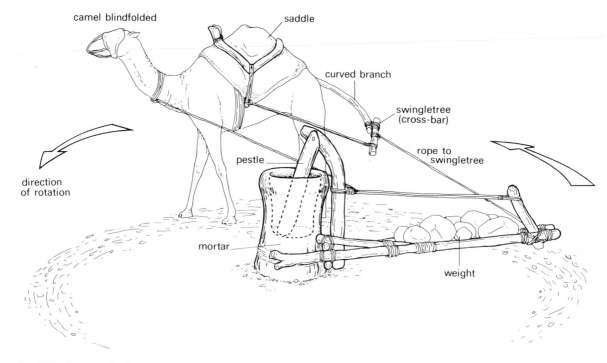

fig. 10.13 A camel oil mill

Kababish Arabs of Nòrthern Kordofan. *Sudan Notes Rec.*, **45**, 45–58.

Barthe, M. L. (1905). *La composition du lait de la chamelle. J. Pharm. Chim.*, **21**, 386–388.

Bhargava, K. K., Sharman V. D. and Singh, M. (1965). A study of birth weight and body measurements of camel. *Indian J. Vet. Sci.*, **35**, 358–362.

Blagověsčenskiǐ, V. (1963). Reserves in the production of milk and meat, (trans.). *Konevod Konnya Sport.*, **33**(10), 8–9 (in Russian, abstracted in Animal Breeding Abstracts).

Boué, R. (1949). *Essai de barymétrie chez le dromadaire Nord-africain. Rev. Elev. Méd. vét. Pays trop.*, **3**, 13–16.

Boustead, J. E. H. (1934). The Camel Corps of the Sudan Defence Force. *J. Royal United Services Inst.*, **1934**, 547–557.

Bremaud, O. (1969). *Notes sur l'élevage camelin dans les districts du nord de la Republique du Kenya*. Institut d'Elevage et de Médecine Vétérinaire des Pays Tropicaux: Maisons Alfort, France.

Burgemeister, R. E. (1975) *Elevage de chameaux en Afrique du Nord*. Office Allemand de la Coopération Technique: Eschborn, West Germany.

Capot-Rey, R. (1962). The present state of nomadism in the Sahara. in: *The problems of the arid zone*. UNESCO: Paris, France.

Congiu, S. (1953). *Indagine sulla resa al macello, sulla distribuzione ponderale sulla correlazione fra le diverse parti del corpo del dromedario nomade, Zootec. vet.*, **8**, 188–191.

Dahl, G. and Hjort, A. (1976). *Having herds: Pastoral herd growth and household economy*. University of Stockholm: Stockholm, Sweden.

Davies, W. L. (1939). *Indian indigenous milk pro-

dúcts. Thresher Spink: Calcutta, India.

Dhingra, D. R. (1934). The component fatty acids and glycerides of the milk-fat of Indian camels. *Biochem. J.*, **28**, 73-78.

El-Bahay, G. M. (1964). *Normal contents of Egyptian camel milk*. Thesis, University of Cairo: Giza, Egypt.

Faulkner, D. E. (1978). *The future of the camel*. Manuscript paper for presentation at the Conference of Ministers of Agriculture of the Gulf States and Arabian Peninsula.

FAO (1972) *Manual on the employment of draught animals*. FAO: Rome.

Field, C. R. (1979). *Ecology and management of camels, sheep and goats in northern Kenya*. UNESCO: Nairobi, Kenya.

Gillespie, I. A. (1962). Riding camels of the Sudan. *Sudan J. Vet. Sci. Anim. Husb.*, **3**, 37-42.

Institute für Tropische Veterinärmedizin (1973). *Kamelmilch*. Merkblatt, No. 21. ITV: Geissen, West Germany.

Khan, K. U. and Appanna, T. C. (1967). Carotene and vitamin A in camel milk. *J. Nutrition Dietetics*, India., **41**, 17-20.

Khatami, K. (1970). *A new promising approach to the solution of the meat and protein problems in the arid and semi-arid countries of the world*. Ministry of Agriculture: Teheran, Iran.

Knoess, L. (1977). The camel as a meat and milk animal. *World Anim. Rev.*, **22**, 39-44.

Kon, S. K. (1972). *Milk and milk products in human nutrition*. FAO Nutrition Studies, No. 27. FAO: Rome.

Kulaeva, V. (1964). The production of the Bactrian camel, (trans.) *Konnevod. Konnya Sport.*, **34**, 9-10 (in Russian, abstracted in Animal Breeding Abstracts).

Lakoza, J. (1962). A valuable source for production of meat, milk and wool, (trans.). *Konnevodstvo.*, No. 12, 2-5 (in Russian, abstracted in Animal Breeding Abstracts).

Leese, A. S. (1927). *A treatise on the one-humped camel in health and disease*. Haynes & Sons: Stamford, Lincs, UK.

Leupold, J. (1968). *Le chameau, important animal domestique des pays subtropicaux*. *Les cahiers bleus vét.*, No. 15, 1-6.

Lewis, I. M. (1955). *Peoples of the Horn of Africa*. International African Institute: London.

Mares, R. G. (1954). Animal husbandry, animal industry and animal disease in the Somaliland Protectorate. *Brit. Vet. J.*, **10**, 411-423, 470-481.

Mason, I. L. and Maule, J. P. (1960). *The indigenous livestock of eastern and southern Africa*. Common. Bur. Anim. Breed. Genet. Tech. Comm. No. 14. Commonwealth Agricultural Bureaux: Farnham Royal, UK.

Monod, Th. (1967). *Notes sur le harnachement chamelier. Bull. IFAN*, **29B**, 234-306.

Morgan, W. T. W. (1972). *East Africa, its peoples and resources*. Oxford University Press: Oxford, UK.

Musil, A. (1928). *The manners and customs of the Rwala Bedouins*. New York, USA.

Nanda, P. N. (1957). *Camels and their management*. Indian Council of Agricultural Research: New Delhi, India.

Nasr, S., El-Bahay, G. & Moursy, A. W. (1965). Studies on camel meat. I. The effect of age and sex on the components of camel meat. *J. Arab Vet. Med. Assoc.*, **25**, 253-258.

Nicolaisen, J. (1963). *Ecology and culture of the pastoral Tuareg*. National Museum; Copenhagen, Denmark.

Pratt, D. J. and Gwynne, M. D. (1977). *Rangeland management and ecology in East Africa*. Hodder and Stoughton: London.

Purchase, M. S. (1943). Some experiments in the making of butter, ghee and cheese from camel's milk. *E. Afr. Agric. J.*, **9**, 39-41.

Rao, M. B., Gupta, R. C. and Dastur, N. N. (1970). Camel's milk and milk products. *Indian J. Dairy Sci.*, **23**, 71-78.

Sharma, V. D. and Bhargava, K. K. (1963). The Bikaneri camel. *Indian Vet. J.*, **40**, 639-643.

Singh, H. (1966). Camel care. *Intensive agric. (India)*, No. 9.

Spencer, P. (1973). *Nomads in alliance: Symbiosis and growth among the Rendille and Samburu of Kenya*. Oxford University Press: Oxford, UK.

Swift, J. J. (1979a). *The economics of traditional nomadic pastoralism: The Twareg of the Adrar n Iforas(Mali)*. Thesis, University of Sussex: Brighton, UK.

Swift, J. J. (1979b). The development of livestock trading in a nomad pastoral economy: The Somali case. *In: Pastoral production and society*, pp. 447–465. Cambridge University Press: Cambridge, UK.

Wilson, R. T. (1976). Some quantitative data on the Tigre salt trade from the early 19th century to the present day. *Ann. Ist. univ. orient Napoli.*, **36**, 157–164.

Wilson, R. T. (1978a). Studies on the livestock of Southern Darfur, Sudan. V. Notes on camels. *Trop. Anim. Hlth Prod.*, **10**, 19–25.

Yasin, S. A. and Abdul Wahid (1957). Pakistan camels – a preliminary survey. *Agric. Pakistan*, **8**, 289–295.

11 The future for the camel

"The blessings of this world, until judgement day, are tied to the forelocks of our horses, sheep are a benediction and the Almighty in making animals created nothing preferable to the camel".

Mohammed, the Prophet of God.

In the modern world, after some 40 to 50 centuries of domestication, the camel seems to be an anachronism. Unfortunately we are in no position to decide whether to 'advanced' people throughout the ages it has ever appeared to be anything else. That it has always been confined to the most extreme conditions of heat and aridity and that it has always been of service to only a relatively few people cannot be disputed.

The camel is a triple-purpose animal providing milk, meat and transport; it also provides hair and hide in some areas. Its comparative advantages over other domestic animals as possible replacements within the camel's optimal environmental limits are as follows.

1   Its water economy resulting from the ability to reduce water loss to a very considerable degree.
2   Its ability to support a very high degree of water loss amounting to as much as 30 per cent of its initial body weight.
3   Its massive capacity for making up water loss in a very short time when water becomes available, drinking up to 180 litres within 24 hours.
4   The three previous factors enable the camel to go voluntarily without water for up to 10 days (quite apart from the special occasions of winter grazing described in Chapter 9).
5   The camel does not lose its appetite for food as it dehydrates, unlike other food-producing domestic animals.
6   The ability of the camel to fluctuate its body temperature coupled with anatomical and behavioural adaptations enable considerable savings in energy to be made.
7   Factors 4 and 5 together, supported to varying degrees by 6 vastly increase the ranging area of camels in comparison with other domestic animals.

8   Range may be further increased by the greater speed of camels.
9   The camel is primarily a browsing animal enabling it to make use of fodder often not relished by other domestic animals.
10   Where it might be in competition for browse plants its relative height and the elevation at which it eats reduces competition between it and other domestic species.
11   The large range (7 and 8 above) and the dietary factors (9 and 10 above) enable a greater biomass to be carried more evenly over a given area served by one watering point thus reducing possible consequences of erosion.
12   The huge plate-like feet themselves are less damaging to soil structure than the smaller cloven hooves of the other common domestic species.

Some of the arguments above have been used against the camel. That is eats plants not normally touched by cattle, sheep and goats; that it eats parts that they cannot reach in areas they cannot use; and that it opens up areas of rangeland to penetration by other stock which then eat the field layer and contribute further to degradation. There may be some truth in this alternative hypothesis. On balance it would appear that the advantages of the camel considerably outweigh the disadvantages. It does make use of areas that cannot be used by other stock and it turns this use to milk, meat and motive force. There are those who contend that the camel is the least efficient of all domestic animals in producing, per unit of weight, these factors. It is not certain that in terms of overall efficiency camels are at a disadvantage: we do not know enough of their energy and production needs in terms of food to assess this in any objective way. Daily gains of 1·4 kg by males and 0·9 kg by females in Iran on a diet mainly of low-cost products indicate that the camel is quite efficient. The argument is, in any case, largely irrelevant. No-one suggests that the days of cattle are numbered because they are less efficient than goats or than rabbits. They fulfil a different role and occupy a different niche. The camel, we stress again, is an animal of semi-arid and arid areas where there is little alternative hope of production.

A further current argument is that the camel has outlived its usefulness because it no longer fulfils a transport function, this having been taken over by mechanical power. This is probably also fallacious. That most goods are now transported by other means is not in dispute. That they are goods that would have been transported by the camel is very much in dispute. No number of camels could possibly transport the amount of stuff that is moved nowadays due to the very rapid economic and social changes which have taken place in the last few decades. The camel, in spite of this, still moves very considerable tonnages at the primary level, between households and villages and to and from collecting centres where mechanised transport would be neither economic nor practicable. It provides power for transport or agricultural or industrial purposes on renewable resources. It is, as we have said elsewhere, mainly in the areas most suitable to the camel that the most far-reaching changes due to oil have been possible. No-one considers that the oil will last forever and that prosperity will expand indefinitely.

The future for the camel has not been irretrievably lost with its transport and communications role, if indeed these roles have been lost. Napoleon's *Corps de Dromadaires* in Egypt occupied the working lives of a maximum of 700 camels for less than 2 years. The Camel Corps of the Sudan Defence Force had 400 riding camels and a 'few' baggagers for something like 30 years. The loss of its military role has hardly been a mortal blow. Within the last 10 years more than 2 000 camels have been observed in one caravan in one day transporting salt.

But it has to be admitted that the transport role is limited. The future lies in the ability of the camel to produce meat and milk from natural resources which would otherwise hardly be utilised. The labour requirements are low (the labour formerly required in transport now works on the oil fields or on trucks) and the potential is considerable. Very little research has been done on these aspects and perhaps now is the time to take it up. Fundamental research on physiology and on the anatomy of the reproductive tract is interesting and rewarding to the scientist involved. Improved production from research on feeding and management is equally so and is likely to benefit more people.

The camel population of the world is currently equivalent to only 1·6 per cent of the total biomass of cattle, buffalo, sheep, goats and camels. Nonetheless at the average levels of production for meat and milk given in Chapter 10 a sustained offtake equivalent to 369 863 kg of meat and to more than 20 million litres of milk per day is being achieved. These far from negligible amounts can form a base for improved and improving output.

Glossary

adaptation In evolutionary terms, a characteristic which improves the chance of survival in a given environment. In physiological terms a change in an organism as a result of exposure to environmental conditions resulting in its reacting more effectively to those conditions. Thus, adaptive cooling.

adductor Muscle used in bringing one part of the body towards or in contact with another part.

albedo A measure of reflectivity.

alveolus Normally a cavity in the jaw bone into which a tooth fits.

analagous Similar or resembling. When referring to organs, meaning to have the same function but of different origin. Compare **homologous**.

antidiuretic hormone A hormone secreted from the pituitary which stimulates water reabsorption by the kidney and diminishes the flow of urine. Also known as vasopressin.

aponeurotic Not containing nervous tissue.

artefact A man-made object, e.g. the pottery and stone implements found at archaeological sites.

articulated Attached by means of a movable joint.

autovaccine Shortened form of 'autogenous vaccine'. A vaccine from the specific sub-culture of the animal or group of animals to be vaccinated and not from a stock or general culture.

benign Not malign. Usually mild in nature and not causing death.

biomass The weight of all animals occupying a given area. We have limited the term in this book to domestic herbivores but it can be applied to all forms of life including plants.

biotic factors Influences arising from activities of living organisms. In the specific case of the camel on its southern African limit this includes human cultural resistance and disease-causing organisms.

browse Vegetation such as the leaves or small branches of trees. Not commonly eaten and does not normally form a large part of the diet of the usual domestic animals except camels and goats. The act of eating such vegetation.

buccal Of the mouth. The buccal cavity is lined with a derivative of the ectoderm.

carrying capacity The ability of an area of land to support a given number of animals or a certain amount of herbivore biomass on a sustained basis. (That no ecological degradation takes place is usually implied in this definition – see **stocking rate**).

cirrhosis Yellow matter secreted as a result of disease; most often associated with the liver and other internal organs.

coccygeal Pertaining to the tail.

collagen Fibrous protein. Collagen fibres have high tensile strength (as in tendons) but little reversible extensibility (see **elastin**).

contagious Spreading by contact.

corpus luteum (plural **corpora lutea**) The yellow body, unlike in most other mammals, develops in camels only after fertilisation. Formation normally occurs as a result of secretion of luteinising hormone. See also **Graafian follicle**.

dermatitis Inflammation or disease of the skin.

dermis The innermost of the two layers of skin: it is much thicker than the **epidermis**.

diaphragm The sheet of tissue, composed of muscle and tendon, which separates the thoracic from the abdominal cavity.

digitigrade Walking on the ventral surface of the toes as opposed to **unguligrade**, walking on the tips of the toes only.

elastin Fibrous protein, highly extensible and elastic.

epidermis The outer of the two layers of skin.

extensor Muscle which extends or straightens a part of the body (see **flexor**).

evaginate To turn inside out; to unsheath. Refers to the appearance of the soft palate during rut in male camels.

F_1 or first filial generation The offspring resulting from crossing two species or two different types of animals (or plants). Generally exhibit strong hybrid vigour (see **heterosis**).

feral Reverted to the wild state. Domestic animals escaped from captivity and living wild.

figurine A small statue of baked clay, wood or metal. Often of significance in archaeological work, in conjunction with **artefacts**, in establishing periods of occupation and cultures.

flexor Muscle used to bend a part of the body (see **extensor**).

follicular wave The recurring cycle of events associated with female sexual activity in animals, such as the camel, in which the stimulus of copulation is required for luteinising hormone to be released. See also **oestrus**.

ganglia (singular **ganglion**) Small solid masses of nervous tissue. In vertebrates the ganglia occur in the peripheral nervous system.

gestation The period during which the foetus grows in the uterus.

globidiosis The disease caused by the protozoan parasite *Globidia* spp. which is characterised by dermatitis.

glomerular filtration rate The rate of flow of urine (water and dissolved substances) through the glomerulus of the kidney. The glomerulus is a mass of capillaries in the kidney.

Graafian follicle A spherical vesicle in the ovary containing an oocyte. After growth and rupture it becomes the **corpus luteum**; in the camel this occurs only after impregnation, unlike in most other domestic animals.

heterosis Increased vigour (of growth, fertility, production) in a cross between genetically different lines when compared with the same characters in either parental line.

homologous Of similar origin, structure and/or position.

inappetance Lack of appetite.

intercostal Between the ribs.

isotonic Of a solution that neither gains nor loses water by osmosis when separated by a semi-permeable membrane from another solution.

lobulated Divided into a number of small lobes.

lumbar Of the region of the waist. The lumbar vertebrae are between those of the chest or **thoracic** vertebrae and those of the hip or **sacral** region.

luteinising hormone Secreted by the anterior lobe of the pituitary and normally initiates formation of the **corpus luteum** towards the end of the oestrus cycle. In camels produced only after copulation.

mean population weight (MPW) The average weight of animals in a herd calculated from the weight of animals of a specific age group and the percentage contribution of that age group to the total number of animals.

meatus A passage.

meninges Membranes which cover the central nervous system.

mesenteric Relating to the mesentery, a double layer of peritoneum attaching the soft abdominal parts to the peritoneal cavity.

metabolic rate The rate of energy expenditure of an animal at rest. Normally expressed per unit weight as the output in kilojoules per square metre of body surface per unit of time (kJ/per m^2 kg s). Q_{10} is the temperature coefficient and is the increase in rate of a process (in this case metabolic rate) for an increase in temperature of $10°C$: for biological processes it is usually of the order of 2.

morphology The external or visible shape or form.

motility Movement. Particularly in the case of spermatozoa, the speed and amount of activity.

mucosa Mucous membrane: a name applied to moist epithelium which usually secretes mucus. A term applied particularly to the gut lining or to the linings of the genital and urinary systems.

necrosis Death.

neural Concerned with the nervous system. The neural spines (which project from the neural arch through which the spinal cord runs) serve as muscle attachments along the vertebrae of the spinal column.

niche The place occupied by an animal in an ecosystem. Camels are high-level browsers, as opposed to goats which are low-level browsers and cattle and sheep which are mainly grazers.

oedema Swelling of tissue by increase of its fluid content, mainly intercellular fluid.

oestrus The recurrent period of receptivity to males by females, resulting from the regular series of hormonal events known as the oestrus cycle.

oocysts A phase in the life cycle of protozoan parasites.

papules Small fleshy swellings often associated with particular diseases. Usually dry.

pathogen, pathogenic A disease-producing organism, or one capable of producing disease.

phagocytosis The process by which cells (phagocytes) engulf particles from their surroundings. An important defence mechanism against bacterial invasion.

prehensile Adapted to seizing or grasping.

prophylactic A medicine used in the prevention, rather than in the cure, of disease.

pustule A swelling containing pus.

pyogenic Pus forming: bacteria implicated in the formation of an abcess.

Q₁₀ See **metabolic rate.**

sacral See **lumbar.**

salivation The process of secretion of fluid from salivary glands: this is a reflex response to the presence of food in the mouth.

serum A clear liquid which separates from the blood on clotting.

sphincter A ring of smooth muscle in the wall of a cylindrical organ which, by its contraction, closes or narrows the opening.

spirochaete A micro-organism which is spiral in morphology.

sternum The breast bone. Sternal ribs are attached to this as well as to the spinal column. Asternal ribs are attached only to the spine.

stocking rate The number of hectares per unit of animal biomass, however this latter may be expressed. May be, and now often considered to be, considerably in excess of **carrying capacity.**

sympatric Occurring together geographically. Used of species whose ranges overlap.

syndrome A complex of symptoms occurring together. A clinical condition due to several concurrent and probably additive causes.

taxonomic Relating to taxonomy or the classification of organisms according to their similarities and differences.

temporal fossae Depressions lying on either side of the central line of the head.

thoracic See **lumbar.**

transhumance Seasonal movements of animals and people in search of grazing and/or water but, as opposed to nomadism, always returning to a fixed base or a recognised home area. Originally applied to the seasonal movements to and from summer grazing in the European Alps.

vesicles Small bladders or cavities, e.g. the seminal vesicles which store sperm in male animals.

zoonosis (plural **zoonoses**) Disease of animals capable of being transmitted to man.

Bibliography

Abdalla, A. B. (1979). Structure of the secretory cells of the salivary glands of the dromedary camel. *Sudan J. Vet. Sci. Anim. Husb.* **20**, 65–76.

Abdalla, M. A. (1973). *Anatomical study of the urinary system of the camel (Camelus dromedarius).* M.V.Sc. Dissertation. Khartoum University.

Abdalla, M. A. and Abdalla, O. (1979). Morphometric observations on the kidney of the camel *Camelus dromedarius. J. Anat*, **129**, 45–50.

Abdalla, O. (1960). *Anatomical study of the female genital system of Camelus dromedarius with special reference to the histology of its mucous membranes.* M.V.Sc. Dissertation. Khartoum University.

Abdalla, O. (1965). Anatomical study of the female genital system of the one-humped camel. 1. Ovaries. *Sudan J. Vet. Sci. Anim. Husb.* **6**, 41–52.

Abdalla, O. (1967). Anatomical study of the female genital system of the one-humped camel. 2. The oviducts. *Sudan J. Vet. Sci. Anim. Husb.* **8**, 67–77.

Abdalla, O. (1968). Anatomical study of the female genital system of the one-humped camel. 3. The uterus and placenta. *Sudan J. Vet. Sci. Anim. Husb.* **9**, 477–500.

Abdalla, O., Fahmy, M. F. A. and Arnautovic, I. (1970). Anatomical study of the lacrymal apparatus of the one-humped camel. *Acta Anat.* **75**, 638–650.

Abdalla, O., Arnautovic, I. and Fahmy, M. F. A. (1971). Anatomical study of the liver of the camel. I. Topography and morphology. *Acta Morph. Neerlando-Scandinavica.* **9**, 85–100.

Abdel Aziz, M. A. (1970). *The incidence of TB in camels and pigs and typing of the isolated organisms.* M.D. Thesis. Cairo University.

Abdel Aziz Neumani-Bey (1911). *The comparative osteology of the camel.* Cairo.

Abdel-Ghaffar, M. (1960). El-Dabab: a new indicator for its detection. *Proc. 1st. Ann. Vet. Congr., Cairo.* 107–313.

Abdelhamid, B. (1973). *Les convolutes cerebrales du dromadaire.* Thèse DMV. ENV: Lyon.

Abdel-Latif, R. (1958). The incidence of diseases caused by inter-corpuscular blood parasites in camels in Egypt. *Vet. Med. J., Giza* **4**, 43–54.

Abdel-Latif, R. (1959). *Vet. Med. J., Giza.* **5**, 123–137.

Abdel Magid, A. M. and Abdel Razag, A. I. (1975). Relationship and possible function of the nasal sacs and glands of the one-humped camel *Camelus dromedarius. Acta Anat.* **91**, 423–428.

Abdel-Raouf, M. (1965). Studies on reproduction in camels (*Camelus dromedarius*). III. Testicular hypoplasia. *Proc. 6th Annual Vet. Congr., Cairo.* 125–130.

Abdel-Raouf, M. and El-Naggar, M. A. (1964). Studies on reproduction in camels (*Camelus dromedarius*). I. Mating techniques and collection of semen. *J. Vet. Sci. UAR.* **1**, 113–119.

Abdel-Raouf, M. and El-Naggar, M. A. (1965). Studies on reproduction in camels (*Camelus dromedarius*). II. The morphology of the camel spermatozoon. *J. Vet. Sci. UAR.* **2**, 1–11.

Abdel-Raouf, M. and Owaida, M. M. (1974). Studies on reproduction in camels (*Camelus dromedarius*). IV. Gross changes in the morphology of the testis in relation to age and season. *Assiut Vet. Med. J.* **1**, 213–223.

Abdel-Raouf, M., El-Bab, M. R. F. and Owaida, M. M. (1975). Studies on reproduction in camels (*Camelus dromedarius*). V. Morphology of the testis in relation to age and season. *J. Reprod. Fert.* **43**, 109–116.

Abdel-Raziq, M. T. and Yagi, A. I. (1975). The Tabanidae of 'Rahad Turda' in Eastern Kordofan Province, Sudan. *Rev. Zool. Afr.* **89**, 117–123.

Abdel-Wahab, M. F. and Hassan, Y. M. (1967). Vitamin determination in dairy products in the Sudan. I. Vitamin C in milk. *Sudan J. Vet. Sci. Anim. Husb.* **8**, 108–114.

Abdel-Wahab, M. F. and Osman, A. M. (1971). Iodine metabolism in domestic animals in the Sudan using I^{131}. *Endokrinologie.* **58**, 198–208.

Abdel-Wahab, M. F., Abdo, M. S., Megahed, Y. M. and El Mougy, S. A. (1974). Thyroxine content in the thyroid gland of domestic animals. Part VII. Iodinated tyrosines and tyronines in the serum of she-camel at various reproductive stages. *Endokrinologie.* **63**, 116–121.

Abdo, M. S., Al-Gawabi, A. S. and Al-Kafawi, A. A. (1969a). Studies on the ovaries of the female camel during the reproductive cycle and in conditions affected with cysts. *Cornell Vet.* **59**, 418–425.

Abdo, M. S., Al-Kafawi, A. A. and Al-Gawabi, A. S. (1969b). Thyroid function of the she-camel during the various phases of the reproductive cycle and in cases of cystic ovaries. *Vet. Med. J., Giza.* **16**, 183–190.

Abdo, M. S., Farahat, A. A. and Fahmy, F. A. (1974). Further studies on prostaglandins. I. Effect of crude prostaglandins extracted from prostate glands of camels (*Camelus dromedarius*) on the endocrine glands of immature male and female rats. *Biol. Zentralbl.* **93**, 697–705.

Abdou, A. H. (1965). Incidence and public health importance of hydatidosis in the Middle East with special reference to UAR. *J. Vet. Sci. UAR.* **2**, 125–134.

Abdou, M. S. S., El Wishy, A. B., Abdo, M. S. and Elsawaf, S. A. (1971). Hormonal activities of the placenta of the one-humped camel *Camelus dromedarius.* Part I. Gonatrophic, adrenocortitrophic and thyrotrophic hormones. *J. Anim. Morph. Physiol.* **18**, 11–16.

Abdulrahman, M. (1973). The socio-cultural problems of settling camel nomads in South Jordan (the El Jafr region) (in German). *Informationsdienstkartei (AGLBO) Bonn.* D-74-02592.

Abdunazarov, N. Kh. (1970). Biological characteristics of reproduction in the one-humped camel (in Russian). *Trudy Turkmen Sel'-khz Inst.* **15**, 134–141.

Abdunazarov, N. Kh. (1971). Calving season and parturition in Turkmen dromedaries (in Russian). *Trudy Turkmen Sel'-khz Inst.* **16(3)**, 29–37.

Abdussalam, M. and Raouf, A. (1957). Coccidia of camels. *Proc. 9th Pakistan Sci. Conf., Peshawar.* Part III: 125–126.

Abul-Hab, J. and Al-S'adi, H. (1973). Seasonal occurrence of *Hypoderma* spp. (Diptera, Oestridae) warble flies on cattle in Baghdad area, Iraq. *Bull. End. Dis.* **14**, 73–81.

Abul-Hab, J. and Al-Affass, N. N. (1977). Seasonal occurrence of the domestic camel bot fly *Cephalopina titillator*, Diptera, Oestridae in Central Iraq. *Bull. Biol. Res. Cent. (Baghdad).* **8**, 97–104.

Abu-Yaman, I. K. (1978). Insects and other pests affecting man and animals in Saudi Arabia. *Ang e wandte Parasitologia.* **19**, 31–33.

Ackerman, K. (1898). *Cross-breeding of animals. Volume II. The Vertebrates.* Weber und Weidemeyer: Kassal.

Acland, P. B. E. (1932). Notes on the camel in eastern Sudan. *Sudan Notes Rec.* **15**, 119–149.

Adam, J. G. (1966). Composition chimique de quelques herbes mauritaniennes pour dromadaires. *J. Agric. Trop. Bot. Appl.* **13**, 337–342.

Adam, S. E. I., Obeid, H. M., Ashour, N. and Tartour, G. (1974). Serum enzyme activities and haemotology of normal and diseased ruminants in the Sudan. *Acta Vet. Brno.* **43**, 225–231.

Adam, W. (1832). On the osteological symmetry of the camel (refers to Bactrian). *Trans. Linn. Soc.*

Adamsons, K., Engel, S. L., Dyke, H. B. van, Schmidt-Nielsen, B and Schmidt-Nielsen, K. (1956). The distribution of oxytocin and vasopression (antidiuretic hormone) in the neurohypophysis of the camel. *Endocrinology.* **58**, 272–278.

Addo, P. B. (1980). A serological survey for evidence of Q Fever in camels in Nigeria. *British Vet. J.* **136(5)**, 519.

Afifi, M. A. (1972). Comparative studies on the digestibility of beef, buffalo, camel and mutton fats for chicks. *British J. Nutr.* **27**, 97-100.

Afifi, A., Kraft, W. and Arif, H. (1979). Values of R-T_3, T_4, total T_3 and cholesterol of some farm animals in Egypt. *Indian Vet. J.* **56**, 16-18.

Afram, M. S. and Saleh, S. M. (1977). The slide agglutination test for the diagnosis of filariasis in camels. *Trop. Anim. Hlth Prod.* **9**, 241-244,

Afshar, A. (1978). Camels at Persepolis. *Antiquity.* **52**, 223-231.

Afshar, A., Nazarian, J. and Baghban-Baseer, B. (1971). A survey of the incidence of hydatid cyst in camels in South Iran. *British Vet. J.* **127**, 544-546.

Afshar, A. and Kayvanfar, H. (1974). Occurrence of precipitating antibodies to blue-tongue virus in sera of farm animals in Iran. *Vet. Rec.* **94**, 233-235.

Agius, M. L. (1951). Le Sahara: la vie au desert. *J. Inst. Afr. N.* **4**, 109-110.

Ahmed, A. A., Awad, Y. L. and Fahmy, F. (1977). Studies on some minor constituents of camel's milk. *Vet. Med. J., Giza.* **25**, 51-56.

Ahmed, K. Z. S. (1979). *Some anatomical studies of the trigeminal nerve of the one-humped camel.* Fac. Vet. Med. Zagazig University, Egypt.

Ahmedaly, M., Soliman, K. Z. and Moustafa, M. S. E. (1980). Some anatomical studies of the trigerminal nerve (N Trigerminus) of the one-humped camel (*Camelus dromedarius*) in Egypt. *Zentralbl. Vet. Med.* **9**, 176.

Akhtar, S. A. (1937). *Chabertia rishati* n.sp. A new nematode parasite of camels. *Proc. Indian Acad. Sci., Sect. B.* **5**, 45-47.

Al-Abassy, S. N., Altaif, K. I., Jawad, A. K. and Al-Saqur, I. M. (1980). The prevalence of hydatid cysts in slaughtered animals in Iraq. *Ann. Trop. Med. Parasit.* **74**, 185-188.

Al-Aubaidi, J. M., Ern, H. and Al-Shammary, J. (1978). Recovery and identification of *Acholeplasma oculi* from camels. *Zentralbl. Bakt. Parasit. Infekt. Hyg.* **241A**, 260-261.

Al-Baghdadi, F. A. K. (1964). The thyroid gland of the camel. *Nord. Vet. Med.* **16**, 1004-1012.

Al-Baghdadi, F. A. K. (1966). The tongue of the camel (*Camelus dromedarius* and *Camelus bactrianus*). *Nord. Vet. Med.* **18**, 337-346.

Al-Baghdadi, F. A. K. (1969). The adrenal gland of the camel (*Camelus dromedarius*). *Zentralbl. Vet. Med.* **16A**, 354-364.

Albright, W. F. (1942). *Archaeology and the religion of Israel.* John Hopkins Press: Baltimore.

Albright, W. F. (1950). The origins of the camel. *Zeutschr. für die alttestamentliche Wissensch.*: Berlin. **CXII** 315.

Albright, W. F. (1961). *The archaeology of Palestine.* Penguin Books: Baltimore.

Al-Delaimy, K. S. and Barakat, M. M. F. (1971). Antimicrobial and preservation activity of garlic on fresh ground camel meat. I. Effect of fresh ground garlic segments. *J. Sci. Food Agr.* **22**, 96-98.

Ali, H. A., Moniem, K. A. and Tingari, M. D. (1976). Some histochemical studies on the prostate, urethral and bulbo-urethral glands of the one-humped camel (*Camelus dromedarius*). *Histochem. J.* **8**, 565-578.

Ali, H. A. Tingari, M. D. and Moniem, K. A. (1978). On the morphology of the accessory male glands and histochemistry of the *ampulla ductus deferentis* of the camel (*Camelus dromedarius*). *Anatomy.* **125**, 277-290.

Alim, K. A. (1976). The livestock and meat industry of Egypt. *Wld Rev. Anim. Prod.* **12(4)**, 59-68.

Alimen, M. H. and Chevaillon, J. (1959). Hadjret el Kteba: station rupestre cameline de la Saoura (Sahara nord-oriental). *Bull. Soc. Préhist.*, France. **56**, 441-447.

Alongi, G. and Balboni, A. (1935). Camel trypanosomiasis in Tripolitania (in Italian). *Clin. Vet.*, Milano. **58**, 110-131.

Altaif, K. I. (1974). Helminths in camels in Iraq. *Trop. Anim. Hlth Prod.* **6**, 55-57.

Altmann, D. (1975). *The most important diseases of old-world and new-world camels.* Diseases of Zoo Animals. Proc. XVII Intnl. Symp. 4-8 June 1975, Tunis. Akademie-Verlag: Berlin, GDR.

Alwan, A. S. (1968). Socio-economic issues of nomads' settlement in the Western Desert of the UAR. *Land Reform.* **1**, 28.

Alwar, V. S. and Achuthan, H. N. (1960). On a new species of whipworms *Trichuris raoi* from a camel. *Indian Vet. J.* **37**, 500-501.

Amand, W. B. (1974). Paratuberculosis in a dromedary camel. *American Assoc. Zoo. Vet. Ann. Proc.*, Atlanta, Georgia. 150-153.

Ambwani, V. R. and Jatkar, P. R. (1969). Sensitivity of *E. coli* and salmonellae isolated from camel (*Camelus dromedarius*) to various antibiotics. *Indian Vet. J.* **46**, 934-938.

Ambwani, V. R. and Jatkar, P. R. (1973). Salmonella infections of camel in Bikaner. *Indian Vet. J.* **50**, 100-102.

Anand, O. P. (1968). Saddle galls - camel. *J. Remount Vet. Corps.*, Hissar (India). **7**, 50-55.

Andersen, H. T. (1966). Desert, man and camel (in Norwegian). *Nord. Med.* **75**, 61-63.

Anderson, C. R. and Casals, J. (1973). Dhori virus, a new agent isolated from *Hyalomma dromedarii* in India. *Indian J. Med. Res.* **61**, 1416-1420.

Andreani, E., Prosperi, S., Arush, M. A. and Salim, A. (1978). Salmonella carriers among cattle, sheep, goats and dromedaries in the Somali Democratic Republic (in Italian). *Ann. Fac. Med. Vet., Pisa.* **31**, 65-72.

Andrée, J. (1928). *Tuberculosis in camels (in German).* Dissertation. Hanover.

Angelotti, S. (1947). *Cystercercus dromedarius* in camels (in Italian). *Bull. Soc. Ital. Med. Ig. Trop.*, Eritrea. **7**, 544-549.

Angrisani, V. (1962). Human tuberculosis due to consumption of cow and camel milk in Somalia (in Italian). *Arch. Ital. Sci. Med. Trop. Parasit.* **43**, 205-210.

Anon. Epizootic intestinal strongylosis (in Italian). *Arch. Ital. Sci. Med. Colon.* **10**, 145.

Anon. (1934). A short history of surra treatment in the Punjab. *Indian J. Vet. Sci.* **4**, 232-241.

Antonius, O. (1951). On mammalian inter-specific hybrids (in German). *Verh. Zool. Bot. Ges.*, Wien. **92**, 106-115.

Appanna, T. C. and Vyas, C. R. (1969). Effect of dietary camel milk protein on urinary creatinine excretion of rats. *J. Nutr. Diet.*, India. **6**, 105-110.

Arbusov, P. N. (1940). Normal titre of camel serum in relation to brucellosis (in Russian). *Sovyet Vet.* **No. 5**, 47-48.

Archibald, R. G. (1910). Acid-fast baccilli in a camel's lung. *J. Comp. Path. Therap.* **23**, 56-57.

Archier, (Cne) (1953). Note sur les chameaux-jouets. *Bull. Liais. Sahar.* **15**, 19-38.

Arkell, A. J. (1961). *A history of the Sudan from earliest times to 1821.* University of London. The Athlone Press: London.

Arnautovic, I. and Abdalla, O. (1969). Elastic structures in the foot of the camel. *Acta Anat.* **72**, 411-428.

Arnautovic, I. and Abdalla, O. (1969). Unusual blind sac on the face of the one-humped camel. *Acta Anat.* **73**, 272-277.

Arnautovic, I., Abdalla, O. and Fahmy, M. F. A. (1970). Anatomical study of the vomeronasal organ and the nasopalatine duct of the one-humped camel. *Acta Anat.* **77**, 144-154.

Arnautovic, I., Abu Sineina, M. E. and Stanic, M. (1970). A study of induced dysfunction of the facial nerve in one-humped camels. *J. Anat.* **106**, 341-348.

Arnautovic, I., Fahmy, M. F. A. and Abdalla, O. (1972). Anatomical study of the liver of the camel. II. The course and distribution of the portal vein, hepatic artery and hepatic duct. *Acta Morph. Neerlando-Scandinavica*, **9**, 211-220.

Arnautovic, I. and Abdel Magid, A. M. (1974). Anatomy and mechanism of distention of the dulaa of the one-humped camel. *Acta Anat.* **88**, 115-124.

Arora, R. G. and Kalra, D. S. (1973). A note on isolation of *Klebsiella pneumoniae* and diplococci from cases of broncho-pneumonia in camels: *Indian J. Anim. Sci.* **43**, 1095-1096.

Arora, R. G., Kalra, D. S. and Gupta, R. K. P. (1973). Granuloma actinomyces in camel *Camelus dromedarius*. *Arch. Vet.* **10**, 49-52.

Arora, R. G., Kalra, D. S. and Kulshrestha, R. G. (1974). A note on focal lymphoid hyperplasia in the conjunctivae of a camel. *Indian J. Anim. Sci.* **44**, 594-595.

Arshadi, M. G. (1971). Le trypanosomiase en Iran (*T. evansi* du dromadaire). *Bull. Off. Int. Epiz.* **76**, 225-234.

Asad, T. (1964). Seasonal movements of the Kababish Arabs of Northern Kordofan. *Sudan Notes Rec.* **45**, 45-58.

Asad, T. (1970). *The Kababish Arabs: Power, authority and the lineage in a nomadic tribe.* C. Hurst & Co.: London.

Asadov, S. M. (1957). Analysis of the helminth fauna of the dromedary (*Camelus dromedarius* L.) in Azerbaidzhan (in Russian). *Dokl. Akad. Nauk Azerbaidzh.* SSR. **13**, 781-784.

Asadov, S. M., Kolesnichenko, M. L. and Zaidova, U. G. (1965). Helminth fauna of camels in Azerbaidzhan (in Russian). *Trudy Inst. Zool. Akad. Nauk Azerbaidzh.* SSR (Voprosy Parazit.). **24**, 35-42.

Asdell, S. A. (1946). *Patterns of mammalian reproduction.* Constable: London.

Aspock, H., Aspock, U. and Rausch, H. (1980). *Raphidia* (*?Dichrostigma*) *santuzza* n.sp. - a new camel neck fly from Calabria (Neuropteroidea: Raphidioptera: Raphidiidae) (in German). *Entomol. Zp.* **90**, 73-79.

Atabani, Y. I. (1966). Animal industry in the Sudan. *Sudan J. Vet. Sci. Anim. Husb.* **7**, 116-124.

Atai, P. (1978). Recherches anatomiques sur les poumons. Caractères generaux et differences morphologiques de la ramescence bronchique chez le chameau dromadaire (*Camelus dromedarius*) de l'Iran. *Rev. Med. Vét.* **129**, 791-796, 799-802.

Auby, J. C. (1970). *Mémento élémentaire de biologie et de pathologie du dromadaire d'Afrique du Nord.* Centre d'Instruction des Formations vétérinaires de l'Armée, Compiègne.

Aueljbekov, K. (1967). Camel breeding — a profitable field (in Russian). *Konevod. Konni Sport.* **5**, 6-8.

Auguadra, P. (1958). Influenza in camels (in Italian). *Arch. Ital. Sci. Med. Trop. Parasit.* **34**, 212-215.

Auguadra, P. (1963). Prophylaxis and therapy of trypanosomiasis in Somalia and in the Congo by using Antrycide, Naganol and Berenil (in Italian). *Clin. Vet.*, Milano. **86**, 467-474.

Australia (1973). *Animal Helminthology.* S. Australia Inst. Med. Vet. Sci.: Adelaide (34th Ann. Rep. Council July 1971-June, 1972).

Awad, F. I., Salem, A. A. and Fayed, A. A. (1976). Studies of clinical signs observed on experimentally infected animals with *Pasteurella multocida* type I. *Egyptian J. Vet. Sci.* **13**, 53-56.

Awad, F. I., Salem, A. A. and Fayed, A. A. (1976). Studies on the viability of *Pasteurella multocida* type I under simulated environmental conditions in Egypt. *Egyptian J. Vet. Sci.* **13**, 57-60.

Awad, Y. L. (1959). The icteric index in cows, buffaloes and camels in Egypt (in Flemish). *Vlaams Diergeneesk Tydschr.* **28**, 140-148.

Awad, Y. L. and Berschneider, F. (1977). Values for certain minerals and trace elements in some tissues of the camel (*Camelus dromedarius* L.). *Egyptian J. Vet. Sci.* **14**, 31-35.

Awad, Y. L. and Berschneider, F. (1977). Selenium content of internal organs of the camel (*Camelus dromedarius* L.). *Egyptian J. Vet. Sci.* **14**, 71-75.

Awkati, A. and Bagdadi, F. (1971). Lacrimal glands of the camel (*Camelus dromedarius*). *American. J. Vet. Res.* **32**, 505-510.

Awkati, A. J. and Al-Khatib, G. M. (1972). Trypanosomiasis in domestic animals of Iraq. *J. Egyptian Vet. Med. Assoc.* **32**, 203-206.

Ayoub, M. H., Awad, Y. L. and Bayyazeed, L. A. (1960). Chlorides in serum of Egyptian farm animals. *Indian J. Vet. Sci.* **30**, 34-37.

Ayyoub, M. H., Awad, Y. L. and Bayyazeed, L. A. (1960b). Calcium level in Egyptian farm animals. *Indian J. Vet. Sci.* **30**, 43-49.

Azab, E. A. Al and Musa, B. Early detection of pregnancy in the camel by using biological methods. *Zuchthygiene.* **11**, 166-168.

Azimov, Sh. A. and Zhakhidov, A. T. (1973). Trematode infections in camels a possible source of infection for cattle (in Russian). *Shornik Rabot Uzbekskoi Nauk-Issle Vet. Inst.* **21**, 11-12.

Badanine, N. V. (1933). Use of stomach tube on camels (in German). *Deutsche Tierarztl. Wschr.* **41**, 166.

Badanine, N. V. (1935). Experimental qualitative and quantitative census of parasitic worms of camel studied by method of total helminthological dissections. *Trudy Turkmen Sel'-khz Inst.* **1**, 3-13.

Badanine, N. V. (1938). *Sur la question d'helmintofauna du chameau en Turkmenie.* Livro Jubilar Prof. L. Travassos: Inst. Oswaldo Cruz, Rio de Janeiro.

Badawi, H. and El-Bab, M. R. F. (1974). Anatomical and histological studies on the nasal cavity of the camel (*Camelus dromedarius*). *Assiut Vet. Med. J.* **1**, 1-14.

Badawi, H. and El-Shaieb, M. (1975). Comparative anatomical studies on the *N. mandibularis* of caprine and *Camelus dromedarius* in Egypt. *Assiut Vet. Med. J.* **2**, 3-19.

Badawi, H., El-Shaieb, M. and Kenawy, A. (1975). The arterial blood supply of the brain of the camel (*Camelus dromedarius*). *Assiut Vet. Med. J.* **2**, 21-29.

Badawi, H., El-Shaieb, M. and Kenawy, A. (1977). The arteria maxillaris of the camel (*Camelus dromedarius*). *Anat. Histol. Embryologia.* **6**, 21-28.

Baghat Mostafa, A. M., Moustafa, I. H. and Soliman, M. K. (1968). Histochemical studies on keto-enol granules (KEG) in normal and infected camel liver with *Echinococcus granulosis* cysts. *Vet, Med. J., Giza.* **15**, 145-151.

Baimukanov, A. (1969). Milk production of camels (in Russian). *Vest. Sel'-khoz Nauk Alma-Ata.* **9**, 48-50.

Baimukanov, A. (1974). Machine milking of female camels (in Russian). *Proc. III All-Union Symp/Phys. Principles Machine Milking.* Borovsk, Sept. 1972. 67-84.

Balfour, A. (1911). *Microfilaria camelensis. Fourth Ann. Rep. Wellcome Trop. Res. Lab.*

Bali, M. K., Vashishta, M. S. Singh, R. P. and Gautam, O. P. (1978). Studies on the therapeutic effects of thiophanate in pica-infected camels. *Trop. Anim. Hlth Prod.* **10**, 61-62.

Balis, J. (1977). Note sur la toxicité de l'Isométamidium par injection intraveineuse chez quelques mamifères domestiques et spécialement chez le dromadaire. *Rev. Elev. Méd. Vét. Pays Trop.* **30**, 373-375.

Balis, J. and Richard, D. (1977). Action trypanocide du chlorhydrate de chloruxe d'Isométamidium sur *Trypanosoma evansi* et essai de traitement de la trypanosomiase du dromadaire. *Rev. Elev. Méd. Vét. Pays Trop.* **30**, 369-372.

Balis, J. and Richard, D. (1977). Action of the chlorhydrate of isometamidium chloride on *Trypanosoma evansi* and attempt at treating dromedary trypanosomiasis. *Ethiopian Vet. Bull.* **3**, 32-36.

Balsan, F. (1954). *A travers l'Arabie inconnue.* Amiot Dumont: Paris.

Banerjee, S., Bhattacharjee, R. C. and Singh, T. I. (1962). Hematological studies in the normal adult Indian camel (*Camelus dromedarius*). *American J. Physiol.* **203**, 1185-1187.

Banerjee, S. and Bhattacharjee, R. C. (1963). Distribution of body water in the camel (*Camelus dromedarius*). *American J. Physiol.* **204**, 1045-1047.

Banerjee, S. and Bhown, A. S. (1964). Studies on camel haemoglobin. *Biochem. Biophys. Acta.* **86**, 502-520.

Bansal, S. R., Gautam, O. P. and Gulati, R. L. (1969). Trials with Banminth against parasitic infestation in camels, sheep and goats. *J. Res. Punjab Agric. Univ.* **6**, 967-981.

Bansal, S. R., Gautam, O. P., Sarup, S. and Hibbs, J. W. (1971). Studies on pica in camels - some aspects of etiology, haematology, biochemistry and therapeutics. *J. Res. Haryana Agric Univ.* **1**, 82-89.

Bansal, S. R., Gautam, O. P. and Banerjee, D. P. (1979). Thiaben-dozole in gastro-intestinal nematodiasis. *J. Res. Haryana Agric. Univ.* 9, 181–183.

Barakat, A. A., Sayoub, E. and Fayed, A. A. (1976). Investigation of an outbreak of anthrax in camels in the Western Desert. *J. Egyptian Vet. Med. Assoc.* 36, 183–186.

Barakat, M. Z. and Abdel-Fattah, M. (1970). Biochemical analysis of normal camel blood. *Zentralbl. Vet. Med.* 17A, 550–557.

Barakat, M. Z. and Abdel-Fattah, M. (1971). Seasonal and sexual varia-tions of certain constituents of normal camel blood. *Zentralbl. Vet. Med.* 18A, 174–178.

Barakat, M. Z., El Kirdassy, Z. H. M. and Hegazy, M. I. (1978). Biochemical analysis of camel spleen. *Vet. Med. J., Giza.* 26, 29–43.

Barbour, E. H. and Schultz, C. B. (1939). A new giant camel, *Gigan-tocamelus fricki*, gen. et sp.nov. *Bull. Univ. Nebraska State Mis.* 2, 17–27.

Barès, J. F. (1968). *Contribution à l'étude de la pathologie infectueuse du dromadaire au Tchad.* Thèse DMV. ENV: Toulouse. No. 65.

Barhat, N. K., Chowdhary, M. S. and Gupta, A. K. (1979). Note on relationship among gestation length, birth weight and intra-uterine development index in Bikaneri camel. *Indian J. Anim. Res.* 13, 115–117.

Barhat, N. K. and Chowdhary, M. S. (1980). Note on the inheritance of birth weight in Bikaneri camel (*Camelus dromedarius*). *Indian J. Anim. Sci.* 50, 665–666.

Barker, H. M. (1961). *Camels and the outback.* Angus & Robertson: London.

Barmintsev, Y. N. (1951). Rectal examination of reproductive organs of camel (in Russian). *Konevodstvo.* 21, 38–42.

Barnet, R. D. (1960). *Assyrian Palace Reliefs.* Batchworth: London.

Barone, R. and Belemlih, A. (1973). Le développement du dromadaire (*Camelus dromedarius* L.). *Anat. Histol. Embryologia.* 2, 301–315.

Barotte, J. (1925). Les trypanosomes de l'Afrique du Nord. *Mem. Soc. Sci. Nat. Maroc.* 11.

Barotte, J. and Velu, H. (1924). Contribution à l'étude du kystic hydati-que en Afrique du Nord. L'echinococcose au Maroc. *Bull. Soc. Path. Comp.* 266, 805–830, 857–882.

Barron, N. S. (1960). A note on camels. *Vet. Rec.* 72, 164–165.

Bartels, H., Hilpert, P., Barbey, K., Betke, K., Riegel, K., Lang, E. M. and Metcalfe, J. (1963). Respiratory function of blood of the yak, llama, camel, Dzboaski deer and African elephant. *American J. Physiol.* 205, 331–336.

Bartenbach, G. (1973). *Characteristics and classification of a camelpox virus.* Inaugural dissertation, Tierartzliche Facultat, München.

Bartha, V. R. (1971). The physiological adaptability of camels to the en-vironmental conditions of the vast arid zones (in German). *Der Tropenlandwirt.* 72, 138–148.

Barthe, M. L. (1905). La composition du lait de la chamelle. *J. Pharm. Chim.* 21, 386–388.

Barus, V., Amin, A., Blazek, K. and Moravek, F. (1976). Nematodes parasitizing domestic animals in Afghanistan. *Folia Parasit.* 23, 207–216.

Baskakov, V. P. (1924). Fauna of parasitic worms of Turkestan camels. *Tra. Gosudarst. Inst. Expt. Vet.* 2, 102–103.

Bassal, T. T. M. (1974). Biochemical and physiological studies of certain ticks (Ixodoidea). Activity of juvenile hormone analogs during embryo-genesis in *Hyalomma* (H) *dromedarii* Koch (Ixodidae). *Zeit. Parasit.* 45, 85–89.

Basset, R. (1905). Le nom du chameau chez les berbères. *Actes Congrès Orientalistes XIV, Alger.* 69–80.

Batelli, C. (1949). Il *C. dromedarii* Pellagrini 1945 in Eritrea (in Italian). *Bull. Soc. Ital. Med. Ig. Trop.,* Eritrea. 9, 289–294.

Bauer, C., Rollema, H. S., Till, H. W. and Braunitzer, G. (1980). Phosphate binding by llama and camel haemoglobin. *J. Comp. Physiol. Deu.* 136, 67–70.

Baxby, D. (1972). Smallpox virus from camels in Iran. *Lancet.* 1063.

Baxby, D. (1974). Differentiation of smallpox and camelpox viruses in cultures of human and monkey cells. *J. Hyg*: London. 72, 751.

Baxby, D., Ramyer, H., Hessami, M. and Ghaboosi, B. (1975). Response of camels to intradermal inoculation with smallpox and camelpox viruses. *Infect. Imm.* 11, 617–621

Baylis, H. A. (1932). Three notes on parasitic nematodes. *Ann. Mag. Nat. Hist.* 10, 497–502.

Baylis, H. A. (1936). *The Fauna of British India. Nematodes I. Ascaroidea and Strongyloidea.* Taylor and Francis: London.

Baylis, H. A. and Daubney, R. (1923). A further report on parasitic nematodes in the collection of the zoological survey of India. *Rec. Indian Mus.,* Calcutta. 25, 551–578.

Bazanova, N. V., Stepankina, M. K. and Skaja, M. F. (1953). A method of study of the activity of the digestive tube in the dromedary (in Russian). *Physiol. Zh. SSR.* 39, 632–633.

Bazanova, N. V. and Tachenov, K. T. (1959). Secretory activity of the parotid gland in a water-deprived camel (in Russian). *Trudy Alma-atinshogo Zoovet.* 11, 405–420.

Beccaloni, G. (1980). *Camels – a literature search by subject order.* In *Workshop on Camels,* Khartoum, Sudan, 18–20 Dec. 1979. Intnl. Foundation for Science, Stockholm, Sweden. 472–486.

Beebe, W. (1940). Camels and men. Domesticated for thousands of years, the dromedary and Bactrian still complain of the burdens they must carry. *Bull. New York Zool. Soc.* 48, 117–126.

Béjot, (Lt.) *Therapeutique arabe des maladies du chameau.* Unpub. Rep. Gouv. Gen. Algerie.

Béjot (Lt.). (1925). Le Méhari. *Rev. Vēt. Milit.* 77, 619–627.

Belemlih, A. H. (1973). *Le plissement cérébral du dromadaire.* Thèse DMV. ENV: Lyon. No. 34.

Belloni, G. G. (1960). *Roman money of the Republican period (in Italian).* Commune di Milano: Milano.

Belokobylenko, V. T. (1978). Principles for the selection of female camels for machine milking (in Russian). *Vest. Sel'-khz. Nauk Kazakhzh. SSR.* 11, 65–68.

Belokobylenko, V. T. and Cherepanova, V. P. (1974). Characteristics of machine milking of camels (in Russian). *Proc. III All-Union Symp. Phys. principles of machine milking, Borovsk*; Sept. 1972: Borovsk, USSR; VNIIFBPSZh. 68–69.

Ben Danou (1905). Note sur les Camelidés et leur laine. *Suppl. Bull. Off. Gouv. Gen. Algerie.*

Bendson, H. S. (1972). Camelpox and smallpox. *Lancet.* No. 7789, 1235.

Benhazera, M. (1908). *Six mois chez les Touareg d'Ahaggar.* Algers.

Bennett, S. C. J. (1927). Trypanosomiasis. *Ann. Rep. Vet. Dept. Sudan Govt.*

Bennett, S. C. J. (1929). The mercuric chloride test for trypanosomiasis in camels. *J. Comp. Path. Therap.* 42, 118–126.

Bennett, S. C. J. (1929). Camel trypanosomiasis in the Sudan. *Proc. Pan-African Agric. Vet. Conf.,* Pretoria.

Bennett, S. C. J. (1933). The control of camel trypanosomiasis. *J. Comp. Path. Therap.* 46, 67–77.

Bennett, S. C. J. (1934). Control of camel trypanosomiasis. *Ann. Rep. Sudan Vet. Service, 1933.*

Bennett, S. C. J. (1936). Camel trypanosomiasis control. *Ann. Rep. Sudan Vet. Service, 1935.*

Bennett, S. C. J. and Kenny, P. A. C. (1928). Mercuric chloride as a diagnostic agent for trypanosomiasis in camels. *J. Comp. Path. Therap.* 41, 341–353.

Bennett, S. C. J., John, E. R. and Hewison, J. W. (1948). *Animal Husbandry.* Ch. XXII in Tothill, J. D. (ed) *Agriculture in the Sudan.* Oxford University Press: London. 663–687.

Ben Osman, F. Considerations épidémiologiques sur l'hydatidose animale en Tunisie. *Arch. Inst. Pasteur,* Tunis. 42, 409–418.

Bent, J .T. (1900). *Southern Arabia.* Smith, Elder: London.

Berdyev, A. (1971). Parasitism of livestock by *Hyalomma asiaticum asiaticum* Schulze and Schlottke in Southern Turkmenia (in Russian). *Izvest. Akad. Nauk Turkmen SSR (Biol. Nauk).* No. 4, 79–82.

181

Berdyev, A. S. (1972). Present position of toxoplasmosis in Turkmenia (in Russian). *Izvest. Akad. Nauk Turkmen SSR (Biol. Nauk)*. No. 6, 46-51.

Berdyev, A. (1974). Observations on the ecology of *Hyalomma detritum* (Parasitiformes Ixodidae) in Turkmenia (in Russian). *Zoolog. Zh.* **53**, 551-556.

Berdyev, A. and Meledzhaeva, M. A. (1974). The fauna of Ixodid ticks of central Karakum (in Russian). *Izvest. Akad. Nauk Turkmen SSR (Biol. Nauk)*. No. 3, 34-37.

Berg, R., Taher el S. and Moustafa, M.S.el Din. (1968). Comparison of prenatal growth of some organs in the camel (*Camelus dromedarius*) and the Egyptian water buffalo (*Bos bubalus bubalis* L.). *Zentralbl. Vet. Med.* **15A**, 438-447.

Berg, R., Taher, el S. and Moustafa, M.S.el Din. (1969). Comparative studies on the prenatal growth of the brain, thymus, stomach and oesophagus in the camel (*Camelus dromedarius*) and the Egyptian water buffalo (*Bos bubalus bubalis* L.). *Zentralbl. Vet. Med.* **16A**, 659-663.

Bergeon, P. and Balis, J. (1974). Contribution à l'étude de la repartition des tiques en Ethiopie (enquête effectuée de 1965 à 1969). *Rev. Elev. Med. Vet. Pays Trop.* **27**, 285-299.

Bernard, F. (1956). Recherches sur la biologie du chameau. *Bull. Liais. Sahar.* **7**, 13-15.

Bernard, J. (1969). Quelques parasites nouveau ou non encore signalés en Tunisie. *Arch. Inst. Pasteur, Tunis.* **46**, 397-409.

Bernus, E. (1969). Maladies humaines et animales chez les Touaregs Sahéliens *J. Soc. Africanistes*. **39**, 111-137.

Bernus, E. (1974). *Les Illabakan (Niger). Une tribu touareg sahélienne et son aire de nomadisation*. ORSTOM: Paris.

Bernus, E. (1975). Jeu et élévage. Vocabulaire d'élévage utilisé dans un jeu de quadrillage par les Touaregs (Iullemmenden Kel Dinnik). *J. Agron. Trop. Bot. Appl.* **22**, 167-176.

Bernus, E. (1976). Vocabulaire relatif aux techniques d'adoption par les animaux en milieu Touareg (Niger). *C. R. Coll. Ethnosci.* 23-26 nov 1976. *Mus. Hist. Nat.*, Paris.

Berque, J. (1959). Nomades et nomadisme en zone aride. *Rev. Int. Sci. Sociales*. **11**, 501-517.

Bettini, T. M. (1940). Livestock raising in Migiurtinia (in Italian). *Agric. Colon. Ital.* **35**, 51-77.

Bettini, T. N. and Salerno, A. (1950). Paper presented by the Italian delegation to the Cairo International Congress for the discussion of problems relating to livestock production in tropical and sub-tropical regions (in Italian). FAO: Rome.

Bettini, T. N., Mohamed, A. A. and Dubal, A. I. (1980). Nutrition of the dromedary in Somalia. A tentative inventory of the vegetation (in Italian). *Riv. Agric. Subtrop. Trop.* **74**, 151-203.

Beveridge, I., Barker, I. K., Rickard, M. D. and Burton, J. D. (1974). Experimental infection of sheep with *Camelo-strongylus mentulatus* and associated gastritis. *Australian Vet. J.* **50**, 36-37.

Bezrukov, N. I. (1972). *Changes in the ovarian follicles of camels during their growth and maturation* (in Russian). In *Obshch. zakonomernosti morfogeneza i regeneratsii*: Alma-Ata, USSR. 164-168.

Bezrukov, N. I. (1976). The growth oocyte and follicle in Tylopoda (in Russian). *Arkh. Anat. Histol. Embriol.* **70**, 32-38.

Bezzi, A. (1930). The introduction of the camel to Libya (in Italian). *Clin. Vet.*, Milano.

Bhargava, A. K. (1973). Infection of soft palate in camels. *Indian Vet. J.* **50**, 1213-1214.

Bhargava, A. K., Mehrotra, P. N. and Banerjee, S. (1964). Biochemical studies on Indian camel (*Camelus dromedarius*) 5. Serum proteins and their variation with age, sex, pregnancy, rut and infection. *Indian J. Exp. Biol.* **2**, 52-54.

Bhargava, A. K. and Vyas, U. K. (1967). 'Chloral mag' anesthesia in the camel (*Camelus dromedarius*). *Vet. Rec.* **80**, 332.

Bhargava, A. K., Heath, R. B., Rudy, R. L. and Gabel, A. A. (1969).

Clinical trials of halothane anacin in a camel (*Camelus dromedarius*). *Indian Vet. J.* **46**, 999-1001.

Bhargava, K. K., Sharma, V. D. and Singh, M. (1963). A study of mortality rate, sex ratio and abortions in camel (*Camelus dromedarius*). *Indian J. Vet. Sci.* **33**, 187-188.

Bhargava, K. K., Sharma, V. D. and Singh, M. (1965). A study of birth weight and body measurements of camel. *Indian J. Vet. Sci.* **35**, 358-362.

Bhatia, Y. S., Misra, S. S., Lavania, J. P. and Angelo, S. J. (1978). Surgical management of bilateral mandibular fracture in camel. *Indian Vet. Med. J.* **2**, 85-87.

Bhatia, J. S., Goshal, A. K. and Vyas, U. K. (1971). Collection and examination of cerebrospinal fluid. (CSF) in camels suffering from kumri. *Indian Vet. J.* **48**, 796-798.

Bhatt, P. L. and Kohli, R. N. (1959). A preliminary study of camel's blood sedimentation rate. *Indian Vet. J.* **36**, 375-378.

Bhatt, P. L., Kohli, R. N. and Rathore, U.S. (1960). The normal body temperature, respiratory frequency and heart rate of the camel. *Indian Vet. J.* **37**, 456-462.

Bhatt, P. L. and Kohli, R. N. (1961). A study on the normal serum-albumin level of the camel. *Indian Vet. J.* **38**, 246-249.

Bhatt, P. L. and Kohli, R. N. (1962). Quantitative biochemical studies on camel's blood Part II. Inorganic phosphorus and sodium content. *Indian Vet. J.* **39**, 201-202.

Bhattacharjee, R. C. and Banerjee, S. (1962). Biochemical studies on Indian camel (*Camelus dromedarius*) 2. Inorganic constituents of serum. *J. Sci. Indust. Res.* **21C**, 106-107.

Bhattacharyulu, Y., Chaudhri, R. P. and Gill, B. S. (1975). Transstadial transmission of *Theileria annulata* through common Ixodid ticks infesting Indian cattle. *Parasitology*. **71**, 1-7.

Bhown, A. S. and Banerjee, S. (1963). Biochemical studies on Indian camel (*Camelus dromedarius*). 4. Camel haemoglobin. *Indian J. Exp. Biol.* **1**, 164-166.

Bhown, A. S. and Banerjee, S. (1972). Biochemical studies of Indian camel (*Camelus dromedarius*) haemoglobin: alkali resistance. *Indian J. Biochem. Biophys.* **9**, 214-215.

Bibby, G. (1970). *Looking for Dilmun*. Collins: London.

Biehler, B. (1959). Képis rouges et méharistes. *Rev. Corps. Vet. Armée.* **14**, 75-78.

Bilke, E. and Koppe, J. (1972). A visit to the Egyptian animal breeding stations (in German). *Umschau*. **27**, 230-231.

Blagovescenskii, V. (1963). Reserves in the production of milk and meat (in Russian). *Konevod. Konnyi Sport.* **33**, 8-9.

Blainville, H. M. de D. (1864). *Ostéographie des mammifères; 4ème vol*. Baillière: Paris.

Blaizot, C. (1976). *Etude des parasites gastro-intestinal du dromadaire dans la région de Diré-Dawa (Sud Est Ethiopie) at essais therapeutiques*. Thèse DMV. ENV: Alfort. No. 9.

Blanc, G., Bruneau, J., Martin, L. A. and Maurice, A. (1948). Quelques données nouvelles sur le virus de la Q fever marocaine. *C. R. Séances Acad. Sci.* **226**, 607-608.

Blanc, G., Martin, L. A. and Bruneau, J. (1949). Q fever expérimentale de quelques animaux domestique. *Ann. Inst. Pasteur, Maroc*. **77**, 99-107.

Blanc, G., Bruneau, J. and Chabaud, A. (1951). *Ann. Inst. Pasteur, Maroc*. **79**, 298-303.

Blanchard, R. (1901). *Bull. Acad. Med.* **20**.

Blaudin de Thé, B. (1955). *Historique des campagnes méharistes (1902-1952)*. Imp. Gouv.-Gen. Algerie: Alger.

Blenkinsop, L. J. and Rainey, J. W. (eds) (1925). *Veterinary Services*. In *History of the Great War based on Official Documents*. 625-626.

Bligh, J. and Harthoorn, A. M. (1965). Continuous radiotelemetric records of the deep body temperature of some unrestrained African mammals under near natural conditions. *J. Physiol.* **176**, 145-162.

Bligh, J., Cloudsley-Thompson, J. L. and MacDonald, A. G. (1976).

Environmental Physiology of Animals. Blackwell: Oxford.

Boas, J. E. V. (1890). On the morphology of the stomachs of the Camelidae and the Tragulidae and on their bearing on systematic position. *Morph. Jahrb*. **16**, 494 – 524.

Bodenheimer, F. S. (1953). *Problems of animal ecology and physiology in deserts*. Desert Research Special publ. Research Council of Israel & UNESCO: Jerusalem. **No. 2**.

Bodenheimer, F. S. (1954). *Problems of the physiology and ecology of desert animals*. In Cloudsley-Thompson, J. L. *Biology of Deserts*.

Bodenheimer, F. S. (1957). *The ecology of mammals in arid zones*. In *Ecologie Humaine et Animale*. Zone Aride, UNESCO: Paris.

Boev, S. N. (1959). Lung helminthosis of domestic ruminants in the USSR. *Proc. 16° Int. Vet. Cong*. **11**, 575 – 577.

Boev, S. N. and Orlov, N. P. (1958). Les maladies parasitaires des animaux d'élévage au Kazakhstan et les moyens permettant de les combattre. *Bull. Off. Int. Epiz*. **49 bis**, 187 – 205.

Boever, W. J. and Rush, D. M. (1975). *Microsporum gypseum* infection in a dromedary camel. *Vet. Med. Small Anim. Clin*. **70**, 1190 – 1192.

Bohlken, H. (1960). Remarks on the stomach and the systematic position of the Tylopods. *Proc. Zool. Soc. London*. **134**, 207 – 215.

Boid, R., Luckins, A. G., Rae, P. F., Gray, A. R., Mahmoud, M. M. and Malik, K. H. (1980). Serum immunoglobin levels and electrophoretic patterns of serum proteins in camels infected with *Trypanosoma evansi*. *Vet. Parasit*. **6**, 333 – 346.

Boid, R., Mahmoud, M. M. and Gray, A. R. (1980). Changes in the levels of some serum enzymes in dromedary camels infected with *Trypanosoma evansi*. *Res. Vet. Sci*.

Bokori, J. (1974). Contribution to the haemograms of the buffalo and of the camel. *Acta. Vet. Acad. Sci. Hungaricae*. **24**, 73 – 76.

Bokori, J. (1974). Haematology of dromedaries and buffaloes (in Hungarian). *Magyar Allartorvosok Lapja*. **29**, 418 – 419.

Boltz, C. L. (1955). The camel riddle answered. *Discovery*, London. **16**, 338.

Bondestan, L. (1975). The famine in Ethiopia and its causes (in Swedish). *Forum for utviklingsstudier*. **4 – 6**, 49 – 68.

Bonnet-Dupeyron, F. (1946). *Carte pour l'elevage et la transhumance au Sénégal et en Mauritanie*. ORSTOM: Paris.

Borgne (Capt. le) (1953). Vocabulaire technique du chameau en Mauritanie (dialecte hassanya). *Bull. IFAN*. **15**, 292 – 380.

Boris, G. (1951). *Documents linguistiques et ethnographiques sur une région du sud-tunisien (Nefzaoua)*. Adrien Maisonneuve: Paris.

Boris, G. (1951). *Le chameau chez les Marazig (Sud Tunisien). Notes lexicographiques, presentées par J. Quemeneu*. Publ. Inst. Belles Lettres Arabes; Tunis

Borisovich, Yu. F. (1973). *Camelpox*. In Orlov, F. M. (ed) *Little-known contagious diseases of animals*. Izdatel 'stvo Kolos, USSR 32 – 42.

Born, M. (1965). *Central Kordofan: Farmers and nomads in the savanna zone of the Sudan (in German)*. Marburg

Borovskii, V. A., (1972). Epizootiology of hydatid in the koyubinsk region. *Vest. Sel '-khoz. Nauk Alma-Ata* **11**, 56 – 58.

Borricand, P. (1948). La nomadisation en Mauritanie. *Trav, Inst. Rech. Sahar., Alger* **5**, 81 – 93

Bossi, (1901). *Research on the dentition and knowledge of age of Camelus dromedarius from the R. Mandria of S. Rossare* (in Italian). Tipografia Simoncini: Pisa.

Botros, B. A. M., Awad, A. Y., Kozman, A. R., Hildebrandt, P. K. and Maronpot, R. R. (1970). Hematologic, blood electrolyte and blood biochemical values of Egyptian domesticated animals. *J. Egyptian Med. Assoc*. **30**, 53 – 61.

Botros, B. A. M., Soliman, A. E. M., Kerkor, M. E. and Bucci, T. J. (1980). Investigation of El Gabal El Asfar camel farm. I. Parasitologic survey and hematologic values. *J. Egyptian Soc. Parasit*. **10**, 239 – 246.

Botting, D. (1958). *Island of the Dragon's Blood*. Wilfrid Funk: New York.

Boucheman, A. (1935). *Matériel de la vie bédouine – Syrie*. Docs. études orient.

Boué, A. (1945). Fibromatose du dromadaire. *Arch. Inst. Pasteur*; Alger.

Boué, A. (1946). Le Méhari Reguibi. *Rev. Vét. Milit*. **2**, 136 – 144.

Boué, A. (1946). Principales plantes et arbustes à chameau de la zone de nomadisation des Reguibat. *Rev. Vét. Milit*. **1**, 145 – 148.

Boué, A. (1947). Le pasteur di Sud algérien: esquisse psychologique. *Rev. Vét. Milit*. **2**, 250 – 255.

Boué, A. (1947). De quelques relativités dans les fractures costales chez le dromadaire de bât nord-africain. *Rev. Vét. Milit*. **2**, 348 – 353.

Boué, A. (1948). La masse sanguine chez le chameau. *Rev. Elev. Méd. Vét. Pays Trop*. **2**, 117.

Boué, A. (1948). Cicatrisation imparfaite de l'ouraque chez une chamelle. *Rev. Elev. Méd. Vét. Pays Trop*. **2**, 117.

Boué, A. (1948). La résistance des hématies à l'hémolyse chez le chameau. *Rev. Elev. Méd. Vet. Pays Trop*. **2**, 117 – 118.

Boué, A. (1948). Les chameaux de l'ouest saharien. *Rev. Elev. Méd. Vét. Pays Trop*. **2**, 193 – 201.

Boué, A. (1949). Essai de barymétrie chez la dromedaire Nord-africain. *Rev. Elev. Méd. Vét. Pays Trop*. **3**, 13 – 16.

Boué, A. (1949). Un cas de fibromatose cervicale diffuse chez le chameau. *Rev. Elev. Méd. Vét. Pays Trop*. **3**, 45 – 46.

Boué, A. (1949). Quelques anomalies dentaires chez le chameau. *Rev. Elev. Méd. Vét. Pays Trop*. **3**, 46 – 47.

Boué, A. (1949). Etude de la toxicité d'une composée saharienne, *Perralderia coronopifolia* Cosson, et ses variétés pour les animaux. *Arch. Inst. Pasteur, Alger* **27**, 322 – 333.

Boué, A. (1950). La remonte d'une unité méhariste: son caractère polymorpe, conditions d'une homogeneité moyenne. *Rev. Elev. Méd. Vét. Pays Trop*. **4**, 139 – 144.

Boué, A. (1951). Les chameaux de l'Ouest saharien. *Elev. Cult. Afrique Nord* **40**, 9 – 11.

Boué, A. (1951 – 52). L'originalité du chameau. *Rev. Elev. Méd. Vét. Pays Trop*. **5**, 109 – 114.

Boué, A. (1953). L'élévage au Sahara algérien. *Elev. Cult. Afrique française noire*. **60**

Boué, A. (1956). Le chameau dans l'économie tunisienne. *Elev. Cult. Afrique française noire*. **92**, 5 – 11.

Boué, A., Castagnez, H. and Daudel, (1962). L'initiation au dromadaire. *Service biologique et vétérinaire des armées*.

Bouin, A. R. (1921). Filariose et microfilariose des animaux domestiques dans le Sud marocain. *Bull. Soc. Cent. Méd. Vét*. **74**, 464 – 467.

Bouin, A. R. and Jazas, P. (1920). L'echinococcose dans la region de Marrakesh. *Bull. Soc. Cent. Méd. Vét*. **73**, 470 – 475.

Boulenger, C. L. (1921). On some nematode parasites of the camel in India. *Parasitology*. **12**, 311 – 314.

Boulanger, C. L. (1924). The filarid of the camel *Acanthocheilonema evansi* (Lewis). *Parasitology*. **16**, 419 – 423.

Bourlière, F. (1955). *Mammals of the World. Their Life and Habits*. Harrap: London

Bourounoff, Y. (1959). *Contribution a l'étude de la castration du chameau*. Thèse DMV. ENV: Alfort. **No. 45**.

Boustead, J. E. H. (1934) The Camel Corps of the Sudan Defence Force. *J. Royal Utd. Serv. Inst*. **1934**, 547 – 557.

Bouvier, C. (1976). *Etude des parasites gastro-intestinaux dromadaire dans la région de Diré-Dawa (Sud-est Ethiopie) et essais therapeutiques*. Thèse DMV. ENV: Alfort. **No. 9**.

Bovill, E. W. (1956). The camel and the Garamantes. *Antiquity*. **30**, 19 – 21.

Bowman, I. (1924). *Geog. Rev*. **14**

Bowman, J. C. (1977). *Animals for Man*. Studies in Biology No. 73 Edward Arnold: London.

Box, T. W. (1968). Range resources of Somalia. *J. Range Manag*. **21**, 388 – 392.

Box, T. W. (1971). Nomadism and land use in Somalia. *Econ. Dev. Cult Change*. **19**, 222–228.

Boyer, J. R. (1963). *Contribution à l'étude de l'élévage camelin au Sahara occidental. Le Reguiebat et son chameau.* Thèse DMV. ENV: Alfort. **No.3**.

Bozzi, L. and Triulzi, G. A. (1953). Observations on the domestic animals of Somalia (in Italian). *Riv. Agric. Subtrop. Trop.* **47**, 266–294.

Brahmi, C. (1973). *L'hydatidose humaine et animale en Tunisie.* Thèse DMV. ENV: Lyon. **No. 10**.

Braudel, F. (1972). *The Mediterranean and the Mediterranean World in the Age of Philip II.* Collins: London.

Braunitzer, G. (1980) Phosphate: haemoglobin interaction in relation to the human foetus, to adult humans and to llamas and dromedaries (in German). *Klin. Wschr. Deutsche.* **58**, 701–708.

Braunitzer, G., Schrank, B., Stangl, A. and Weisner, H. (1979). Breathing at high altitudes. Phosphate: Protein interaction and the sequence of the haemoglobins in the Guinea-pig and dromedary (in German). *Z. (Hoppe-Seyler's) Physiol. Chem.* **360**, 1941–1946.

Bremaud, O. (1969). *Notes sur l'élevage camelin dans les districts du nord de la République du Kenya.* IEMVT: Maisons Alfort.

Bremaud, O. and Pagot, J. (1962). *Pâturage, nomadisme et transhumance en zone sahélienne.* In *Problems of the Arid Zone* UNESCO: Paris.

Brentjes, B. (1960). *The camel in the ancient Orient* (in German). Klio **38**, 23–52.

Briouga, J. (1974). *Echinococcose-hydatidose au Maroc. Epidémiologie et prophylaxie.* Thèse DMV. ENV: Alfort. **No, 43**.

Brogan, O. (1954). The camel in Roman Tripolitania. *Pap. British School*; Rome (ns). **9**, 126–131.

Brogan, O. (1955). The fortified farms of Ghirza, Libya. *Illustrated London News.* Jan 22, 138–142, Jan 29, 182–185.

Brown, B. (1929). A Miocene camel bed-ground. *Nat. Hist. New York*. **29**, 658–662.

Brown, R. D. (1956). Demonstration by serological tests of the presence of Q fever in domestic animals in Kenya. *Bull. Epiz. Dis. Afr.* **4**, 115–119.

Browne, E. G. (1956). *A Literary History of Persia.* Cambridge University Press: Cambridge.

Brownlow, W. J. and Dedeaux, J. D. (1964). Leptospirosis in animals of upper Egypt. *American J. Trop. Med. Hyg.* **13**, 311–318.

Brumpt, (1909). Castration du chameau. *Comm. Soc. Cent. Méd. Vét.*

Bruner, D. W. and Moran, A. B. (1949). Salmonella infections of domestic animals. *Cornell Vet.* **39**, 53–63.

Buchholzer, J. *The Horn of Africa.* Angus & Robertson: London.

Buchnev, K. N. and Sadykov, R. G. (1967). *Contribution to the study of camelpox (relationship of the virus to vaccinia)* (in Russian). In *Aktual'nye voprosy veterinarnoi virusologii,* Tom 2 Moscow Vet. Acad.: Moscow; USSR. 152–153.

Buchnev, K. N. and Sadykov, R. G. (1969). On camelpox in Kazakhstan. *Nauchno-issledov. vet. Inst. Alma-Ata.* **15**, 12.

Buchwalder, R. (1962). Comparative studies on the camels *(Camelus dromedarius, Camelus bactrianus)* in the Berlin Zoo. *Arch. Expt. Veterinarmed.* **16**, 413–431.

Bulliet, R. W. (1969). Le chameau et la roue au Moyen Orient. *Annales: Econ. Soc. Civ.* **24**, 1092–1103.

Bulliet, R. W. (1975). *The Camel and the Wheel.* Harvard University Press: Cambridge, Mass.

Bump, J. D. (1933). A South Dakota camel *(Poëbrotherium).* *Black Hills Engineer*, Rapid City. **21**, 28–29.

Burchak-Abramovich, N. I. (1974). Domestic camels in the Mingechaur area of the Caucasus in ancient times. *Byull. Mosk. Obshch. Ispyt Prirody, Otdel Biol.* **78**, 127–138.

Burckhardt, J. L. (1830). *Notes on the Bedouins and Wahabys.* Henry Colburn & Richard Bentley: London.

Buren, E. D. van (1930). Clay figures of Babylonia and Assyria. *Yale Orient. Ser. Research.* **16**, 1–287.

Buren, E. D. van (1939). *The Fauna of Ancient Mesopotamia as represented in Art.* Pontificium Inst. Bib., Rome.

Burgemeister, R (1974). *Problems of keeping and breeding dromedaries in Southern Tunisia* (in German). Thesis. Justus Liebig Univ.: Geissen.

Burgemeister, R. (1975). *Elevage de Chameaux en Afrique du Nord.* Office Allemand de la Cooperation Techniques S.A.R.L.

Burgemeister, R. (1976). Distribution and use of dromedaries (in German). *Tropenlandwirt.* **77**, 43–53.

Burgemeister, R., Leyk, W. and Gossley, R. (1975). Studies on the occurrence of parasites and bacterial and viral infections in southern Tunisian dromedaries (in German). *Deutsche Tierartzl. Wschr.* **82**, 352–354.

Burgemeister, R., Leyk, W. and Gossler, R. (1976). Parasites and infectious diseases in dromedaries in southern Tunisia. *Anim. Res. Dev.* **4**, 110–117.

Canavan, W. P. (1929). Nematode parasites of vertebrates in the Philadelphia Zoological Gardens and Vicinity. *Parasitology.* **21**, 63–108.

Canavan, W. P. (1931). Nematode parasites of vertebrates in the Philadelphia Zoological Gardens and vicinity II. *Parasitology.* **23**, 196–228.

Cardaspe-Couchet, T. (1956). Le chameau dans l'armée d'autrefois. *Bull. Liais, Sahar.* **7**, 109–110.

Capot-Rey, R. (1942). Le nomadisme pastoral dans le Sahara français. *Trav. Inst. Rech. Sahar. Univ. Alger.* **1**.

Capot-Rey, R. (1949–53). *L'Afrique blanche française, Vol. II. Le Sahara français.* Presses universitaire de France: Paris.

Capot-Rey, R. (1959). Plaidoyer pour le chameau. *Gazette Soc. Nat. Pétroles, Aquitaine.* **1959**, 24–26.

Capot-Rey, R. (1962). *The present state of nomadism in the Sahara.* The Problems of the Arid Zone. UNESCO: Paris.

Capot-Rey, R. (1964). Les problèmes du nomadisme au Sahara. *Rev. Intern. Trav., Genève,* **90**, 531–546.

Caprun, A. A. (1935). Biology including descriptions of egg, larva, pupa and adult *Cephalopsis titillator* (in Russian). *Trudy vecsojuz. Inst. Sksp. Vet.* **11**, 136–151.

Carbuccia, J. L. (1853). *Du dromadaire comme bête de somme et comme animal de guerre.* J. Dumaine: Paris.

Carpano, M. (1932). *Bull. Sez. Ital. Sci. Int. Microbiol.* **1932**, 4108.

Carpano, M. (1937). A preliminary note on severe infections in camels caused by Corynebacteria. *Ann. Rep. Vet. Serv. Egypt, 1932–1933.* 138–140.

Carson, G. (1980). Jefferson Davis's Camel Corps. *Nat. Hist.*, New York. **30(5)**, 70–79.

Casati, R. (1957). Observations on a case of tuberculosis in a camel (in Italian). *Atti. Soc. Ital. Sci. Vet.* **11**, 551–554.

Caskel, W. (1954). *The Bedouinization of Arabia.* In Grunebaum, G. E. von (ed) Studies in Islamic History. *American Anthrop.* **56**.

Castagnera, H. (1957). Le chameau: manuel technique. *Manuel technique: Service Vet. des Troupes de l'AOF,* Dakar.

Castagnera, H. and Lebailly, J. (1959). Harnachement et materiel méharistes. *Rev. Corps Vet. Armée.* **14(2)**, 56–63.

Caton-Thompson, G. (1934). The camel in Dynastic Egypt. *Man,* London. **34(24)**, 21.

Caton-Thompson, G. (1944). The tombs and Moon Temple of Hureidha (Hadhramaut). *Rep. Res. Comm. Soc. Antiq.* London. **13**, 1–191.

Cauvet, G. (1920). Le dromadaire d'Afrique. *Bull. Soc. Geog.,* Alger. **1920**, 175–196.

Cauvet, G. (1925–26). *Le chameau (2 tomes)* Baillière: Paris.

Cauvet, G. (1929). Dromadaires à 34 dents et dromadaires à 36 dents. *Bull. Soc. Hist. Nat. Afrique Nord.* **20**, 247–256.

Cauvet, G. (1934). Le harnachement du méhari ou dromadaire de selle. *Erritala.* **3**.

Cauvet, G. (1937). Le dromadaire de l'Oued Itel. *Bull. Soc. Hist. Nat. Afrique Nord.* **28**, 513–525.

184

Cauvet, G. (1948). La rahla, selle du dromadaire d'Afrique. *Vert et Rouge, Rev. Légion Etrangère.* **4(18)**, 32.

Cazalbon, L. (1903). Note sur un trypanosome du dromadaire au Soudan, français. *Bull. Acad. Méd.* **49**, 807.

Cazalbon, L. (1906). Sur un embryon de filaire hépatique observé en Afrique occidentale. *Bull. Soc. Cent. Méd. Vét.* **60**, 596-597.

Centre des Hautes Etudes Musulmanes (1953). *L'économie pastorale sahélienne.* Centre des Hautes Etudes Musulmanes. Notes et Etudes Documentaires. **No. 1730**.

Cerenpuncag, S. (1969). Meat production in camels (in Russian). *Konevod. Konnyi Sport.* **10**, 34.

Cerenpuncag, S. and Davaa, R. (1967). Camel breeding in Mongolia (in Russian). *Mezhdunar Sel'-khoz. Zh.* **11**, 107-108.

Cervani, G. (1962). *Pasquale Revoltella's 'Journey in Egypt' (1860-1862)* (in Italian). ALUT: Trieste.

Cessnola, L. P. di. (1877). *Cyprus: its ancient cities, tombs and temples.* London.

Chahrasbi, H. and Radmehr, B. (1974). Studies on the anatomy and histology of rumen water sacs in the camel (*Camelus dromedarius*) in Iran. *J. Vet. Fac. Univ. Teheran.* **30(3)**, 14-25.

Chahrasbi, H. and Radmehr, B. (1974). Etudes anatomiques des differences morphologiques et facteurs specifiques de la circulation arterielle de la cervelle du dromadaire (races de la zone de Teheran). *Cah. Méd. Vét.* **43**, 106-109.

Chahrasbi, H. and Radmehr, B. (1975). Anatomical and histological structures of female genital system in camel in Iran (*Camelus dromedarius*). *Proc. 20th Wld. Vet. Cong.* Thessalonika, Greece, Summaries. **Vol. 1**, 41-42.

Chahrasbi, H. and Radmehr, B. (1975). Recherches anatomiques et histologiques sur le troisième réservoir gastrique chez le chameau dromadaire des races de l'Iran. *Cah. Méd. Vét.* **44**, 106-109.

Chahrasbi, H., Radmehr, B. and Goulbazhagh, F. (1975). Anatomy and histology of the reproductive organs of the Iranian camel (*Camelus dromedarius*). *J. Vet. Fac. Univ. Teheran.* **30(4)**, 42-50.

Chahrasbi, H. and Goulbazhagh, F. (1976). An anatomico-histological study of the accessory genital glands of the one-humped male camel (*Camelus dromedarius*) in Iran (in Persian with English summary). *J. Vet. Fac. Univ. Teheran.* **31**, 38-54.

Chand, K. and Singh, R. P. (1970). A study on the reliability of the mercuric chloride test in the diagnosis of surra amongst different species of domestic animals. *J. Res.*, Ludhiana. **7**, 108-110.

Chandler, A. C. (1930). Specific characters of the genus *Trichuris* with a description of a new species *Trichuris tenus* from a camel. *J. Parasit.* **16**, 198.

Chandrasekaran, K., Nair, K. P. D., Sundaram, R. K. and Peter, C. T. (1970). On the use of 'Thiabendazole' against *Trichostrongylus* and *Trichuris* infections in camel (*Camelus dromedarius*). *Kerala J. Vet. Sci.* **1**, 129-132.

Chandrasekaran, K., Nair, K. P. D., Sundaram, R. K. and Peter, C. T. (1971). Anthelmintic activity of parbendazole (Helmatac Premix) in camel (*Camelus dromedarius*) and Nilgiri Tahr (*Hemitragus hylocrius*). *Kerala J. Vet. Sci.* **2**, 135-138.

Chandrasekaran, K., Nair, K. P. D., Sundaram, R. K. and Peter, C. T. (1972). A note on a clinical trial with tetramisole (Nilverm) in camel (*Camelus dromedarius*) with Nilgiri Tahr (*Hemitragus hylocrius*) infected with gastro-intestinal helminths. *Kerala J. Vet. Sci.* **3**, 120-126.

Chandrasekaran, K., Nair, K. P. D., Sundaram, R. K. and Peter, C. T. (1973). Use of morantel tartrate (Banminth II) as an anthelmintic in zoo animals. *Kerala J. Vet. Sci.* **4**, 193-195.

Chandrasena, L. G., Emmanuel, B. and Gilanpour, H. (1979). A comparative study of glucose metabolism between the camel (*Camelus dromedarius*) and the sheep (*Ovis aries*). *Comp. Biochem. Physiol.* **62A**, 837-840.

Chandrasena, L. G., Emmanuel, B., Hamar, D. W. and Howard, B. R. (1979). A comparative study of ketone body metabolism between the camel (*Camelus dromedarius*) and the sheep (*Ovis aries*). *Comp.*

Biochem. Physiol. **64**, 109-112.

Chapelle, J. (1957). *Nomades noirs du Sahara.* Plon: Paris.

Charnot, Y. (1953). De l'evolution des camelides: apparition du dromadaire au Maroc. *Bull. Soc. Sci. Nat. Phys.*, Maroc. **33**, 207-230.

Charnot, Y. (1958). Reactions physiologiques du dromadaire à la privation d'eau. *C. R. Séances Soc. Sci. Nat. Phys.* Maroc. **24**, 177-178.

Charnot, Y. (1958). *Répercussion de la déshydratation sur la biochimie et l'endocrinologie du dromadaire.* Thèse. Univ. de Paris.

Charnot, Y. (1959). A propos de l'écologie des Camelides. *Bull. Soc. Sci. Nat. Phys.*, Maroc. **39**, 29-

Charnot, Y. (1960). Répercussion de la déshydratation sur la biochimie et l'endocrinologie du dromadaire. *Travaux de l'Institut scientifique Chérifien*, Rabat. **No. 20**.

Charnot, Y. (1961). Equilibre mineral tissulaire dans la déshydratation du dromadaire. *J. Physiol.*, Paris. **53**, 793-806.

Charnot, Y. (1963). Synchronisation de la croissance du voile du palais et des testicules pendant le cycle sexuel chez le dromadaire. *Bull. Soc. Sci. Nat. Phys.*, Maroc. **43**, 49-54.

Charnot, Y. (1963). Premiers observations sur les parathyroides du dromadaire. *Bull. Soc. Sci. Nat. Phys.*, Maroc. **43**, 281-284.

Charnot, Y. (1963). Cycle sexuel et déshydratation chez le dromadaire. *C. R. Séances Soc. Sci. Nat. Phys.* Maroc. **29**, 138-141.

Charnot, Y. (1963). Le développement du voile du palais selon l'état physiologique chez le dromadaire. *J. Physiol.*, Paris. **55**, 226-227.

Charnot, Y. (1964). Endocrinologie sexuelle chez le dromadaire mâle. *J. Physiol.*, Paris. **56**, 547.

Charnot, Y. (1964). Le cycle testiculaire du dromadaire. *Bull. Soc. Sci. Nat. Phys.*, Maroc. **44**, 37-45.

Charnot, Y. (1965). Endocrinologie sexuelle et déshydratation chez le dromadaire mâle. *C. R. Seances Soc. Biol.* **159**, 1103-1105.

Charnot, Y. (1967). Regulation endocrinienne du metabolisme de l'eau chez le dromadaire. *Bull. Soc. Sci. Nat. Phys.*, Maroc. **47**, 215-226.

Charnot, Y. and Racadot, J. (1963). Mise en évidence de catégories cellulaires distinctes dans le lobe antérieur de l'hypophyse du dromadaire. *Bull. Microsc. Appl.* **13**, 144.

Chatterjee, A., Chakraborty, P., Chattopadhyay, D. and Sengupta, D. N. (1978). Isolation of *Trichophyton schoenleinii* from a camel. *Indian J. Anim. Hlth.* **17**, 79-81.

Chatty, D. (1972). *Structural forces of pastoral nomadism with special reference to camel pastoral nomadism.* Inst. Soc. Stud., The Hague.

Chaumard, R. (1954). La lutte contre la trypanosomiase cameline (debab) dans l'Ouest saharien. *Ann. Inst. Agric. Serv. Rech.*, Alger.

Chaumard, R. (1955). La trypanosomiase cameline dans l'Quest saharien Bilan de quatre années de lutte (1950 à 1954). *Rev. Corps. Vet. Armée.* **10**, 1-90.

Chavanne, P. and Boué, A. (1950). Taux normaux de l'urée et du glucose sanguine chez le dromadaire nord-africain. *Rev. Elev. Méd. Vét. Pays Trop.* **4**, 183.

Cheikh Diak. (1963). *L'élevage en Mauritanie.* Thèse DVM. ENV: Alfort.

Chen, B. X. and Yuan, Z. X. (1980). *Reproductive pattern of the Bactrian camel.* In *Workshop on camels*, Khartoum, Sudan, 18-20 Dec. 1979. Intnl. Foundation for Science: Stockholm, Sweden. 251-270.

Chen, B. X. and Yuan, Z. X. (1980). *Pregnancy diagnosis by rectal examination.* In *Workshop on camels*, Khartoum, Sudan, 18-20 Dec. 1979. Intnl. Foundation for Science: Stockholm, Sweden. 271-278.

Chen, P. M., Kang, C. L., Yuen, Z. X. and Ge, Y. G. (Ko, Y. G.) (1980). Reproductive pattern of the Bactrian camel 2. Sexual behaviour (in Chinese). *Acta Vet. Zootech. Sinica.* **11**, 65-76.

Chevrier, L. (1959). Epidémiologie de la rage au Maroc. *Rev. Elev. Méd. Vét. Pays Trop.* **12**, 115-120.

Cheyne, I. A., Pegram, R. G. and Cartwright, C. F. (1977). An outbreak of salmonellosis in camels in north-east Somalia. *Trop. Anim. Hlth Prod.* **9**, 238-240.

Chichibabin, E. S. (1971). Brucellosis in camels. I. Comparison of serological tests (in Russian). *Trudy Kazakh Nauch. Vet. Inst.* **14**, 25-27.

Chichibabin, E. S. (1971). Brucellosis in camels. II. Agglutination test using heated serum (in Russian). *Trudy Kazakh Nauch. Vet. Inst.* **14**, 28-30.

Chineme, O. N. (1980). A case report of coccidiosis caused by *Eimeria cameli* in a camel (*Camelus dromedarius*) in Nigeria. *J. Wildl. Dis.* **16**, 377-380.

Chiodi, H. (1971). Comparative study of the blood gas transport in high altitude and sea level Camelidae and goats. *Resp. Physiol.* **11**, 84-93.

Choudhury, S., Balaya, S. and Mohaptra, L. N. (1971). Serological evidence of *Coxiella burnetii* function in domestic animals in Delhi and surrounding areas. *Indian J. Med. Res.* **59**, 1194-1202.

Clair, M. N. (1962). *De la résistance du chameau à la soif.* Thèse DMV. ENV: Alfort. **No. 9.**

Clairambault, S. (1938). Influence de la politique de l'eau et de la libre nomadisation sur la transhumance des Regueibat Sahel. *Bull. Serv. Zoot. Epizoot. AOF.* **4**, 55-57.

Clark, J. D. *The Prehistoric Cultures of the Horn of Africa.* Cambridge University Press: Cambridge.

Cleland, J. B. (1909). Diurnal variations in the temperature of camels. *Proc. Linn. Soc.* New South Wales. **34**, 268-271.

Clerget, M. (1934). *Le Caire: étude de géographie urbaine et d'histoire économique.* Paul Geuthner: Paris.

Clutton-Brock, J. (1962). *An analysis of the mammalian remains from three prehistoric sites in India and Western Asia.* Ph.D. Thesis. Univ. of London.

Cochi, I. (1858). Sur la naturalisation du dromadaire en Toscane. *Bull. Soc. Imp. Zool. Acclim.* **5**, 479.

Cockrill, W. S. (1973). *The Camel Project.* FAO: Rome.

Colbert, E. H. The osteology and relationships of Archaeomeryx, an ancestral ruminant. *American Mus. Novitates.* **1135**, 1-24.

Cole, D. P. (1975). *Nomads of the nomads: the Al Murrah Bedouin of the Empty Quarter.* Aldine Publishing Co.: Chicago.

Colombari, F. (1853). *Les Zemboureks. Artillerie de campagne à dromadaire dans l'armée persane.* Paris.

Combelles, H. and Petit, O. (1964). *Le livre des nomades.* Hatier, Didier: Paris.

Congiu, S. (1953). A study of dressing percentage, body proportions and various correlations of the Somali camel (in Italian). *Zootec. e Vet.* **8**, 188-191.

Conti, G. (1913). A serious prophylactic problem - rinderpest in the camel. *Mod. Zoot.* **1913**, 3-12.

Cook, G. C. and Al-Torki, M. T. (1975). High intestinal lactase concentrations in adult Arabs in Saudi Arabia. *British Med. J.* **5976**, 135-136.

Corancez, L. A. O. de. (1816). *Itinéraire d'une partie peu connue de l'Asie Mineure.* J. M. Ebehrard: Paris.

Cordier, J. A. (1893). Recherches sur l'anatomie comparée de l'estomac des Ruminants. *Ann. Sci. Nat. (Zool.)* **7(16)**, 1-178.

Cordier, J. A. (1893). Observations d'anatomie comparée sur l'estomac des Camelidés. *Bull. Soc. Zool.*, France. **18**. 75-78.

Cornevin, C. and Lesbre, F. X. (1894). *Traité de l'âge des animaux domestiques d'après les dents et les productions epidermiques.* Baillière: Paris.

Cottier, H. (1939). L'élevage en Tunisie. *Rec. Méd. Exot.* **12**, 50-51.

Cousi, N. (1951). L'echinococcose en Tunisie. *Arch. Inst. Hidatid.* **12**, 53-61.

Couston, F. (1918). Le chameau de trait le Sahara algérien. *J. Agric. Prac.* **N.S. 31**, 408-411.

Cozzi, P. (1965). Livestock rearing in Somalia (in Italian). *Riv. Agric. Subtrop. Trop.* **59**, 4-6.

Crombe, C. V. (1957). *Au sujet des pertes de chameaux subies par la compagnie méhariste du Sud tunisien au cours des derniers mois.* Rapp. Min. Def. Nat. Forces Armée, Paris.

Cross, H. E. (1917). A note on Jhooling in camels. *Bull. Agric. Res. Inst.*, Pusa. **No. 72.**

Cross, H. E. (1917). *The camel and its diseases: being notes for veterinary surgeons and commandants of camel corps.* Baillière, Tindall & Cox: London.

Cross, H. E. (1918). Some camel feeding experiments. *Bull. Agric. Res. Inst.*, Pusa. **No. 77.**

Cross, H. E. (1918). Are camels susceptible to blackquarter, haemorrhagic septicaemia and rinderpest? *Bull. Agric. Res. Inst.*, Pusa. **No. 80.**

Cross, H. E. (1919). Camel trypanosomiasis. *Ann. Rep. Camel Specialist*, Punjab.

Cross, H. E. (1920). Camel trypanosomiasis. *Bull. Agric. Res. Inst.*, Pusa. **No. 95.**

Cross, H. E. and Patel, P. G. (1921). *Vet. Bull. Dept. Agric.*, Punjab. **No. 6**, 1-3.

Cross, H. E. and Patel, P. G. (1922). *Vet. Bull. Dept. Agric.*, Punjab. **No. 8**, 1-19.

Croveri, P. (1929). A new strongylide *Anthostrongylus somaliensis* Croveri 1917 (n.g.; n.sp.), a parasite of dromedaries in Somalia, and intestinal strongylosis of the dromedary (in Italian). *Arch. Ital. Sci. Med. Colon. Parasit.* **10**, 143-170.

Curasson, G. (1918). Une maladie du dromadaire analogue au farcin du boeuf. *Bull. Soc. Cent. Méd. Vét.* **72**, 491-496.

Curasson, G. (1920). *Hygiène et maladie du dromadaire en Afrique Occidentale Française.* Imprimerie du Gouvernement Générale: Gorée, Sénégal.

Curasson, G. (1943). *Traité de protozoologie vétérinaire et comparée (3 tomes).* Vigot Frères: Paris.

Curasson, G. (1946). *Maladies infectieuses des animaux domestiques (2 tomes).* Vigot Frères: Paris.

Curasson, G. (1947). Les tests anatomiques de l'adaptation du chameau au milieu désertique. *Rev. Elev. Méd. Vét. Pays Trop.* **1**, 29-36.

Curasson, G. (1947). Les avortements chez la chamelle. *Encyclopéd. Vét. Périod.* **4**, 74-76.

Curasson, G. (1947). *Le Chameau et ses Maladies.* Vigot Frères: Paris.

Custer, R., Kramer, L., Kennedy, S. and Bush, M. (1977). Haematologic effects of Xylazine when used for restraint of Bactrian camels. *J. American Vet. Assoc.* **171**, 899-901.

Dada, B. J. O. (1978). Incidence of hydatid disease in camels slaughtered at Kano abattoir. *Trop. Anim. Hlth Prod.* **10**, 204.

Dada, B. J. O. (1980). Taeniasis, cysticerosis and echinococcosis/hydatidosis in Nigeria: II - prevalence of bovine and porcine cysticercosis, and hydatid disease in slaughtered food animals based on retrospective analysis of abattoir records. *J. Helminth.* **54**, 287-291.

Dada, B. J. O. (1980). Taeniasis, cysticerosis and echinococcosis/hydatidosis in Nigeria: III - prevalence of bovine and porcine cysticercosis, and hydatid cyst infection based on joint examination of slaughtered food animals. *J. Helminth.* **54**, 293-297.

Dada, B. J. O. and Belino, E. D. (1978). Prevalence of hydatidosis and cysticercosis in slaughtered livestock in Nigeria. *Vet. Rec.* **103(14)**, 311-312.

Dada, B. J. O. and Belino, E. D. (1979). Hydatid disease in food animals slaughtered in Sokoto State, Nigeria. *Int. J. Zoon.* **6**, 115-116.

Dada, B. J. O., Adegboye, D. S. and Mohammed, A. N. (1980). The epidemiology of *Echinococcus* infection in Kano State, Nigeria. *Ann. Trop. Med. Parasit.* **74**, 515-517.

Dade, J. E. M., Zaklama, N. S., Imam, I. Z. E. and Wanees, M. (1973). Serological survey for Q fever in Egyptian domestic animals. *J. Egyptian Pub. Hlth Assoc.* **48**, 101-108.

Dagain, R. (1947). Le service vétérinaire au groupe d'unites sahariennes de l'Est à Ouargla. *Rev. Vét. Milit.* **2**, 43-44.

Dagain, R. (1947). Thérapeutique cameline indigène chez les Touareg Ajjer. *Rev. Vét. Milit.* **2**, 334-340.

Dagg, A. L. (1974). Locomotion of the camel. *J. Zool.* London. **174**, 67-78.

Dahl, G. and Hjort, A. (1976). *Having Herds: Pastoral Herd Growth and Household Economy.* Univ. of Stockholm: Stockholm.

Dailey, M. D. and Sweatman, G. K. (1965). The taxonomy of *Echinococcus granulosus* in donkey and dromedary in Lebanon and Syria. *Ann. Trop. Med. Parasit.* **59**, 463-477.

Dajani, R. M., Frayha G. J., Samia, L. H. and Sweatman, G. K. (1973). Carbon dioxide fixation by the nymphs of the tick, *Hyalomma dromedarii. J. Parasit.* **59**, 897-899.

Dakkuri, A., Naccache, P. and Sha'afi, R. I. (1972). Sodium and potassium transport in camel red cells. *Comp. Biochem. Physiol.* **43A**, 1019-1023.

Dallon, M. (1935). Mission au Tibesti (1930-1931). *Mem. Acad. Sci.,* Paris.

Danho, W. O. (1973). Pituitary lactogenic hormone from the camel (*Camelus dromedarius*). Purification and amino acid composition. *J. Fac. Med.,* Baghdad. **15**, 57-62.

Danho, W. O., Gattner, H. G. and Nissen, D. (1975). B-chain shortening of matrix-bound insulin with pepsin. II. Preparation and properties of camel dis-pentapeptide (B26-30) and dis-Phe-B¹-dis-pentapeptide (B26-30) insulin. *Z. (Hoppe-Seyler's) Physiol. Chem.* **356**, 1405-1412.

Daniels, C. (1970). *The Garamantes of Southern Libya.* Oleander Press: New York.

Dareste, A. (1857). Rapport sur l'introduction projetée du dromadaire au Brésil. *Bull. Soc. Imp. Zool. Acclim.* **4**, 190.

Dareste, A. (1857). Acclimatisation of the dromedary to the plains of northern Brazil and of the cultivation of tamarind, being a translation of the presentation of Monsieur A. Dareste to the Imperial Society of Zoological 11 Acclimatisation of Paris (in Portuguese). *Typographia Nacional:* Rio de Janeiro.

Daumas, G. (1854). *Bull. Soc. Imp. Zool. Acclim.* **1**, 20.

Davidson, P. (1923). *Alticamelus alexandrae,* a new camel from the Barstow upper Miocene of the Mohave desert. *Univ. Calif. Publ. Geol.* **14**, 397-408.

Davies, F. G., Mungai, J. N. and Shaw, T. (1975). Characteristics of a Kenyan camelpox virus. *J. Hyg.,* Cambridge. **75**, 381-385.

Davies, R. (1957). *The Camel's Back.* John Murray: London.

Davin, M. F. (1857). Notice industrielle sur le poil de chameau. *Bull. Soc. Imp. Zool. Acclim.* **4**, 253-257.

Dayal, P., Sohal, H. S. and Narain, D. (1973). The sex chromatin in Purkinje cells of artiodactyla. *J. Anat. Soc.,* India. **22**, 81-85.

Daynes, P. and Richard, D. (1974). Note sur les helminths (et quelques autres parasites) du dromadaire en Ethiopie. *Rev. Elev. Méd. Vét. Pays Trop.* **27**, 53-56.

Daynes, P. and Graber, M. (1974). Principales helminthoses des animaux domestiques en Ethiopie. *Rev. Elev. Méd. Vét. Pays Trop.* **27**, 301-306.

Decker, R. A. and McDermid, A. M. (1977). Nutritional myopathy in a young camel (*Camelus dromedarius*). *J. Zoo. Anim. Med.* **8**, 20-21.

Dekeyser, P. L. (1954). Les chameaux. *Naturalia.* **1**, 7-11.

Dekker, N. D. M. and Schaaf, A. van der. (1962). Open tuberculosis in a camel. *Diergeneesk Tydschr.* **87**, 1133-1140.

Decker, R. A., Hruska, J. C. and McDermid, A. M. (1979). Colloid goiter in a newborn dromedary camel and an aborted foetus. *J. American Vet. Med. Assoc.* **175**, 968-969.

Delanoe, P. (1922). Myiases du bétail du cercle de Doukkala causées par les larves d'une mouche sarcophile *Wohlfahrtia magnifica* Schiner, 1862. *Bull. Soc. Sci. Nat. Phys.,* Maroc. **2**, 132.

Delavenay, R. P. (1978). Emploi du Nitroxynil chez le dromadaire. *Rev. Elev. Méd. Vét. Pays Trop.* **31**, 171-177.

Del Bono, G. and Arispici, M. (1978). Visceral cysticercosis in dromedary (*Camelus dromedarius*) (in Italian). *Ann. Fac. Med. Vet.,* Pisa. **31**, 320.

Del Bono, G., Arispici, M. and Rindi, S. (1978-79). Visceral cysticerciasis in the dromedary (*Camelus dromedarius*) (in Italian). *Pubb. Fac. Med. Vet.,* Perugia. **14**, 129-139.

Dellman, H. D. and Fayez, M. (1964). Investigation on the microscopic anatomy of the forestomach and stomach of *Camelus dromedarius. J. Vet. Sci.,* UAR, **1**, 99-112.

Dellman, H. D., Fayez, M. and Helmy, M. M. (1965). Investigations on the topography and distribution of the cervical, thoracic, abdominal and pelvic parts of the autonomous nervous system of *Camelus dromedarius. Acta Vet.,* Hungary. **15**, 269-280.

Dellman, H. D., Blin, P. C. and Fahmy, M. F. A. (1968). Contribution a l'étude de l'anatomie microscopique du tube digestif chez le chameau. *Rev. Elev. Méd. Vét. Pays Trop.* **21**, 1-32.

Delpy, L. (1936). Sur les maladies contagieuses des animaux domestiques observées en Iran de 1930 à 1935. *Bull. Acad. Vet.,* France. **9**, 206-210.

Delpy, L. (1937). Description de *Hyalomma dromedarii* (Koch 1844). Morphologie de la larve et de la nymphe. *Ann. Parasit. Hum. Comp.* **15**, 481-486.

Delpy, L. (1946). Protozoaires observés en Iran dans le sang des animaux domestiques. *Bull. Soc. Path. Exot.* **39**, 122-126.

Delpy, L. and Gouchey, S. H. (1937). Biologie de *Hyalomma dromedarii* (Koch 1844). *Ann. Parasit. Hum. Comp.* **15**, 487-499.

Delpy, L. and Rafyi, A. (1947). La trypanosomiase du dromadaire en Iran. Etude expérimental de *Trypanosoma evansi* (Steel 1885). *Arch. Inst. d'Hessarck.* **5**, 33-50.

Demougeot, E. (1960). Le Chameau et l'Afrique du Nord romaine. *Annales: Econ. Soc. Civ.* **15**, 209-247.

Denis, P. (1953). La justice chez les grandes nomades Reguibat. *Doc. CHEAM.* No. 2353.

Denis, P. (1970). *Observations sur le comportement du dromadaire.* Thèse. Fac. Sci. Univ. de Nancy.

Denisse, R. (1957). Pratique divinatoire préalable a l'enterprise d'un voyage. *Bull. Liais. Sahar.* **8**, 128-129.

Dennig, H. K. (1971). The influence of splenectomy on *Trypanosoma evansi* infections in camels. *Proc. 19th Wld. Vet. Cong.,* Mexico City. **2**, 631-632.

Dennig, H. K. (1972). Use of xylazine in dromedarii for diagnostic splenectomy (*Trypanosoma evansi* infections) (in German). *Vet. Med. Rev.* **3**, 243-246.

Dennig, H. K. (1972). The use of Rompun in the dromedary in diagnostic splenectomy (infection with *Trypanosoma evansi*/surra). *Vet. Med. Rev.* **3**, 239-242.

Deschamps, L. (1909). Le méhariste saharien. *Bull. Soc. Geog.,* Oran.

Descheins, R. (1960). Considerations générales, épidémiologiques et sanitaires sur l'hydatidose dans le bassin méditerranéen et en Corse. *Bull. Soc. Path. Exot.* **53**, 971-990.

Deshayes, J. (1969). *Les Civilisations de l'Orient Ancien.* Arthaud: Paris.

Devé, F. (1923). Enquête etiologique sur l'echinococcose en Tunisie. *Rev. Vet. Milit.* **75**, 133-165.

Dhablania, D. C., Tyagi, R. P. S. and Vig, M. M. (1971). Stringhalt in camels - case reports. *Indian Vet. J.* **18**, 416-419.

Dhillon, S. S. (1959). Incidence of rinderpest in camels in Hissar district. *Indian Vet. J.* **36**, 603-607.

Dhingra, D. R. (1934). The component fatty acids and glycerides of the milk-fat of Indian camels. *Biochem. J.* **28**, 73-78.

Diagana, D. (1977). *Contribution a l'étude de l'élevage de dromadaire en Mauritanie.* Thèse DMV. ESIMEV: Dakar, Sénégal. No. 1.

Dickson, H. R. P. (1949). *The Arab of the Desert.* Allen & Unwin: London.

Didier, R. (1975). *Etude des maladies du dromadaire dans le sous-province de Borana (Ethiopie).* Thèse DMV. ENV: Alfort.

Diffloth, P. (1924). *Zootechnie Coloniale, Guide de l'Eleveur.* Vol. II. J.-B. Baillière et Fils: Paris.

Dina, D. and Klintberg, (1977). *Proposals for a rural development training project and study concerned with camel utilization in arid lands in Ethiopia.* Addis Ababa (mimeo).

Dischamps. La production animale au Soudan français. *Rec. Méd. Vét. Exot.* **4**, 207-218.

Dixit, V. P., Agarwal, V. K. and Nangia, O. P. (1970). Plasma protein-bound iodine levels in camels. *J. Endocrinol.* **48**, 463-464.

Dobrynin, M. I. (1968). Role of camels in the epizootiology of

Anoplocephalata infections of ruminants in Turkmenia. *Mater. Konf. Posvy. Pamyati N. V. Badanina*, Tashkent. 68-69.

Dobrynin, M. I. (1969). Helminths of the dromedary in Turkmenia (in Russian). *Izvest. Akad. Nauk Turkmen SSR (Biol. Nauk)*. **4**, 31-36.

Dobrynin, M. I. (1970). The discovery of *Trichonema* sp. (Nematoda: Trichonematidae) in *Camelus dromedarius*. In Tashliev, A. D. & Shagaline, C. M. (eds), Ashkhalad Izdat 'Ilim'. 105-110.

Dobrynin, M. I. (1972). *Musca lucidula* as the intermediate host of *Thelazia lessei*, a parasite of camels (in Russian). *Izvest. Akad. Nauk Turkmen SSR (Biol. Nauk)*. 73-77.

Dobrynin, M. I. (1972). Epidemiology of *Thelazia* infection in the dromedary (in Russian). *Izvest. Akad. Nauk Turkmen SSR (Biol. Nauk)*. **5**, 55-59.

Dobrynin, M. I. (1974). The development of *Thelazia leesie* Raillet and Henry, 1910, in the body of an intermediate host (in Russian). *Izvest. Akad. Nauk Turkmen SSR (Biol. Nauk)*. **5**, 39-45.

Doherty, A. G. (1910). *Ann. Rep. Dept. Agric.* British E. Africa. 1909-1910.

Dollfus, R. P. (1962). Cyclophyllidés de quelques oiseaux mammifere Miscellanea Helminthologica Maroccana XXXIV: Cestode anoplocéphale chez un dromadaire. *Arch. Inst. Pasteur*, Maroc. **6**, 387-391.

Domenech, J. (1977). Enquête sérologique sur la brucellose du dromadaire en Ethiopie. *Rev. Elev. Méd. Vét. Pays Trop.* **30**, 141-142.

Domenech, J. (1980). Etude bactériologique de *Corynebacterium pseudotuberculosis* et de *Corynebacterium pyogenes* isolés chez le dromadaire en Ethiopie. *Rev. Elev. Méd. Vét. Pays Trop.* **33**, 123-126.

Domenech, J., Guidot, G. and Richard, D. (1977). Les maladies pyogènes du dromadaire en Ethiopie. Symptomatologie - Etiologie. *Rev. Elev. Méd. Vét. Pays Trop.* **30**, 251-258.

Domizio, G. di (1918). *Clin. Vet.*, Milano. **41**, 391-413.

Domizio, G. di and Tarantino, G. B. (1935). On the incidence of *Trypanosoma brucei* in dromedaries in Italian Somalia (in Italian). *Arch. Ital. Sci. Med. Colon*. **16**, 193-293.

Donatien, A. (1921). El ghedda, septicémie hémorragique des dromadaires. *Arch. Inst. Pasteur, Afrique Nord*. **1**, 242-249.

Donatien, A. and Larrieu, M. (1922). Nouvelle épizootie de ghedda à M'raier (Sahara). *Arch. Inst. Pasteur, Afrique Nord*. **2**, 316-319.

Donatien, A. and Lestoquard, F. (1923). Bull. Soc. Path. Exot. **16**, 168-170.

Donatien, A. and Boué, A. (1944). Une epizootie de ghedda dans la region de l'Oued Guir (Saharra oranais). *Arch. Inst. Pasteur*, Alger. **22**, 171-174.

Doncenko, V. V. (1956). The one-humped camel in Turkmenistan and methods for improving the breed. *Trudy Inst. Zool. Akad. Nauk Turkmen SSR*. **No. 1**, 292-308.

Donchenko, A. S., Donchenko, V. N., Fatkeeva, E. A., Kibasov, M. and Zernova, L. A. (1975). Destruction of tubercle bacilli in camel's milk and 'shubat', a lactic acid product (in Russian). *Vet.*, Moscow. **2**, 24-26.

Donchenko, A. S., Donchenko, V. N. and Kenzheev, Sh. (1975). Influence of the tuberculin test on blood proteins in camels and cows (in Russian). *Vet.*, Moscow. **9**, 52-53.

Donchenko, A. S. and Donchenko, V. N. (1979). Residual nitrogen, protein and protein fractions of blood serum in camels (in Russian). *Vest. Sel.-khz. Nauk Kazakh*. **3**, 57-60.

Dostal, W. (1959). The evolution of Bedouin life. In Gabrieli, F. (ed), *L'Antica Societa Beduina*. Centro di studi semitici, Ist. studi orientali Univ.: Roma.

Dotoum, B. (1975). Note sur la situation sanitaire en matière des trypanosomiases animales au Tchad au cours de la période 1971-1975. *Circonscr. Elev. Sud-est Sarh. Moyen-Chari, Tchad*. 135-148.

Dougbag, A. S. A. M. and Berg, R. (1980). Morphological observations on the normal cardiac glands of the camel (*Camelus dromedarius*). Anat. Anz. **148**,258-264.

Dougbag, A. S. A. M. and Berg, R. (1980). Histological and histochemical studies on the mucosa of the initial dilated and middle long narrow part of the third compartment of the camel's stomach *Camelus dromedarius*. *Zentralbl. Vet. Med.* **9**, 155-163.

Dougherty, J. F. (1940). Skull and skeletal remains of the camel *Paratylopus cameloides* (Wortman) from the John Day deposits, Oregon. *Carnegie Inst. Publ.* **No. 514**, 49-58.

Doutressoulle, G. (1947). *L'Elevage en Afrique Occidentale Française*. Imprimerie de Mortainais: Mortain, France.

Doutressoulle, G. (1948). *L'Elevage au Soudan Français*. Imprimerie de Mortainais: Mortain, France.

Doutressoulle, G. and Traore, S. (1949). L'élevage dans la Boucle du Niger. *Rev. Elev. Méd. Vét. Pays Trop.* **3**, 29-37.

Dowling, D. F. and Nay, T. (1962). Hair follicles and sweat glands of the camel (*Camelus dromedarius*). *Nature*, London. **195**, 578-580.

Doyle, G. (1956). Camels in Texas. *San Jacinto Mus. Hist. Assoc.*

Drake-Brockman, R. E. (1912). *British Somaliland*. Hurst & Blacket: London.

Draz, O. (1974). The use of 'Gammexane' in the treatment of sarcoptic mange in camels. *Vet. Rec.* **59**, 548-549.

Draz, O. (1956). Improvement of animal production in Yemen. *Bull. Inst. Dés.*, Egypte. **6**, 79-110.

Drerup-Eilker, K. (1980). *Studies on the infestation of livestock with ticks (Ixodidae: Ixodidae) in Egypt* (in German). Thesis. Hanover Veterinary University.

Droandi, I. (1915). Notes on the camel (in Italian). *Governo della Tripolitania*; Tripoli.

Droandi, I. (1920). The castration of the camel (in Italian). *Agric. Colon. Ital.* **5**.

Droandi, I. (1920). Camel raising (in Italian). *Agric. Colon. Ital.* **5**, 201-218.

Droandi, I. (1921). The racing camels of Barca (Eritrea) (in Italian). *Agric. Colon. Ital.* **14/15**, 1-47.

Droandi, I. (1936). The Natural History, Anatomy, Physiology, Husbandry and Pathology of the Camel (in Italian). *Istituto Agricolo Coloniale*: Firenze.

Droandi, I. (1939). Is the world camel population declining? (in Italian). *Regio Istituto Agronomico per l'Africa Italiana*, Firenze.

Droandi, I. (1939). Castration of camels (in Italian). *Riv. Milit. Med. Vet.*, Roma. **2**, 568-570.

Droandi, I. (1940). The Camelidae - exceptional ruminants (in Italian). *Riv. Milit. Med. Vet.*, Roma. **3**, 177-198.

Duba, D. R. and Ellis, J. E. (1979). *Food habits and forage quality for camels, sheep and goats in the Arabian Shield*. Min. of Agric. and Water: Saudi Arabia.

Dubey, J. P. and Pande, B. P. (1964). On Eimerian oocysts recovered from Indian camel (*Camelus dromedarius*). *Indian J. Vet. Sci.* **34**, 28-34.

Duboc (General) (1946). *Méharistes Coloniaux*. L. Fournier: Paris.

Dunham, D. (1957). *Royal Tombs at Meroë and Barkal*. Museum of Fine Arts, Boston.

Dunkel, R. (1973). Therapeutic trial with proteolytic enzymes in camelpox. *Tierdrztl. Umschau*. **28**, 580; 582-584.

Dupas (1938). Le commerce caravanier entre les confins algéro-tunisiens et l'AOF (Mauritanie et Soudan) à travers le Sahara occidental. *Doc. CHEAM.* **No. 1357**.

Durand, M. (1952). Le problème de l'eau et des puits en Mauritanie. *Bull. Info., AOF*. **No. 137**, 15-19.

Durand, M. and Kchouk, M. (1958). Le 'krafft', une osteopathie dystrophique du dromadaire. *Arch. Inst. Pasteur*, Tunis. **35**, 107-152.

Durand, M. and Kchouk, M. (1958). Etude de quelques constantes hématologiques et chimiques chez le dromadaire. *Bull. Acad. Vét. France*. **31**, 197-198.

Duran-Jorda, F. (1948). The eosinphil cell: Studies in horse and camel. *Lancet*. **255**, 451-452.

Duran-Jorda, F. (1950). Secretion of red blood corpuscles as seen in the camel. *Nature*, London. **165**, 280.

Durdyev, B. D. (1976). Quantitative data for blood morphology in young dromedaires (in Russian). *Izvest. Akad. Nauk Turkmen SSR (Biol. Nauk)*. No. 6, 84-85.

Durdyev, B. D. and Kozlov, P. V. (1975). Carotene content in blood serum of young Arabian camels during postnatal development (in Russian). *Izvest. Akad. Nauk Turkmen SSR (Biol. Nauk)*. No. 2, 81-83.

Dyson, R. H. (1953). Archaeology and the domestication of animals in the old world. *American Anthr.* 55, 661-673.

Dzhumagulov, I. K. (1969). The use of PMS in camel breeding (in Russian). *Konevod. Konnyi. Sport.* 5, 32.

Dzhumagulov, I. K. (1976). Milk production and their inheritance in Bactrian camel-dromedary hybrids (in Russian). *Izvest. Akad. Nauk Kazakh. SSR (Biol. Nauk)*. 14, 69-75.

Dzhumagulov, I. K. (1977). Chemical composition of camel milk and heritability of milk components during interbreeding hydridization (in Russian). *Izvest. Akad. Nauk Kazakh. SSR. (Biol. Nauk)*. 4, 79-81.

Dzhumagulov, I. K. (1977). Pregnancy diagnosis in camels (in Russian). *Konnevod. Konnyi Sport.* 10, 29.

Dzhumagulov, I. K. and Baimukanov, A. B. (1971). Physiological characters of lactation and milking rate in the camel. *Vest. Sel'-khz. Nauk Alma-Ata.* 14(9), 46-49; 117.

Dzhuraev, A. (1973). Comparative evaluation of castration methods for male camels. *Vest. Sel'-khz. Nauk Alma-Ata.* 16(4), 61-64; 121.

Eddin, S. (1955). Rapport général sur la situation sanitaire de l'Egypte en ce qui concerne les maladies parasitaires. *Bull. Off. Int. Epiz.* 43, 204-213.

Edelsten, R. M. and Pegram, R. G. (1974). Contagious skin necrosis of Somali camels associated with *Streptococcus agalactiae*. *Trop. Anim. Hlth Prod.* 6, 255-256.

Edney, E. B. (1966). *Animals of the desert*. In Hills, E. S. (ed.). *Arid lands: a geographical appraisal*. Methuen: London.

Egger, E; (1864). A quelle époque le chameau a-t-il été introduit en Egypte comme bête de somme? *C. R. Acad. Inscr. Belles Lettres.* 8, 329-330.

Eguchis, (1938). Endoparasites of several zoo beasts with reference to their kinship with human parasites. *Parasitology.* 1, 168.

Eisa, M. and El Amin, M. A. G. (1972). Adenovirus precipitating antibodies in the sera of some domestic animal species in the Sudan. *Sudan J. Vet. Sci. Anim. Husb.* 13, 45-51.

Eissa, S. M. and Abdel-Fattah, R. F. (1974). Haematological studies on the young and adult Arabian camel (*Camelus dromedarius*) from Kuwait. I. Some haematological constants. *J. Univ. Kuwait (Science).* 1, 123-127.

Eitan, A., Aloni, B. and Livne, A. (1976). Unique properties of the camel erythrocyte membrane. II. Organization of membrane proteins. *Biochem. Biophys. Acta.* 426, 647-658.

El-Abdin, Y. Z. and Hamza S. M. (1972). Acid and alkaline phosphatases in normal sheep and camels. *J. Egyptian Vet. Med. Assoc.* 32, 247-249.

El-Abdin, Y. Z., Abdel-Rahman, M. S., Hamza, S. M. and Abdel-Wahab, R. M. (1975). Comparative studies on some serum constituents and some serum enzyme activities of normal and nematode infested camels. *Egyptian J. Vet. Sci.* 12, 31-43.

El Afifi, A., Zahi, R. and Farrag, H. (1953). Incidence and typing of tuberculosis in camels in Egypt. *Vet. Med. J., Giza.* 1, 1.

El-Ahwal, A. M. (1969). Rabies problem and eradication in UAR. *J. Egyptian Vet. Med. Assoc.* 29, 121-129.

Elamin. F. M. (1980). The dromedary camel of the Sudan. In *Workshop on Camels*, Khartoum, Sudan, 18-20 Dec. 1979. Intnl. Foundation for Science: Stockholm, Sweden.

Elamin, F. M. and Saha, N. (1980). Blood protein polymorphism in the one-humped camel (*Camelus dromedarius*) in the Sudan. *Anim. Blood Groups Biochem. Genet.* 11, 39-42.

El Azab, E. A. and Musa, B. E. (1976). Early detection of pregnancy in the camel by using biological methods. *Zuchthygiene.* 11, 166-168.

El Badawi, El-K. S., Eisa, A. M., Slepenev, N. K. and Saad, M. B. A. (1979). Hydatidosis of domestic animals in the central region of the Sudan. *Bull. Anim. Hlth Prod. Afr.* 27, 249-251.

El Badry, A. A., El Mougy, S. A., Aziz, M. A. and Fat-Halla, M. M. (1978). The effect of feeding placental tissues of she-camel on the growth rate and dressing percentage in Fayoumi chickens. *Vet. Med. J., Giza.* 26, 385-393.

El Badry, A. A., El Mougy, S. A., Aziz, M. A. and Fat-Halla, M. M. (1978). The effect of feeding camel placenta on the blood picture of Fayoumi chickens. *Vet. Med. J., Giza.* 26, 395-400.

El-Bahay, G. M. (1962). Normal contents of Egyptian camel milk. *Vet Med. J., Giza.* 8, 7.

El-Bahay, G. M. (1964). *Normal Contents of Egyptian camel milk*. DVM Thesis. Univ. of Cairo.

El-Dashlouty, M. S., Foda, Y. H., El-Gharabawi, M. I., Abdalla, M. A. and El-Sanafiry, N. Y. (1976). Effect of enzymes on camel meat. 3. Histological studies on enzymatic tenderization of camel meat. *Agric. Res. Rev.*, Egypt. 54, 137-146.

El-Etreby, M. F. (1970). Myocardial sarcosporidiosis in the camel. *Path. Vet.* 7, 7-11.

El Fourgi, M. (1950). *Le Chameau Tunisien*. Thèse DMV. ENV: Toulouse. No. 48.

El Fourgi, M. (1972). L'élevage en Tunisie. *Bull. Off. Int. Epiz.* 77, 103-106.

El Gaafary, M. A. and Aly, A. A. (1979). Anatomical studies on the arterial supply of the testis and epidymis of the dromedary camel. *Assiut Vet. Med. J.* 4, 11-23.

El-Garhy, M. T. and Selim, M. K. (1957). Incidence of echinococcosis in camels slaughtered for meat production in Egypt. *Vet. Med. J., Giza.* 4, 191-200.

El-Ghannam, F., El-Azab, E. A. and El-Sawai, (1974). Preliminary study on the application of Cuboni test pregnancy diagnosis in the camel. *Zuchthygiene.* 9, 46.

El-Gharabawi, M. I., Abdalla, M. A. and El Goundy, M. S. (1974). Studies on some market meats in Egypt. I. Changes in nitrogenous compounds during ageing, freezing and storage. *Libyan J. Agric.* 3, 125-130.

El-Gharabawi, M. I., Fodha, Y. H., and El-Dashlouty, M. S. (1975). Studies on some market meats in Egypt. II. Histological characteristics as influenced by ageing freezing and storing. *Libyan J. Agric.* 4, 13-17.

El-Gindy, E. M. M., El-Hagri, M. A., Mostafa, M. S. and El-Khaligi, G. E. M. (1976). Some post-natal morphological studies on the mid-brain (mesancephalon) of the one-humped camel (*Camelus dromedarius*). *J. Egyptian Vet. Med. Assoc.* 36, 11-17.

El-Gohary, M., Abdel Majid, A. M. and Taib, N. T. (1978). Fine structure of the nasal glands of the one-humped camel (*Camelus dromedarius*). *Anat. Anz.* 190, 390.

El Hagri, M. A. A. and Morcos, M. B. (1954). Quelques caractéristiques anatomiques des systèmes nerveux et musculaire du membre thoracique du chameau. *Rev. Elev. Méd. Vét. Pays Trop.* 7, 81-85.

El Hagri, M. A. A. and Morcos, M. B. (1954). Etude du système arteriel du membre thoracique du chameau, *Rev. Elev. Méd. Vét. Pays Trop.* 7, 165-169.

El Hagri, M. A., El Gindy, E. M., Mostafa, M. S. and El Khaligi, G. E. (1976). The cerebral meninges of one-humped camel (*Camelus dromedarius*). *J. Egyptian Vet. Med. Assoc.* 36, 5-9.

Eljack, A. H. (1980). The anatomy of the male genital system of the one-humped camel (*Camelus dromedarius*). *Zentralbl. Vet. Med.* 90, 92.

Eljack, A. H. (1980). On the penis and prepuce of the male camel (*Camelus dromedarius*). *Anat. Histol. Embryologia.* 9, 180.

El Kordy, M. I. (1946). On the incidence of hydatid diseases in domestic animals in Egypt. *J. Egyptian Med. Assoc.* 29, 265.

Elmossalami, E., Siam, M. A. and El Sergany, M. (1971). Studies on tuberculous-like lesions in slaughtered camels.. *Zentralbl. Vet. Med.* 18B, 253-261.

Elmoty, I. A., El Mulla, A. and Elmossalami, S. (1967). The influence of various orally and intramuscularly administered vitamin A preparations on the blood plasma level of vitamin A in buffaloes and camels. *Acta Vet., Hungary.* **17**, 87–90.

El-Naggar, M. and Abdel-Raouf, M. (1976). Studies on reproduction in camels (*Camelus dromedarius*). VII. The acid and the alkaline phosphatase activities of the seminal plasma. *Indian Vet. J.* **53**, 823–828.

El-Naggar, M. and Abdel-Raouf, M. (1977). Studies on reproduction in camels (*Camelus dromedarius*). VIII. The electrophoretic pattern and the amino acid content of the seminal plasma protein. *Indian Vet. J.* **54**, 239–243.

El Nasri, M. (1962). A serological survey for the detection of Q fever antibodies in the sera of animals in Sudan. *Bull. Epiz. Dis. Afr.* **10**, 55–57.

El-Nouty, F. D., Yousef, M. K., Magdub, A. B. and Johnson, H. D. (1976). Thyroid secretion hormones in Camelidae and Equidae. *Fed. Proc.* **35**, 216.

El Sergany, M. A., Elmossalami, E. and El-Newawy, F. (1970). Histopathological studies on camel meat infested with *Cysticercus dromedarii*. *J. Vet. Sci., UAR.* **7**, 191–200.

El-Shaieb, M. (1976). Topography of the nerves of the hind limbs of the camel (*Camelus dromedarius*). *Assiut Vet. Med. J.* **3**, 1–9.

El-Shaieb, M. (1976). The brachial plexus of the camel (*Camelus dromedarius*). *Assiut Vet. Med. J.* **3**, 11–20.

El-Shaieb, M. (1979). Anatomical studies on the *n. facilis* of *Camelus dromedarius*. *Assiut Vet. Med. J.* **6**, 15–27.

El-Shaieb, M. and Aly, A. E. M. (1977). Investigations on the topography and distribution of the vague nerve of *Camelus dromedarius*. *Assiut Vet. Med. J.* **4**, 1–9.

El-Shaieb, M. and Majeed, Z. Z. (1979). Special morphological features of the hyoid bone of *Camelus dromedarius*. *Assiut Vet. Med. J.* **6**, 29–35.

El Sheikh, A. S. and Rasheed, A. A. (1966). Histological changes in the foetal thyroid of the dromedary (*Camelus dromedarius*). *J. Anat.* **100**, 831–837.

Elwishy, A. B. and Elsawaf, S. A. (1971). Functional activity of the ovaries and uterine horns in fat-tailed sheep and camels (*Camelus dromedarius*). *Fortpfl., Besamung und Aufzucht Haust.* **7**, 181–187.

Elwishy, A. B., Mobarak, A. M. and Fouad, S. M. (1972). The accessory genital organs of the one-humped male camel (*Camelus dromidarius*). *Anat. Anz.* **131**, 1–13.

Elwishy, A. B. and Omar, A. M. (1975). On the relation between testis size and sperm reserves in the one-humped camel (*Camelus dromedarius*). *Beit. Trop. Lanwirt. Veterinarmed.* **13**, 391–398.

Elyan, A. and Dawood, M. M. (1954). A serological survey of Q fever in Egypt. *J. Egyptian Public Hlth Assoc.* **29**, 185–190.

Ema, A. N. and Tulpule, S. S. (1980). Some observations on the gross anatomy and histology of the one-humped camel (*Camelus dromedarius*) - Gastrointestinal studies. *Zeut. Vet.* **9**, 180.

Emelin, V. and Zeiss, H. (1928). *Rev. Microbiol. Epidémiol. Parasitol.* **7**, 462–463.

Emmanuel, B. (1980). Oxydation of butyrate to ketone bodies and CO_2 in the rumen epithelium, liver, kidney, heart and lung of camel (*Camelus dromedarius*), sheep (*Ovis aries*) and goat (*Capra hircus*). *Comp. Biochem. Physiol.* **65B**, 699–704.

Emmanuel, B. (1980). Comparative biochemical studies between the camel and other ruminants. *Provis. Rep., Intnl. Foundation for Science.* **No 6**, 321–345.

Emmanuel, B., Howerly, B. R. and Emady, M. (1976). Urea degradation in the camel. *Canadian J. Anim. Sci.* **56**, 595–601.

Emmanuel, B. and Nahapetian, A. (1980). Fatty acid composition of depot fats and rumen wall of the camel (*Camelus dromedarius*). *Comp. Biochem. Physiol.* **57B**, 554–556.

Epstein, H. (1954). Le dromadaire dans l'Ancien Orient. *Rev. Hist. Sci.,* Paris. **7**, 247–268.

Epstein, H. (1971). *The Origin of the Domestic Animals of Africa 2 Volumes.* African Publishing Corporation: New York.

Eraskov, S. G. (1953). Camel's milk and its products (in Russian). *Konevodstvo.* **23(11)**, 35–37.

Eraskov, S. G. (1955). The milk production of the camel (in Russian). *Shorn Dokl 3 vsesojuz Moloc Delu. 1955,* 174–176.

Erencin, Z. (1949). *Histology and morphology of the provenitriculum of the camel* (in Turkish). DVM Thesis, Ankara.

Erman, A. (1927). *The literature of the Ancient Egyptians (Translated by A. M. Blackburn).* London.

Erofeev, M. G. (1935). Anatomie normale du voile du palais du dromadaire. *Trav. Inst. Agric.,* Turkmenistan **1**, 81–92.

Erola, T. (1949). *Camel Herds.* Africa, Madrid **Aug/Sept. 1949,** 329–332

Ershov, (1961). La lutte contre l'echinococcose et la coenurose. *Bull. Off. Inst. Epiz.* **56**, 977–992.

Esterabadi, A. H., Entessar, F., Hedayati, H., Narimani, A. A. and Sadri, M. (1975). Isolation of *Corynebacterium pseudotuberculosis* from camel in Iran. *Arch. Inst. Razi.* **27**, 61–66.

Etemadi, A. A. (1966). Diaphragm and os diaphragmaticum in *Camelus dromedarius*. *Acta Anat.* **65**, 551–560.

Etemadi, A. A. (1975). Carotid body of *Camelus dromedarius*. *Acta Anat.* **92**, 110–120.

Euting, J. (1906). *The Bedouin camel saddle* (in German). In Bozold, C. (ed.) *Orientalische Studien: Theodor Nöldeke zum siebzigsten Geburtstag (2 März 1906).* Alfred Töpelmann: Giezen.

Evans, A. J. (1895). *Cretan Pictographs and Prae-Phoenician Script.* Bernard Quantch: London.

Evans, G. (1880). Report on 'surra' disease in the Dera Ismael Khan district. *Punjab Govt. Milit Dept.* **No. 493**, 4467.

Evans, J. O. and Powys, J. G. (1980). *Camel husbandry to increase the productivity of ranchland.* In *Workshop on Camels,* Khartoum, Sudan, 18–20 Dec. 1979. Intnl. Foundation for Science: Stockholm, Sweden. 241–250.

Evans, J. T. R. (1945). *Ann. Rep. Vet. Dept. Sudan Govt.*

Evans, J. T. R. (1946). *Ann, Rep. Vet. Dept. Sudan Govt.*

Evans, J. T. R. (1948). *Ann, Rep. Vet. Dept. Sudan Govt.*

Evans, J. T. R. (1950/51). *Ann. Rep. Vet. Dept. Sudan Govt.*

Evans, J. V., Roberts, J. and Agar, N. S. (1970). Delta type Merino sheep: a rare blood type with some erythrocyte characteristics approaching those found in the camel. *Australian J. Exp. Biol. Med. Sci.* **48**, 25–32.

Eve and Lewis, (1882). Camel's lung with filaria sanguinis. *J. Comp. Med. Surg.* **8**, 330.

Ezzat, M. A. E. and Tadros, G. (1963). Preliminary trials for treatment of verminous bronchitis of sheep and camels in Egypt. *J. Arab Vet. Med. Assoc.* **22**, 207–216.

Ezzi, A. and Zakarian, B. (1979). A survey on spontaneous atherosclerosis of camel (*Camelus dromedarius*) in Iran. *Trop. Anim. Hlth Prod.* **11**, 102–15.

Fabens, J. W. (1865). *The uses of the camel: considered with a view to his introduction into our western States and Territories.* Carleton Publisher: New York.

Fagbami, A. H., Tomori, O. and Kemp, G. E. (1973). Survey of Nigerian domestic and wild animals for serum neutralizing antibody to indigenous Rift Valley fever virus. *Nigerian Vet. J.* **2**, 45–48.

Fahmy, M. F. A. and El Afifi, A. (1964). Cysticerci of the camel *Zentralbl. Vet. Med.* **11B**, 147–150.

Fahmy, M. F. A., Taher, E. S. and Shahein, Y. M. (1965). A histological study of the adrenal gland of *Camelus dromedarius*. *Vet. Med. J.,* Giza **10**, 271–278.

Fahmy, M. F. A. and Dellman, H. D. (1968). Studies on the microscopic anatomy of the oral cavity of *Camelus dromedarius*. *J. Vet. Sci.* UAR, **5**, 45–51.

Fahmy, M. F. A., Arnautovic, I. and Abdalla, O. (1971). The morphology of the tarsal glands and the glands of the eye-lid in the one-humped camel. *Acta Anat.* **73**, 40–46.

190

Fahmy, M. F. A., Abdalla, O. and Arnautovic, I. (1972). Anatomical study of the liver of the camel. III. The hepatic vein. *Acta Morph. Neerlando-Scandinavica*. **9**, 221-228.

Fakhry, A. (1951). *The Necropolis of el-Bagawat in Kharga Oasis*. Government Press: Cairo.

Falconer, H. and Cautley, P. T. (1836). Note on the fossil camel of the Sivalik hills. *Asiatic Res*. **19**, 115-134.

Falconer, H. and Cautley, P. T. (1869). On the fossil camel of the Sewalik Hills. *Pal. Mem. Hugh Falconer*. **1**, 227-246.

Falluji, M. M. al, Tantawi, H. H. and Shony, M. O. (1979). Isolation, identification and characterization of camelpox virus in Iraq. *J. Hyg.*, London. **83**, 267-272.

FAO (1972). *Manual on the employment of draught animals in Africa*. FAO: Rome

FAO. *Yearbooks*.

Farahat, A. A., Soliman, M. K. and Younis, M. (1978). Some studies on the cellular element of camel foetal blood. *Acta Vet.*, Yugoslvia **28**, 197-203.

Farbrother, E. S. (1941). Smuggling opium and *charas* in stomachs of camels. *Indian J. Vet. Sci*. **11**, 105-106.

Farina, R. and Sobrero, L. (1960). Serological survey for leptospirosis in cattle, goats and camels in Somalia (in Italian). *Zooprofilassi*. **15**, 925-936.

Farrag, H. and El Afify, A. (1956). Salmonella in apparently normal camels. *J. Egyptian Vet. Med. Assoc*. **39**, 698-699.

Farrag, H., Zaki, R. and Hindaur, M. R. (1953). Pneumonia in a camel. *British Vet. J*. **59**, 119.

Fatami, J. A. and Shaad, F. U. (1980). Innervation of the heart of the camel, *Camelus dromedarius*. *Indian J. Zool*. **8(2)**, 15-18.

Fat-Halla, M. M. and Ismail, A. A. (1980). *Seasonal variations in gonadotropins of one-humped male camel (Camelus dromedarius)*. In *9th. Intnl. Cong. on Animal Reproduction and Artificial Insemination*. 16-20 June, 1980. III. Symposia (free communications). Editorial Garsi: Madrid, Spain.

Fath el Bab, M. R. H. (1970). *A histological study on the respiratory system of camel*. Thesis. Assiut, Egypt.

Faulkner, D. E. (1978). *The Future of the Camel*. Paper prepared for discussion at the Conference of Ministers of Agriculture of the Gulf States and Arabian Peninsula (mimeo).

Faure, J. (1949). Contribution a l'étude de l'echinococcose dans le region de Marrakech. *Bull. Inst. Hyg.*, Maroc. **9**, 211-232.

Fayez, M. and Nasr, H. (1963). *Proc. 4th. Ann. Vet. Congr.*, UAR.

Fazil, M. A. (1977). The Camel. *Bull. Anim, Hlth Prod. Afr*. **25**, 435-442.

Fedchenko, V. A. (1971). Tuberculosis in camels. I. Epidemiology in Kazakhstan (in Russian). *Trudy Kazakhskogo Nauch. Vet. Inst*. **14**, 51-56.

Fedchenko, V. A. (1971). Tuberculosis in camels. II. Haematological changes (in Russian). *Trudy Kazakhskogo Nauch. Vet. Inst*. **14**, 57-61.

Federov, V. N. (1960). Plague in camels and its prevention in the USSR (in English). *Bull. World Hlth Org*. **23**, 275-281.

Fedrigo, M. and Ferri, E. (1968). Arterial vascularization of the spinal medulla in a new-born camel (in Italian). *Veterinaria*, Milano **17**, 383-397.

Felinski, L., Kaczmarek, G. and Kurpios, M. (1971). Lipid metabolism in ruminants from the zoological gardens in Poland. II. Characteristics of lipids and free fatty acids of adipose tissue from different body sites of camel, llama and other ruminants (in Polish). *Przeglad Zoologiczny*. **15(2)**, 201-205.

Ferry, R. (1961) *Parasitisme gastro-intestinal du dromadaire au Niger*. These DMV. ENV: Alfort. **No. 100**.

Ficalbi, (1912). The camels of S. Rossore (in Italian). *Monit. Zool*. **23**.

Field, C. R. (1978). The food habits of camels in northern Kenya. *Integrated Project in Arid Lands, Tech. Rep. UNEP/UNESCO*. **No. E-lb**.

Field, C. R. (1979). Ecology and Management of Camels, Sheep and Goats in northern Kenya. *IPAL, Tech. Rep. UNEP/UNESCO*. **No. E-la**.

Field, C. R. (1980). *Camel growth and milk production in Marsabit district, Northern Kenya Preliminary Report*. In Workshop on Camels, Khartoum, Sudan, 18-20 1979. Intnl Foundation for Science: Stockholm, Sweden. 215-240.

Finberg, J. P. M., Yagil, R. and Berlyne, G. M. (1978). Response of renin-aldosterone system in the camel to acute dehydration. *J. Appl. Physiol.: Resp., Env., Exer. Physiol*. **44**, 926-930.

Finbert, E. J. (1938). *La vie du chameau, le vaisseau du désert*. Albin Michel: Paris.

Finelle, P. (1973). Chimiotherapie et chimioprevention de la trypanosomiase animale. Acquisitions récents et situation actuelle. *Cah. Méd. Vét*. **42**, 215-226.

Finkelstein, L. E. (1939). Congenital macrofollicular cystic goiter in a dromedary. *Zoologia*, New York. **24**, 289-292.

Finlayson, R., Keymer, I. F. and Manton, V. J. A. (1971). Calcific cardiomyopathy in young camels (*Camelus spp.*) *J. Comp. Path*. **81**, 71-78.

Fischer, H. (1975). *The raising of sheep, goats, water-buffalo and dromedaries together for livestock production* (in German). Beitrag zur III Vet. Tagung, Ouagadougou, Upper Volta.

Fischer, H. (1976). The contribution of water-buffalo, dromedaries, goats and sheep to the animal production of warm countries (in German). *Tierärztl. Praxis*. **4**, 465-476.

Flamand, G. B. M. (1907). *De l'introduction du chameau dans l'Afrique du Nord*. Act. XIV Cong. Intnl. Orientalistes 1905, 7ème Section. 62-68.

Flaubert, C. (1849). Note sur le dromadaire. *Rec. Med. Vet. Prat*. **6**, 398-404.

Flower, S. S. (1929). *List of the vertebrated animals exhibited in the Gardens of the Zoological Society of London 1828-1927. Vol. 1 Mammals*. Zoological Society: London.

Flower, S. S. (1932). Notes on the Recent mammals of Egypt, with a list of the species recorded from that kingdom. *Proc. Zool. Soc.*, London. **1932**, 369-450.

Floyed, T. M. (1955). Salmonella in domestic animals and fowls in Egypt. *J. Egyptian Publ. Hlth Assoc*. **30**, 177-183.

Foda, Y. H., Abdallah, M. A., El Gharabawi, M. I., El Dashlouty, M. P. and El Sanafiry, N. Y. (1976). Effect of enzymes on camel meat. 1. The effect of the proteolytic enzymes on the water holding capacity of camel meat. *Agric. Res. Rev.*, Egypt. **54**, 117-126.

Foda, Y. H., El Gharabawi, M. I., Abdallah, M. A. and El Dashlouty, M. S. (1976). Effects of enzymes on camel meat. 2. Effects of ficin, bromelin and trypsin on the tenderness of camel meat. *Agric. Res. Rev.*, Egypt. **54**, 127-136.

Foda, Y. H., El Dashlouty, M. S., El Sanafiry, N. Y., El Gharabawi, M. I., Abdalla, M. A. and Labib, W. A. (1976). The effects of enzymes on camel meat. 4. Comparative effectiveness of bromelin, ficin and trypsin on microbial load of camel meat. *Agric. Res. Rev.*, Egypt. **54**, 147-151.

Foley, H. and Meslin, R. (1924). Exploration scientifique des oasis du Gourada et du Touat (mars et avril 1913). *Arch. Inst. Pasteur*, Alger. **2**, 263-302.

Foley, H. and Ceard, L. (1924). Sur des cas d'empoisonnement causés par une liliacee des régions sahariennes (*Ornithogalum amoenum* Batt.). *Arch. Inst Pasteur*, Alger. **2**, 507-516.

Foley, H. and Musso, M. (1925). Les plantes du Sahara toxiques pour les animaux. Presence d'un glucoside cyanhydrique dans le *Lotus jolyi* Battandier. *Arch. Inst. Pasteur*, Alger. **3**, 394-401.

Foley, H., Catanei, A. and Vialatte, C. (1930). Microfilaires du sang de quelques animaux d'Algérie. *Arch. Inst. Pasteur, Alger*. **4**, 485-518.

Fonseca, W. (1977). *The buffalo - synonym for meat, milk, butter and work* (in Portuguese). Ministry of Agriculture: Sao Paulo, Brazil.

Forbes, R. J. (1965). *The coming of the camel*. In *Studies in Ancient Technology. Vol. II. Bull. Leiden. Ch. IV*.

Foster, J. W. and Seager, S. W. J. (1975) Fertility evaluation of the male bactrian camel. *American Assoc. Zoo. Vet. Ann. Proc.* **1975**, 155-161.

Fouad, S. M., Mobarak, A. M. and Aly, M. A. (1979). Micromorphology of the arteries of the penis of the one-humped camel. *Indian J. Anim. Sci.* 49, 377-379.

Foucauld, C. de (1951-52). *Dictionnaire Touareg-Français.*

Fraguier, G. de (1955). Cheval et chameau. *Bull. Liais. Sahar.* 19, 70-77.

Francis, J. (1974). Camels, Australia's uniquely adapted ruminants. *Anim. Quat.* 3(3), 4-8.

Francke, G., Standfuss, R. and Schunke, P. (1933). Observations on 'Surra' in camels (in German). *Berlin Tierarztl. Wschr.* 49, 605-607.

Frandson, (1965). *Anatomy and Physiology of Farm Animals.* Lea and Feiberger: London.

Fraser, A. F. (1968). *Reproductive Behaviour in Ungulates.* Academic Press: London.

Free, J. P. (1944). Abraham's camels. *J. Near East Stud.* 3, 187-193.

Frerking, H. and Andresen, P. (1978). Caesarian section in a dromedary with praecervical uterine torsion (in German). *Praktische Tierärzt.* 59, 128-129.

Frick, C. and Taylor, B. E. (1968). A generic review of the Stenomyline camels. *American Mus. Nov.* 2353, 1-51.

Friese, F. (1975). Elephants, ostriches and a camel (in German). *Kosmos.* 71, 331-334.

Frigeri, F. and Arush, M. A. (1972). Research on the agglutination of immune antibodies of the Parainfluenza 3 virus in the serum of various species (cattle, sheep, goats and camels) in Somalia (in Italian). *Clin. Vet. Ital.*, Milano. 102, 372-376.

Frullini, P. L. (1938). Trypanosomiasis and Piroplasmosis in camels in the Danakil, Italian East Africa (in Italian). *Arch. Ital. Sci. Med. Colon.* 19, 340-343.

Frye, R. N. (1973). *Sasamian Remains from Qasr-i-Abu Nasr.* Harvard University Press: Cambridge, Massachusetts.

Fuchs, P. (1957). Rock paintings and rock engravings in Tibesti, Borku and Ennedi (in German). *Arch. fur Volkerkunde.* 12, 110-135.

Gadd, C. J. (1936). *The Stones of Assyria.* Chatto and Windus: London.

Gadel. (1907). Notes sur les sections méharistes de la région de Zinder. *Rev. Troupes Colon.* 2, 288-303; 427-445.

Gad-el-Mawla, B. I. and Fayad, A. A. (1976). The efficiency of Suramin in the treatment of trypanosomiasis in Egyptian camels under desert conditions. *J. Egyptian Vet. Med. Assoc.* 36, 89-94.

Gadola, A. (1947). Animal production, prophylactic medicine and hygiene in East Africa. Part 1 Ch. 7. Camels (in Italian). *Ist. Sup. San., Fond. Emanuele Paterio*: Rome.

Gaiger *J. Trop. Vet. Sci.* 4, 508.

Gaiger (1915). A revised check-list of the animal parasites of domestic animals. *J. Comp. Path. Therap.* 28, 67-76.

Gardiner, A. H. (1911). *Egyptian Hieratic Texts I. The Papyrus Anastasi.* Leipzig.

Gast, M. (1963). Partage de la viande à Idelés. *Libyca Anthrop., Prehist., Ethnograph.*, Alger. 11, 235-244.

Gast, M., Maubois, J. L. and Adda, J. (1969). *Le Lait et les Produits Laitiers en Ahoggar.* Arts et Métiers Graphiques: Paris.

Gast, M., Maubois, J. L., Adda, J., Blanc-Patin, E. and Jeunet, R. (1969). Les laits et les produits laitiers en Ahoggar. *Cah. Nutr. Diet.* 4, 35-53.

Gates, J. B. (Jr) (1971). A report of halothane anasthesia in a camel. *J. Zoo. Anim. Med.* 2, 26-27.

Gaudefroy-Demombynes, M. Camel - in Arabia. *Encyclopaedia of Religion and Ethics.* 173-174.

Gautam, O. P., Gulati, R. L. and Gera, K. L. (1970). Pulmonary abcess (Malli) in a camel. *Indian Vet. J.* 47, 364-365.

Gautam, O. P. and Sharma, R. K. (1971). Pica - a problem disease of camels successfully tackled. *Haryana Vet.* 10, 64.

Gautam, O. P. and Bansal, R. (1972). Save your camel from pica 'Mitti Khana'. *Indian Fmg.* 21(10), 40-47.

Gautier, E. F. (1927). *Les Siècles obscurs du Maghreb.* Payot: Paris.

Gautier, E. F. (1928). *Le Sahara.* Paris.

Gautier, E. F. *Sahara: The Great Desert.* Columbia University Press: New York.

Gautier, E. F. (1937). *Le passé de l'Afrique du Nord, les siècles obscurs.* Paris.

Gautier, E. F. and Chudeau, R. (1909). *Mission au Sahara.* Paris.

Gauthier-Pilters, H. (1954). Studies on hereditary behaviour of Tylopodes with special consideration of New World forms (in German). *Zeitschr. Tierpsyche.* 11, 213-303.

Gauthier-Pilters, H. (1955). Quelques observations sur le comportement des dromadaires (*Camelus dromedarius*) relevées dans le Sahara nord-occidental. *Bull. Soc. Vet. Zootech.*, Alger. 3, 9-13.

Gauthier-Pilters, H. (1955). Observations éthologiques sur les Tylopodes. *Mammalia.* 19, 399-415.

Gauthier-Pilters, H.(1956). The behaviour of Tylopodes (in German). *Handbuch Zool.*, Berlin Vol. 8, Part 10. No. 22, 1-24.

Gauthier-Pilters, H. (1958). Quelques observations sur l'ecologie et l'éthologie du dromadaire dans le Sahara Nord-Occidental. *Mammalia.* 22(1), 140-151; 294-316.

Gauthier-Pilters, H. (1959). *Of Nomads and camels* (in German). Thomas Verlag: Kempen.

Gauthier-Pilters, H. (1959). A study of the fighting attitudes of male dromedaries: birth and behavioural development in the young (in German). *Z. F. Tierpsyche.* 16(5), 593-604.

Gauthier-Pilters, H. (1961). Observations sur l'écologie du dromadaire dans le Sahara nord-occidental. *Mammalia.* 25, 195-280.

Gauthier-Pilters, H. (1965). Observations sur l'écologie du dromadaire dans l'Ouest du Sahara. *Bull. IFAN.* 27A, 1534-1608.

Gauthier-Pilters, H. (1969). Observations sur l'écologie du dromadaire en Moyenne Mauritanie. *Bull. IFAN.* 31A, 1259.

Gauthier-Pilters, H. (1969). *The Dromedary: Fables and Facts* (in German). In Lorenz, K., Grzimck, B. and Hediger, H. (eds) *Das Tier.*

Gauthier-Pilters, H. (1970). Le dromadaire - fables et réalités. *Miferma-info.* 19, 47-52.

Gauthier-Pilters, H. (1971). *The behaviour and ecology of camels in the Sahara with special reference to nomadism and water management.* In: *Symposium on the behaviour of ungulates and its relation to management.* Alberta, Canada, 2-5 November, 1971.

Gauthier-Pilters, H. (1971). Que valent les pâturages sahariens? *Miferma-info.* 21, 50-56.

Gauthier-Pilters, H. (1972). Le puits pastoral dans le desert. *Miferma-info.* 23, 50-56.

Gauthier-Pilters, H. (1972). Observations sur la consommation d'eau du dromadaire en été dans la région de Beni-Abbes (Sahara nord-occidental). *Bull. IFAN.* 34(1), 219-259.

Gauthier-Pilters, H. (1973). Au rythme lent du dromadaire. *Miferma-info.* 24, 49-56.

Gauthier-Pilters, H. (1973). Les nomades du desert. *Miferma-info.* 25, 51-56.

Gauthier-Pilters, H. (1974). *The behaviour and ecology of camels in the Sahara with special reference to nomadism and water management.* In Geist, V. and Walter, F. (eds) *The Behaviour of Ungulates and its Relation to Management.* IUCN Publ. No. 24.

Gauthier-Pilters, H. (1975). Nomads live to migrate (in German). *Kosmos.* 71, 34-40.

Gauthier-Pilters, H. (1975). Observations sur la végétation d'été du Zemmour mauritanien. *Bull. IFAN.* 37A, 555-604.

Gauthier-Pilters-H. (1976). The camel - wonder of the desert. *Priroda: J. Akad. Sci. USSR.* 1976, 128-137.

Gauthier-Pilters, H. (1977). Contribution à l'étude de l'ecophysiologie du dromadaire en été dans son milieu naturel (moyenne et haute Mauritanie). *Bull. IFAN.* 39A, 365-459.

Gaye, K. (1950). Treatment of trypanosomiasis in camels with dimidium bromide. *Bull. Serv. Elev. Indust. Anim. AOF.* 3, 17-22.

Geddes, L. A., Tacker, W. A. (Jr) and Rosborough, J. P. (1974). Cardiac output in an anesthetized dromedary. *American J. Vet. Res.* **35**, ̄131-133.

Geddes, L. A. and Kidder, H. (1976). Specific resistance of blood at body temperature. *Med. Biol. Engineer.* **14**, 180-185.

Gelb, I. J. (1961). The early history of the West Semitic Peoples. *J. Cuneiform Stud.* **15**, 27.

Gemmell, M. A. (1960). Advances in knowledge on the distribution and importance of hydatid disease as a world health and economic problem during the decade 1950-1959. *Helminth. Abst.* **29**, 355-369.

Gentry, A. W. and Gentry, A. (1970). Fossil camels in Kenya and Tanzania. *Nature*, London. **222 (5196)**, 898.

George, N. (1950). The camel in ancient Egypt. *British Vet. J.* **106**, 76-80.

George, N. (1951). The adrenals of the camel. *British Vet. J.* **107**, 122-124.

George, N. (1957). Some observations on the foetal circulation in the camel. *British Vet. J.* **113**, 219-220.

Gerlach, R. *Pictures from Yemen.* Edition Leipzig: Leipzig.

Gers, J. (1949). Plaidoyer pour le chameau. *Rev. Colon. Belge.* **84**, 208-209.

Gezuli, A. Y. el, Eisa, A. M. and Badawi, El K. S. el (1978). Nemafax against some gastro-intestinal nematodes of camels in the Sudan. *Sudan J. Vet. Sci. Anim. Husb.* **19**, 42-46.

Ghadirian, E. and Arfaa, F. (1973). First report of human infection with *Haemonchus contortus, Ostertagia ostertagi* and *Marshallagia marshalli* (family Trichostrongylidae) in Iran. *J. Parasit.* **59**, 1144-1145.

Ghadirian, E. and Arfaa, F. (1975). Present status of trychostrongylosis in Iran. *American J. Trop. Med. Hyg.* **24**, 935-941.

Ghanmi, A. (1977). *Les dominantes pathologiques du dromadaire.* Thèse DMV. ENV: Toulouse. **No. 54.**

Ghodsian, I., Nowrouzian, I. and Schels, H. F. (1978). A study of some haematological parameters in the Iranian camel. *Trop. Anim. Hlth Prod.* **10**, 109-110.

Ghosal, A. K. (1971). *Water metabolism in camel (Camelus dromedarius).* Ph.D. Thesis, Univ. of Udaipur, Rajasthan.

Ghosal, A. K. and Dwaraknath, P. K. (1971). Normal serum transaminase activities in domestic animals. *Indian J. Anim. Hlth.* **10**, 61-62.

Ghosal, A. K., Appanna, T. C. and Dwaraknath, P. K. (1973). A note on studies on the seasonal variation in serum electrolytes in Indian camel (*Camelus dromedarius*). *Indian J. Anim. Sci.* **43**, 558-559.

Ghosal, A. K., Appanna, T. C. and Dwaraknath, P. K. (1973). Studies on the seasonal variations in the blood constituents of Indian camel (*Camelus dromedarius*). *Indian J. Anim. Sci.* **43**, 642-644.

Ghosal, A. K., Appanna, T. C. and Dwaraknath, P. K. (1973). Some observations on water restriction in Indian camel (*Camelus dromedarius*). *Indian Vet. J.* **50**, 518-520.

Ghosal, A. K., Dwaraknath, P. K. and Patney, J. M. L. (1973). Note on plasma carotene and vitamin A levels in normal camels (*Camelus dromedarius*) of north-west Rajasthan. *Indian J. Anim. Sci.* **43**, 899-900.

Ghosal, A. K., Appanna, T. C. and Dwaraknath, P. K. (1974). Seasonal variation in water compartments of the Indian camel. *British Vet. J.* **130(2)**, xvii-xlix.

Ghosal, A. K., Jatkar, P. R., Dwaraknath, P. K. and Appanna. T. C. (1975). A note on probable role of erythroprotein in the serum of camels (*Camelus dromedarius*). *Indian J. Anim. Sci.* **45**, 69.

Ghosal, A. K., Appanna, T. C. and Dwaraknath, P. K. (1975). A note on the effect of short term water deprivation on certain blood characteristics of the camel. *Indian J. Anim. Sci.* **45**, 105-108.

Ghosal, A. K., Dwarknath, P. K. and Appanna, T. C. (1975). A study of the changes of the blood electrolyte of camel (*Camelus dromedarius*) during water deprivation. *Indian J. Anim. Hlth.* **14**, 113-115.

Ghosal, A. K. and Dwaraknath, P. K. (1976). Plasma carotene and vitamin A levels in cows, sheep and camels in the Thar desert. *Indian Vet. J.* **58**, 640-642.

Ghosal, A. K., Dwaraknath, P. K. and Jatkar, P. R. (1976). A note on serum iron levels in domestic animals of north-western Rajasthan. *Indian J. Anim. Sci.* **46**, 449.

Ghosal, A. K., Appanna, T. C. and Dwaraknath, P. K. (1977). Effect of water deprivation during summer and winter on body water compartments in the camel (*Camelus dromedarius*). *Indian J. Anim. Hlth.* **16**, 31-33.

Gidley, J. W. (1913). Notice of the occurrence of a Pleistocene camel north of the Arctic Circle. *Smithsonian Misc. Coll. Publ. 2173, Vol. 60. No. 26.*

Giles, E. (1889). *Australia Twice Traversed.* Low, Maston, Searle & Rivington: London.

Gill, B. S. (1965). Studies on protective immunity of *Trypanosoma evansi. J. Comp. Path.* **75**, 233.

Gill, B. S. (1973). Studies on surra. XI. Chemotherapeutic susceptibility of *Trypanosoma evansi. Indian J. Anim. Sci.* **43**, 226-229.

Gill, H. S. (1976). Incidence of *Eimeria* and *Infundibulorium* in camel. *Indian Vet. J.* **53**, 897-898.

Gill, H. S. and Prakash, O. (1969). Toxoplasmosis in India: prevalence of antibodies in camels. *Ann. Trop. Med. Parasit.* **63**, 265-267.

Gillespie, I. A. (1962). Riding camels of the Sudan. *Sudan J. Vet. Sci. Anim. Husb.* **3**, 37-42.

Gimbo, A. and Tarantino, A. (1974). An initial report on interstitial cells or testicular type (Leydig cells) in the ovary of *Camelus dromedarius. Experientia.* **30**, 284-285.

Gimbo, A. and Domina, F. (1976). Leydig interstitial cells in the ovary of the dromedary. Histology and histochemistry (in Italian). *Ann. Fac. Med. Vet., Messina*, **13**, 15-27.

Gimbo, A. and Zanghi, A. (1979). Follicular activity in the female *Camelus dromedarius.* Histogenetic observations and consideration of the function of the corpus luteum (in Italian). *Clin. Vet.*, Milano. **102**, 200-225.

Ginawi, M. A. and Shommein, A. M. (1977). Prevalence of Sarcosporidiosis in sheep, goats and camels in the Sudan. *Sudan J. Vet. Sci. Anim. Husb.* **18**, 92-97.

Gipsen, R. and Brand-Saathof, B. (1974). Three specific antigens produced in vaccinia, variola and monkey pox infection. *J. Infect. Dis.* **129**, 289-295.

Girardon, C. A. (1939). *Rev. Milit. Med. Vet.* **2**, 476.

Girardon, C. A. (1939). The livestock resources of the province of Shoa (in Italian). *Coll. Stud. Colon. Ist. Afri. Ital. Sez.*, Milano. **7**, 5-89.

Giroud, P., Roger, F., Dumas, N., Vouilloux, P. and Sacquet, E. (1954). Comportement des animaux domestiques de la région du Tchad vis à vis de l'antigène T 13. *Bull. Soc. Path. Exot.* **47**, 644-645.

Gjerstad, E. (1926). Studies on Prehistoric Cyprus. *Arsskr. Uppsala Univ. (Filhist).* **1**, 1-342.

Gleichen, A. E. (1888). *With the Camel Corps up the Nile.* Chapman and Hall: London.

Gluhbegovic, N. (1976). Collateral ligaments of the knee joint of the dromedary (in German). *Verh. Anat. Gesellschaft.* **70**, 597-603.

Gluhbegovic, N. (1977). Ligaments of the lateral meniscus of the dromedary (in German). *Verh. Anat. Gesellschaft.* **71**, 1397-1403.

Gluhbegovic, N. and Arnautovic, I. (1977). Menisci of the camel knee joint. *Acta Anat.* **99**, 93.

Gode, P. K. (1958). Notes on the history of the Camel in India between BC 500 and AD 800. *Janus.* **47**, 133-138.

Godfrey, D. G. and Killick-Kendrick, R. (1962). *Trypanosoma evansi* of camels in Nigeria: a high incidence demonstrated by the inoculation of blood into rats. *Ann. Trop. Med. Parasit.* **56**, 14-19.

Goel, S. K. and Singh, R. P. (1969). A study on the biochemical analysis of sera of domestic animals both naturally and experimentally infected with *Trypanosoma evansi. Punjab Vet.* **9**, 14-17.

Goel, S. K. and Singh, R. P. (1971). Comparative studies of certain diagnostic tests in the diagnosis of surra. *J. Res. (Ludhiana).* **8**, 404-406.

Goetze, A. (1959). Remarks on the ration lists from Alalokil VII. *J. Cuneiform Stud*. **8**, 37.

Gombe, S. and Oduor-Okelo, D. (1977). Effects of temperature and relative humidity on plasma and gonadal testosterone concentration in camels (*Camelus dromedarius*). *J. Reprod. Fert*. **50**, 107-108.

Gonzalez, P. (1949). *L'alimentation du dromadaire dans l'Afrique française*. These DMV. ENV: Lyon. *No. 38*.

Goor, S. (1953). Infectious diseases of camels in Palestine. *Refuah Vet*. **10**, 174.

Gordon, C. H. (1939). *Western Asiatic seals in the Walters Art Gallery*. Iraq. **6**, 21.

Gorgas, M. (1966). On the skull capacity of Central Asian wild mammals and their domesticated forms. *Zool. Anz*. **176**, 227-235.

Graber, M. (1956). *Rapport de tournée effectuée dans le Nord Ouaddai de juin à septembre 1955*. IEMVT: Paris.

Graber, M. (1959). La cysticercose bovine: son importance dans les zones sahéliennes d'élevage de la République du Tchad. *Rev. Elev. Méd. Vét. Pays Trop*. **13**, 121-143.

Graber, M. (1959). Les parasites des animaux domestiques et sauvages de la République du Tchad. I. Région du Kanem et du Bahr el Ghazal. *Rev. Elev. Méd. Vét. Pays Trop*. **13**, 145-152.

Graber, M. (1964). Les helminthes de quelques artiodacytles sauvages appartenant aux familles des bovidés et des suidés. Ces mammifères en République du Tchad et en RCA, sont-ils des réservoirs de parasites pour les animaux domestiques vivant à leur contact? *Rev. Elev. Méd. Vét. Pays Trop*. **17**, 379-420.

Graber, M. (1966). Etudes dans certaines conditions africaines de l'action antiparasitaire de Thiabendazole sur divers helminthes des animaux domestiques. II. Dromadaire. *Rev. Elev. Méd. Vét. Pays Trop*. **19**, 527-543.

Graber, M. (1967). Etude préliminaire de la biologie d'*Haemonchus contortus* (Raillet & Henry, 1909) du dromadaire (*Camelus dromedarius*). *Rev. Elev. Méd. Vét. Pays Trop*. **20**, 213-225.

Graber, M. (1969). Essais de traitement du parasitisme gastro-intestinal du dromadaire au moyen du Tétramisole. Premières observations. *Rev. Elev. Méd. Vét. Pays Trop*. **22**, 229-236.

Graber, M. (1973). *Helminthes et helminthiases des animaux domestiques et sauvages d'Ethiopie*. Rapport: IEMVT: Paris.

Graber, M. (1975). *Helminthes et helminthiases des animaux domestiques et sauvages d'Ethiopie*. Rapport IEMVT: Paris.

Graber, M. and Gruvel, J. (1964). Etude des agents des myiases des animaux domestiques et sauvages d'Afrique Equatoriale. *Rev. Elev. Méd. Vét. Pays Trop*. **17**, 535-544.

Graber, M., Tabo, R. and Service, J. (1967). Enquête sur les helminthes du dromadaire tchadien. Etude des strongyloses gastro-intestinales et des l'haemoncure à *Haemonchus longistipes*. *Rev. Elev. Méd. Vét. Pays Trop*. **20**, 227-254.

Graells, M. P. (1854). Sur l'acclimatation des animaux en Espagne. *Bull. Soc. Imp. Zool. Acclim*. **2**, 109-116.

Grahame, T. (1944). The ureter and arterial blood supply to the kidney of the camel (*Camelus dromedarius*). *Vet. J*. **100**, 257-261.

Grant, C. P. (1937). *The Syrian Desert*. A. & C. Black: London.

Grassi, F. (1947). Curative treatment of trypanosomiasis in camels with tartar emetic, Naganol and Farma 939 (in Italian). *Bull. Soc. Ital. Med. Igiene Trop*., Eritrea. **7**, 329-332.

Gray, A. R. (1971). *Mammalian Hybrids: A Check-List with Bibliography* Tech. Comm. No. 10. Commonwealth Bureaux of Animal Breeding and Genetics: Farnham Royal, UK.

Gray, A. R. Mahmoud, M. M., Boid, P., Luckins, A. G., Malik, K. H. and Rae, P. (1979). Epidemiological studies on *Trypanosoma evansi* in the Sudan. *Trans. Royal Soc. Trop. Med. Hyg*. **73**, 136-137.

Green, G. W. (1885/86). The Organization and Employment of Camel Corps in Warfare. *J. Royal United Services Inst*. **29**, 521-537.

Greenly, A. H. (1952). Camels in America. *Papers. Bibliographical Soc. America*. **46**, 359-372.

Gregory, J. T. (1939). Two new camels from the late lower Pliocene of South Dakota. *J. Mam*. **20**, 366-368.

Grueber, H. A. (1910). *Coins of the Roman Republic in the British Museum*. British Museum: London.

Gruner, S. A. (1928/29). Bibliographic review on camel husbandry (in Russian). *Trudy Sibirskogo Vet. Inst*. **10**, 329-337.

Gruvel, J. and Graber, M. (1965). Quelques résultats d'enquêtes récentes sur la globidiose du dromadaire au Tchad. Note préliminaire. *Rev. Elev. Méd. Vét. Pays Trop*. **18**, 423-428.

Gruvel, J. and Balis, J. (1965). La trypanosomiase à *Trypanosoma evansi* chez le dromadaire au Tchad et ses principaux vecteurs. *Rev. Elev. Méd. Vét. Pays Trop*. **18**, 435-439.

Gsell, S. (1913). *Histoire ancienne de l'Afrique du Nord; I*. Paris.

Gudat, E. (1964). Contribution to the study of blood constants in the Camelidae (in German). *Monatsch. Vetinärmed*. **19**, 824-826.

Guey, J. (1939). Note sur les livres romains de Numidie et le Sahara au IVe siècle. *Mélanges Archéol. Hist*. Ecole Française, Rome. **No. 178.**

Gulliver, P. H. (1955). *The family herds: a study of two pastoral tribes in East Africa, the Jie and Turkana*. Routledge and Kegan Paul: London.

Gupta, A. K., Chowdhary, M. S. and Barhat, N. K. (1977). A note on optimum time for service in camel (*Camelus dromedarius*). *Indian J. Anim. Sci*. **48**, 324-325.

Gupta, A. K., Vyas, K. K., Dwaraknath, P. K. and Pareek, P. K. (1979). Effect of breeding season, castration and exogenous testosterone on blood glucose level and eosinophil count of male camels (*Camelus dromedarius*). *Indian J. Anim. Sci*. **49**, 554-556.

Gupta, A. K., Vyas, K. K., Dwaraknath, P. K. and Pareek, P. K. (1979). A note on camel blood serum electrolyte studies during rutting and non-rutting seasons and after the exogenous testosterone treatment. *Indian J. Anim. Sci*. **49**, 680-681.

Gupta, G. C., Joshi, B. P. and Rai, P. (1979). Observations on haematology of camel (*Camelus dromedarius* L.). *Indian Vet. J*. **56**, 269-272.

Gupta, P. P. (1979). Report of echinococcosis in a camel from India. *Indian J. Parasit*. **3**, 81.

Gutknecht, P. (1975). Elevage et pathologie néo-natale du chameau au zoo de Mulhouse. In *Disease of Zoo Animals*. Proc. XVII Symp. 4-8 June 1975, Tunis. Akademie Verlag: Berlin, GDR.

Hadani, A. and Rauchbach, K. (1973). The occurrence of myiasis in domestic animals in Israel (in German). *Deutsche Tiёrärztl. Wschr*. **80**, 137-139.

Hafez, M., El-Zaidy, S. and Hefnawy, T. (1970). Biological studies on *Tabanus taeniola* P.de B. adults. *Bull. Soc. Ent*., Egypt. **34**, 327-343.

Hafez, S. M. and Ozawa, Y. (1973). Serological survey of blue-tongue in Egypt. *Bull. Epiz. Dis. Afr*. **21**, 297-304.

Hagid, A. M. A. and Razag, A. I. A. (1975). Relationship and possible function of the nasal sacs and glands of the one-humped camel (*Camelus dromedarius*). Acta Anat. **91**, 423-428.

Haji, C. S. C. (1932). Rinderpest in camels. *Indian Vet. J*. **9**, 13-14.

Halawani, A. (1956). Hydatid disease in Egypt. *Arch. Inst. Hiddid*. **15**, 374-375.

Halternorth, Th. (1953). On the problem of the coagubility of the stomach liquid in camels (in German). *Saugetierk*., Mitteil. **1**, 79-80.

Hamada, S., El-Hidik, M., Sherif, I., El-Sawab, H. and Yousef, M. (1963). Serological investigations on brucellosis in cattle, buffaloes and camels. *J. Arab. Vet. Med. Assoc*. **23**, 173-178.

Hamada, S., El-Sawab, M., Sherif, I., Yousef, M. and Hidik, M. (1963). Salmonella of the mesenteric lymph nodes of slaughtered cattle, buffaloes and camels. *J. Arab. Vet. Med. Assoc*. **23**, 273.

Hamdy, B. H. (1973). Biochemical and physiological studies of certain ticks (Ixodoidea). Cycle of nitrogenous excretion of *Hyalomma dromedarii* Koch (Ixodidae). *J. Med. Ent*. **10**, 345-348.

Hamdy, I. L., Mikhail, E. G. and Soliman, A. A. (1980). A study of hydatidosis in some animals in Egypt. *J. Egyptian Soc. Parasit*. **10**, 43-51.

Hamman, M. A., Hidik, M. E., Sherif, I. and Yousef, M. (1962).

Studies on camel meat. Part I. Chemical composition. *J. Arab. Vet. Med. Assoc.* **22**, 391-396.

Hammer-Purgstall, J. F. von (1855). *Das Kamel.* Denkschriften der kaiserlichen Akademie Wiss., Phil., Hist. Classe 6. Wien.

Hamonier. (1901). Elevage du chaleau dans le cercle de Touggourt. *Rec. Vét. Milit.*

Hamza, A. E. N. (1969). *Comparative assay of the thyroid hormones in cattle, sheep, goats and camels in the Sudan.* M. V. Sc. Dissertation, Khartoum University.

Hansen, H. and Schmidt-Nielsen, K. (1957). On the stomach of the camel with special reference to the structure of its mucous membrane. *Acta Anat.* **31**, 353-375.

Hansen, H. J. and Shams el Din, M. M. (1958). Ostéochondrose cervicothoracique chez le chameau. Etude comparée des lésions des disques invetébraux. *Rev. Elev. Méd. Vét. Pays Trop.* **11**, 439-446.

Harbi, M. S. M. A. and Karim, M. H. A. wad el (1972). Serological investigations into Q fever in Sudanese camels (*Camelus dromedarius*). *Bull. Epiz. Dis. Afr.* **20**, 15-17.

Harlan (General) (1854). Importation of camels. *U.S. Patent Off., Report Agric.* **1853**, 61-63.

Harrington, G. N.(1980). *Grazing arid and semi-arid pastures.* In Morley, F. H. W. (ed.) *Grazing Animals.* Elsevier: Amsterdam.

Hartley, B. J. (1980). Camels in the Horn of Africa. In *Workshop on Camels*, Khartoum, Sudan, 18-20 Dec., 1979. Intnl. Foundation for Science: Stockholm, Sweden. 109-123.

Hartley, B. J., Box, T. W. and Uhlig, A. (1966). *Livestock Development Survey of Somalia.* Rep. Ann. SS 66: 44. FAO: Rome.

Harvey, D. G. and Obeid, H. M. A. (1974). The application of certain liver function tests including serum alkaline phosphatase estimations to domesticated animals in the Sudan. *British Vet. J.* **130**, 544-555.

Hashem, M. M., Tayeb, F. A. and Shoukri, M. M. (1977). Effect of Ditilin (suxamethonium iodide) on rumen motility in goats and ruminal gas fermentation in goats, buffaloes and camels. *Assiut Vet. Med. J.* **4**, 299-301.

Hassan, Y. M. (1968). Blood volume determination in camels (*Camelus dromedarius*). *Isotopen Praxis.* **4**, 73.

Hassan, Y. M. (1971). A note on the effect of dehydration on a camel. *Sudan J. Vet. Sci. Anim. Husb.* **12**, 111-112.

Hassan, Y. M., Hoeller, H. and Hassan, I. M. (1968). Observations on the blood constituents of camels in the Sudan. *Sudan J. Vet. Sci. Anim. Husb.* **9**, 464-476.

Hassan, Y. M. and Wahab, M. F. (1968). Blood volume determination in camels. *Isotopen Praxis.* **4**, 73.

Hassounah, O. and Behbehani, K. (1976). The epidemiology of *Echinococcus granulosus* infections in Kuwait. *J. Helminth.* **50**, 65-73.

Hay, H. P. (1913). Camels of the fossil genus *Camelops. Proc. U.S. Nat. Mus.* **46**, 267-277.

Hay, H. P. (1928). An extinct camel from Utah. *Science.* **N.S. 68**, 299-300.

Heck, H. and Rivenburg, E. (1972). Dosages of M-99 used on hoofed animals at Catskill Game Farm. *Zool. Garten.* **2**, 282-287.

Hedger, R. S., Barnett, I. T. R. and Gray, D. F. (1980). Some virus diseases of domestic animals in the Sultanate of Oman. *Trop. Anim. Hlth Prod.* **12**.

Hegazi, A. H. (1945). *The anatomy of the digestive system of the camel.* Dissertation, Cairo Univ. Fac. Vet. Med., Giza.

Hegazi, A. H. (1949). The soft palate of the camel. *British Vet. J.* **105**, 325-328.

Hegazi, A. H. (1949). The inferior buccal gland in the camel. *Vet. Rec.* **61**, 10-11.

Hegazi, A. H. (1950). The stomach of the camel. *British Vet. J.* **106**, 209-213.

Hegazi, A. H. (1953). The spleen of the camel compared with other domesticated animals. *J. American Vet. Med. Assoc.* **122**, 182-184.

Hegazi, A. H. (1954). The heart of the camel. *British Vet. J.* **110**, 104-108.

Hegazi, A. H. (1954). The liver of the camel as revealed by macroscopic and microscopic examinations. *American J. Vet. Res.* **15**, 444-446.

Hegazi, A. H. (1962). The vascular system of the heart of the camel. *Vet. Med. J.*, Giza. **8**, 153-162.

Heikal, H. A., El Dashlouty, M. S. and Saied, S. Z. (1972). The quality of pastirma as affected by autolysis of the camel meat. *Agric. Res. Rev.*, Egypt. **50**, 235-242.

Heikal, H. A., El Dashlouty, M. S. and Saied, S. Z. (1972). Biochemical, histological and technological changes occurring during the production of sausage from camel meat and beans. *Agric. Res. Rev.*, Egypt. **50**, 243-252.

Heikal, H. A., Saied, S. Z. and El Dashlouty, M. S. (1972). Histological changes in camel meat tissues during pastirma production. *Agric. Res. Rev.*, Egypt. **50**, 253-266.

Hekmati, P., Nowrouzian, I. and Schels, H. F. (1978). A survey on the incidence of foreign bodies in camels at Teheran abattoir. *J. Vet. Fac. Univ. Teheran.* **34**, 9-29.

Heinrich, E. (1937). Uruk-Warke. V. The Tomb-castle in square K XVII of the plan (in German). *Abl. Preuss. Akad. Wiss. (Phil-Hist.)* **1936**, 27-55.

Hell (1936). Testicular necrosis in a dromedary (in German). *Z. Veterinwark.*

Helmy, N., Hosny, Z., Fouad, K. A., Iskandar, M., Farrag, H. and Selim, M. K. (1966). Onchitis and epididymo-onchitis in domesticated animals. *Vet. Med. J.*, Giza. **11**, 179-201.

Helmy, M. M., Mozgov, I. E. and Moursi, H. (1975). Motor functions of the digestive system in *Camelus dromedarius. Proc. 20th Wld. Vet. Cong.* Thessalonika, Greece. Summaries. **Vol. 1**, 64-66.

Henry, A. and Masson G. (1931). Sur une forme coccidienne de l'intestin du chameau. *C. R. Soc. Biol.* **109**, 17-18.

Henry, A. and Masson, G. (1932). Considérations sur le genre *Globidium. Globidium camelus* n:sp. Parasite du dromadaire. *Ann. Parasitol.* **10**, 385-410.

Henry, A. and Masson, G. (1932). La coccidiose du dromadaire. *Rec. Méd. Vét. Exot.* **5**, 185-193.

Henry, A. and Masson, G. (1933). Onchocercose cervicale du dromadaire. *Bull. Acad. Vet. France.* **6**, 208-213.

Heraskov, S. (1938). The milking capacity of camels (in Russian). *Konevodstvo.* **1938(3)**, 46-47.

Heraskov, S. G. (1953). Camel's milk and its products (in Russian). *Konevodstov.* **23(11)**, 35-37.

Heraskov, S. G. (1955). The milk production of the camel (in Russian). *Sborn, Dokl. 3 vsesojuz. Sov. Mol. Delu.* **1955**, 174-176.

Heraskov, S. G. (1965). Camel milk - a valuable food product (in Russian). *Konevod. Konnyi Sport.* **35(8)**, 14-15.

Herbert, S. (1882). The camel: its introduction and acclimation in the United States by Major Herbert C. Wayne, US Army, for Army Transportation purposes in Texas and adjacent territories. *Southern Cultivator and Dixie Farmer.* **May 1882**, 1-11.

Herodotus *The Persian Wars.*

Herrnleben, H. G. (1954/55). Comparative electron microscopical studies of the spermatozoa of various domestic mammals (in German) *Wiss. Z. Humboldt-Univ. Berlin (Math-nature. Reihe No 5).* **4**, 367-378.

Herzog, L. and Lavier, G. (1923). Traitement d'un cas de debab du dromadaire par le 'Bayer 205'. *Ann. Parasit. Hum. Comp.* **1**, 73.

Hifay, A. and Misk, N. A. (1977). The anatomy of the tendons of insertion of the extrinsic muscles of the eyeball in buffalo, cow and camel. *Anat. Histol. Embryol.* **6**, 339-346.

Hilali, M. and Mohamed, A. (1980). The dog (*Canis familiaris*) as the final host of *Sarcoptis cameli* (Mason, 1910). *Tropenmed. Parasit.* **31**, 213-214.

Hilbert, (1908). Sur l'echinoccocose du chameau en Algérie. *Hyg. Viandes Lait.* **2**, 110-113.

Hilzheimer, M. (1913). Survey on the history of research in domestic animals (in German). *Zool. Rundsch., Wurzburg.* **5(4)**, 233-254.

Hintz, H. F., Schryver, H. F. and Halbert, M. (1973). A note on the comparison of digestion by New World camels, sheep and ponies. *Anim. Prod.* **16**, 303-305.

Hintz, H. F., Schryver, H. F. and Halbert, M. (1973). A note on the comparison of digestion by New World camels, sheep and ponies. *Anim. Prod.* **16**, 303-305.

Hippargi, B. S. (1977). How much do you know about camels? Do camels store water? *Livestock Advis.* **22(10)**, 37-38.

Hira, L. M. (1947). Camel breeding in India. *Indian Fmg.* **8**, 504-508.

Hitti, P. K. (1956). *The Arabs.* London.

HMSO (1908). *Animal Management. The Camel.* War Office Vet. Dept..

HMSO (1920). *Handbook of Arabia.* London.

HMSO (1920). *British Somaliland and Socotra.* London.

HMSO (1929). *Sudan Alamanac.* London.

Hoare, C. A. (1972). *The trypanosomes of mammals. A zoological monograph.* Blackwell Scientific Publications: Oxford.

Hogarth, D. G., Woolley, L. and Barnett, R. D. (1952). *Carchemish.* British Museum: London.

Höller, H. and Hassan, Y. M. (1965). The amino acid composition of camel milk casein. *Sudan J. Vet. Sci. Anim. Husb.* **6**, 60-63.

Höller, H. and Hassan, Y. M. (1966). Some blood components of camels in the Sudan (in German). *Deutsche Tierärztl. Waschr.* **73**, 553-556.

Home, E. (1806). Observations on the camel's stomach respecting the water it contains and the reservoirs in which that fluid is enclosed. *Phil. Trans. Royal Soc., London.* **1806**, 355-385.

Hoogstral, H. (1964). A brief review of the contemporary land mammals of Egypt (including Sinai). 3. Carnivora, Hyracoidea Perissodactyla and Artiodactyla. *J. Egyptian Pub. Hlth Assoc.* **39**, 205-240.

Hopfen, H. J. (1969). Farm Implements for Arid and Tropical Regions. *FAO Agric. Dev. Paper No. 91.* FAO: Rome.

Hopkins, M. L. (1955). Skull of fossil camelid from American Falls lake bed area of Idaho. *J. Mam.* **36**, 278-282.

Hoppe, P., Kay, R. N. B. and Maloiy, G. M. O. (1974). Salivary excretion in the camel. *J. Physiol.* London. **244**, 32-33.

Hoppe, P., Kay, R. N. B. and Maloiy, G. M. O. (1976). The rumen as a reservoir during dehydration and rehydration in the camel. *J. Physiol.* London. **254**, 76-77.

Horgan, E. S. and Bennett, S. C. J. (1929). The mercuric chloride test for trypanosomiasis in camels. Mechanism of the reaction. *J. Comp. Path. Therap.* **42**, 188-196.

Houghton, W. (1891). Was the camel known to the early Egyptians? *Proc. Soc. Bibl. Archaeol.* London. **12**, 81-86.

Hughton, W. (1891). Was the camel known to the early Egyptians? *Proc. Soc. Bibl. Archaeol.* London. **13**, 32-33.

Householder, V. H. (1930). Those camels of Arizona. *Arizona Wild Life.* **3**, 4.

Howell, F. C., Fichter, R. and Wolff, R. (1969). Fossil camels in the Omo beds, Southern Ethiopia. *Nature*, London. **223**, 15.

Huard, P. (1960). Contribution à l'étude du cheval, du fer et du chameau au Sahara oriental. *Bull. IFAN sér. B.* **32**, 134-178.

Huard, P. and Feval, J. -C. (1964). Figurations rupestres des confins Algéro-Nigéro-Tchadiens. *Travaux Inst. Rech. Sah.* **23**, 86.

Hubbert, W. T. and Hagstad, H. V. (1979). The need for integrated control programs for zoonoses affecting livestock. *Int. J. Zoon.* **6**, 97-110.

Hudson, J. L. (1934). A list of cestodes known to occur in East African mammals. *J. E. Afr. Uganda Nat. Hist. Soc.* **49**, 205-217.

Huffnagel, (1961). *Agriculture in Ethiopia.* FAO: Rome.

Hulot, F. and Lauvergne, J. J. (1967). The chromosomes of ruminants. *Ann. Génét.* **10**, 86-97.

Humbert, J. (1866). *Corps des dromadaires.* Programme élémentaire d'un cours d'art et d'histoire militaires appliqué à la cavalerie. 165-167.

Hungate, R. E., Phillips, G. D., McGregor, A., Hungate, D. P. and Buechner, H. K. (1959). Microbial fermentation in certain mammals. *Science.* **130**, 1192-1194.

Hunt, J. A. (1951). *A general survey of the Somaliland Protectorate 1944-1950.*

Hunter, F. M. (1877). *An Account of the British Settlement of Aden in Arabia.* Trubner & Co.; London.

Hussein, A. M. and Saad, M. A. G. (1975). Incidence of brucellosis in camels in Kordofan province. *Proc. 7th Ann. Conf. Sudan Vet. Assoc.*

Ibrahim, T. M., Shaker, M. and Salem, F. M. S. (1977). Normal serum cholinesterase level in camel as a diagnostic tool in toxic and diseased conditions. *Egyptian J. Vet. Sci.* **10**, 97-105.

Idris, O. F. and Tartour, G. (1977). *Studies of proteins and certain electrolytes of the camel serum.* In Mustafa, A. A. & el Sanousi, S. M. (eds) *Proc. VIII Cong. Sudan Vet. Assoc.* El Tamaddon Printers Ltd.: Khartoum. 94-98.

Ilemobade, A. A. (1971). Studies on the incidence and pathogenicity of *T. evansi* in Nigeria. I. The incidence of *T. evansi* in camels. *ISCTRC, OAU/STRC. Publ. No. 105*, 157-161.

Ilowarsky, S. A. and Zeiss, H. (1923). 'Bayer 205' in experimental surra in camels (in German). *Rev. Microbiol. Epidemiol.* **2**, 95.

Imam I. Z. E. and Labib, A. (1963). Complement fixing antibodies against epidemic and murine typhus in domestic animals in UAR. *J. Egyptian Publ. Hlth Assoc.* **38**, 101-105.

Imam, Z. E. and Alfy, L. (1966). Evidence of typhus infection in domestic animals in Egypt. *Bull. Wld. Hlth Org.* **35**, 123-126.

Imbert, M. (1859). Mémoire sur le dromadaire. *Mém. Soc. Imp. Cent. Méd. Vét.* **4**, 377-419.

Imperial Ethiopian Government (1972). *A review of animal health and livestock productivity factors in Ethiopia 1965-1971.* Dept. Vet. Serv. MinMag.: Addis Ababa.

Ingram, D. L. and Mount, L. E. (1975). In Schaeffer, K. E. (ed). *Man and Animals in Hot Environments.* Springer-Verlag: Berlin.

Institut für Tropische Veterinärmedizin (1973). *Water economy of the dromadaries* (in German). Markblatt: Geissen.

Institut für Tropische Veterinärmedizin (1973). *Types of dromedaries.* Markblatt: Geissen.

Institute für Tropische Veterinärmedizin (1973). *Some physiological data on the camel* (in German). Markblatt: Geissen.

Institut für Tropische Veterinärmedizin (1973). *Practical performance of camels* (in German). Markblatt: Geissen. NO. 20.

Institut für Tropische Veterinärmedizin (1973). *Camel's milk* (in German). Markblatt: Geissen. No. 21.

Ipatenko, N. G. (1973). *Infectious enterotoxaemia of camels* (in Russian). In Orlov. F. M. (ed.) *Little-known contagious diseases of animals.* 248-255.

Iskander, F. A. and Mikhail, Y. (1966). A morphological study of the adrenal gland of the camel. *J. Arab Vet. Med. Assoc.* **26**, 285-292.

Iskander, F. A. and Naga, I. A. (1973). The effect of old age on the adrenal cortex of man and certain mammals. *J. Egyptian Vet. Med. Assoc.* **33**, 85-89.

Islamy A. (1950). Riding cames around Khash and Iranshah. *Rev. Fac. Med. Vet.*, Teheran **12(2)**, 87.

Ismail, A. A. and Amer, A. A. (1976). Efficacy of dursban, diazinon, lindane and DDT for treatment of mange in camels and buffaloes. *Assiut Vet. Med. J.* **3**, 199-201.

Ismail, F. A. (1975). Preservation of extract from camel meat (in German). *Die Fleischwirtschaft.* **55**, 248-249.

Ismail, F. A. (1975). On the presence of Inossin-5'-Monohosphate in camel meat (in German). *Die Fleischwirtwchaft.* **55**, 1735-1736.

Isoun, T. T., Losos, G. J. and Ikede, B. O. (1972). Diseases of zoo animals in Nigeria. *J. Wldl. Dis.* **8**, 335-339.

Isserlin, B. S. J. (1950). On some possible early occurrences of the camel in Palestine. *Israel Exp. Fund Quarterly.* **82**, 50-53.

Ivashkin, E. E. (1953). Phenothiazine tested against parabronemiasis of camels (*Camelus dromedarius*) (in Russian). *Pap. Helmin. Pres. Akad. Skjabin. Akad. Nauk Moscow.* 254-257.

Ivashkin, V. M. (1956). Elucidation of the life cycle of the nematode *Parabronema skjabini* of ruminants (in Russian). *Dokladi Akad.*

196

Nauk SSR. **107**, 773–775.

Ivashkin, V. M. (1961). Epidemiology and prophylaxis of *Thelazia leesei* infestation in camels (in Russian). *Trudy Gelmint Lab. Akad. Nauk SSR.* **11**, 92–94.

Iwema, S. (1960). The Ship of the Desert. *Veeteelt en Zuivelberichten.* **3**, 390–394.

Jain, N. C. and Keeton, K. S. (1974). Morphology of camel and llama erythrocytes as viewed with the scanning electron microscope. *British Vet. J.* **160**, 288–291.

Jamdar, M. N. (1960). Comparative anatomy of the bony system of the camel (*Camelus dromedarius*). I. Bones of the fore limb of the camel. *Indian Vet. J.* **37**, 235–239.

Jamdar M. N. (1960). Comparative anatomy of the bony system of the camel (*Camelus dromedarius*). II. Bones of the hind limb of the camel. *Indian Vet. J.* **37**, 279–291.

Jamdar, M. N. (1961). Comparative anatomy of the bony system of the camel (*Camelus dromedarius*). III. Axial skeleton. *Indian Vet. J.* **38**, 53–64.

Jamdar, M. N. (1961). Comparative anatomy of the bony system of the camel (*Camelus dromedarius*). IV. Bones of the skull. *Indian Vet. J.* **38**, 325–338.

Jashoski, B. J. and Williamson, W. M. (1958). A fatal nematodiosis in the camel. *J. American Vet. Med. Assoc.* **132**, 35–37.

Jastrzebski, M., Welento, J., Flieger, S. and Lakomy, M. (1979). The olive nucleus, the motor co-ordinating centre of the bulb of the dromedary, from its functional and comparative aspects (in Polish). *Medyeyna Weterynaryjna.* **35**, 629–632.

Jatkar, P. R. (1968). Serum protein fractions of normal adult male camel. *Indian Vet. J.* **45**, 733–734.

Jatkar, P. R., Kohli, R. N. and Bhatt, P. L. (1962). Quantitative study on camel blood 3. *Indian Vet. J.* **39**, 548–549.

Jatkar, P. R. and Singh, M. (1971). Diagnosis of surra in camels by the passive haemagglutination test. *British Vet. J.* **127**, 283–288.

Jatkar, P. R. and Purohit, M. S. (1971). Pathogenesis of anaemia in *Trypanosoma evansi.* I. Haematology. *Indian Vet. J.* **48**, 239–244.

Jatkar, P. R., Ghosal, A. K. and Singh, M. (1973). Pathogenesis of anaemia in *Trypanosoma evansi* infection. III. Studies on serum proteins (in camel). *Indian Vet. J.* **50**, 634–636.

Jatkar, P. R. and Singh, M. (1974). Pathogenesis of anaemia in trypanosome infection. IV. Blood glucose studies. *Indian Vet. J.* **51**, 710–714.

Jatkar, P. R., Rao, P. U. and Singh, M. (1977). Diagnosis of surra: capillary agglutination test. *Indian Vet. J.* **54**, 795–797.

Jean (1930). Utilisation du chameau dans l'armée. *Rev. Vet. Milit.* **14**, 177–187.

Jennison, C. (1927). *Table of Gestation Periods and Number of Young.* A. & C. Black: London.

Jibra'il Jabbur (1967). *The camel: Data from Arkan al Badawa* (in Arabic). Kitab el 'Id, American University of Beirut: Beirut.

Johnson, M. (1978). By ship or by camel. The struggle for the Cameroons' ivory trade in the 19th century. *J. Afr. Hist.* **19**, 539–549.

Joleaud, L. (1931). Succession des faunes de mammifères quaternaires en Berberie. *C. R. 15ᵉ Cong. Int. Anthrop. Archaeol. Préhist.* 220–226.

Joly (1909). Notes géographiques sur la Tunisie. *Bull. Soc. Géog. Algérie.* **1969**, 249–495.

Jomard, M. (1853). *Le régiment des dromadaires à l'armée d'orient (1798–1801).* In *Carbuccia.* 219–244.

Jones, H. L. (translator) (1966). *The Geography of Strabo.* Harvard University Press: Cambridge, Massachusetts.

Jore d'Arces (1953). L'echinococcose en Algérie. *Bull. Off. Int. Epiz.* **40**, 45–52.

Joshi, C. K. (1972). *Studies on certain aspects of reproduction in she-camel.* M.V. Sc. Thesis. University of Udaipur.

Joshi, C. K., Vyas, K. K. and Pareek, P. K. (1978). Studies on oestrus cycle in Bikaneri she-camel (*Camelus dromedarius*). *Indian J. Anim. Sci.* **48**, 141–145.

Joshi, C. K., Pareek, P. K. and Vyas, K. K. (1980). Note on the sexual behaviour of she-camel during oestrus. *Indian J. Anim. Sci.* **50**, 588.

Joshua, H. and Ishay, J. (1973). The haemolytic properties of the oriental hornet venom. *Acta Pharm. Tox.* **33**, 42–52.

Jousselin, M. (1947). Notes sur quelques plantes fourragères du Sahel *Rev. Elev. Méd. Vét. Pays Trop.* **1**, 273–277.

Jousselin, M. (1950). Notes sur la pathologie du dromadaire. De quelques traitements indigènes. *Rev, Elev. Méd. Vét. Pays Trop.* **3**, 105–108.

Jousselin, M. (1950). Notes sur quelques pâturages camelins et la cure de sel dans l'Adras des Iforas et la région de Tombouctou. *Rev. Elev. Méd. Vét. Pays Trop.* **4**, 209–211.

Joyeux, C. (1923). Recherche sur la faune helminthologique africaine Cestodes. *Arch. Inst. Pasteur*, Tunis **12**, 119–167.

Julien, C. A. (1956). *Histoire de l'Afrique du Nord.* Paris.

Julien, C. A. (1961). *Histoire de l'Afrique du Nord.* Payot: Paris.

Juzlikaev, R. D. and Ahmediev, A. (1965). A method of accelerating reproduction in camels (in Russian). *Zhivotnovodstvo*, Moscow **27(12)**, 61–63.

Kacharov, D. N. and Korovine, E. P. (1942). *La vie dans les déserts* (Edition française par Th. Monod). Payot: Paris.

Kagunya, D. K. J. and Waiyaki, P. G. (1978). A serological survey of animal brucellosis in the north-eastern province of Kenya. *Kenya Vet.* **2(2)**, 35–38.

Kakoma, I. and Kinyanjui, M. (1974). Immunogenicity of mycoplasma galactan. *Res. Vet. Sci.* **3**, 397–399.

Kalinin, V. G. and Terentjev, S. M. (1975). Veterinary prophylactic measures in camel breeding (in Russian). *Kolos*, Moscow **1975**, 197–213.

Kamel, H. (1939). *Pneumococcus in camels.* Tech. Sci. Service Bull. No. 226, Min. Ag.; Govt. Press: Cairo.

Kamel, H and Loutf, Z. S. (1963). Types of Salmonella prevailing in apparently healthy camels slaughtered for meat. *Proc. 4th Ann. Arab Vet. Cong.*, Cairo.

Kanan, C. V. (1960). A preliminary study on the pattern of development of the chondrocranium of *Camelus dromedarius.* *Sudan J. Vet. Sci. Anim. Husb.* **1**, 35–41.

Kanan, C. V. (1960). Notes on the vertebral column, ribs and sternum of the camel. *Sudan J. Vet. Sci. Anim. Husb.* **1**, 84–91.

Kanan, C. V. (1960). A study of the development of the auditory capsule of the chondrocranium in *Camelus dromedarius* at 5–4 cm C.R. length stage. *Acta Morph. Neerlando-Scandinavica.* **4**, 1.

Kanan, C. V. (1961). A detailed study of the nasal capsule of the chondrocranium of *Camelus dromedarius* at 5–4 cm C.R. length stage. *Proc. Royal Soc.*, Edinburgh. **68B**.

Kanan, C. V. (1969). Special accessory nerve of the camel (*Camelus dromedarius*). *Acta Anat.* **74**, 623.

Kanan, C. V. (1970). Nuclear configuration of the diencephalaon of *Camelus dromedarius.* *Acta Anat.* **75**.

Kanan, C. V. (1970). The cerebral arteries of *Camelus dromedarius.* *Acta Anat.* **77**.

Kanan, C. V. (1970). Variations in the musculature of the neck of the camel (*Camelus dromedarius*). *Acta Morph. Neerlando-Scandinavica.* **7**, 269–274.

Kanan, C. V. (1971). The arterial blood supply to the diaphragm of the camel. *Acta Morph. Neerlando-Scandinavica.* **8**.

Kanan, C. V. (1971). Observations on the pattern and distribution of the coronary blood vessels of the camel (*Camelus dromedarius*). *Acta Morph. Neerlando-Scandinavica.* **8**, 321–332.

Kanan, C. V. (1972). Observations on the distribution of external and internal ophthalmic arteries in the camel (*Camelus dromedarius*). *Acta Anat.* **81**, 74–82.

Kanan, C. V. (1973). Observations on the arterial supply to the hip joint of *Camelus dromedarius.* *Acta Morph. Neerlando-Scandinavica.* **11**, 209–214.

Kanan, C. V. (1973). The external configuration of the cerebral hemispheres of the camel. *Acta Anat.* **85**.

Kanan, C. V. and Abdalla, O. (1979). Observations on the distribution of the omentum in the one-humped camel (*Camelus dromedarius*). *Acta Morph. Neerlando-Scandinavica.* **17**, 295-300.

Kane, K. K., Boever, W. J., Read, B. W. and Newton, K. A. (1977). Use of human chorionic gonadotropin in a male bactrian camel to increase reproductive behaviour. *J. Zoo. Anim. Med.* **8**, 37-40.

Kangaran-Farahani, J., Samadieh, B., Kargar-Moaakhar, R., Khakpour, M. and Sohrabi-Haghdooot, I. (1979). An attempt to demonstrate the presence of influenzavirus antibodies in the serum of camels (in Persian). *J. Vet. Fac. Univ. Tehran.* **35**, 58-65.

Kapur, I. S. and Sharma, R. K. (1972). A study on effectiveness of thiabendazole in treatment of pica in camels. *Haryana Vet.* **11**, 11-15.

Kassir, S. M., Bashir, N. and Kan, J. A. (1967). *Survey of cattle, buffalo and camel slaughter receipts in Baghdad, Iraq, 1966.* FAO Training Project Tech. Rep. No. 8, FAO: Rome.

Kataitseva, T. V. (1967). Epidemiology of *Dipetalonema evansi* infection in camels (in Russian). *Mater. Konf. Vses. Obsbch. Gel'mint.*, Moscow. **2**, 144-148.

Kataitseva, T. V. (1968). Life cycle of the nematode *Dipetalonema evansi* Lewis 1882 (in Russian). *Dokl. Akad. Nauk SSSR.* **180**, 1261-1264.

Kataitseva, T. V. (1969). Biology of *Dipetalonema evansi* Lewis 1882, a parasite of camels. *Parazitologiya.* **3**, 76-80.

Kaura, R. L. (1957). *Indian Breeds of Livestock.* Prem. Publishers: Lucknow.

Kawashti, I. S. A. (1966). Comparative drought resistance in summer of camels, donkeys, sheep and goats under Egyptian desert conditions. *Bull. Inst. Desert,* Egypt. **16(2)**, 181-204.

Kazanskii, I. I. (1958). *Bull. Off. Int. Epiz.* **49**, 142-156.

Kchouk, M. and Durand, M. (1958). Quelques dosages chimiques dans le sang des dromadaires en Tunisie. *Arch. Inst. Pasteur,* Tunis. **35**, 3-37.

Keikin, D. (1976). Camel breeding can be economical (in Russian). *Konnevod. Konnyi Sport.* **2**, 12-13.

Keimer, L. (1929). On the figure of a camel rider before the flight from Egypt. *Kemi,* Cairo. **2**, 85-90.

Kemp, G. E., Causey, O. R., Moore, D. L. and O'Connor, E. H. (1973). Viral isolates from livestock in northern Nigeria: 1966-1970. *American J. Vet. Res.* **34**, 707-710.

Kendall, S. B. (1974). Some parasites of domestic animals in the Aswan Governorate - Arab Republic of Egypt. *Trop. Anim. Hlth Prod.* **6**, 128-130.

Kennedy, W. (1925). *Ann. Rep. Vet. Dep. Sudan Govt.*

Kenneth, J. H. (1947). *Gestation Periods.* Tech. Comm. No. 5, Imp. Bureau of Animal Breeding and Genetics.

Khalifa, H., Fouad, M. T., Awad, Y. L. and Gregory, M. E. (1973). Application of Fast Gray RA to the spectrophotometric determination of copper in liver of Egyptian camels. *Microchem. J.* **18**, 536-542.

Khalil, G. M. (1976). Prevalence of *Linguatula serrata* infection in animals from the Cairo abattoir. *J. Parasit.* **62**, 126.

Khamis, Y., Fouad, M. T. and Sayed, A. (1973). Comparaison de tranquillisants et sédatifs sur le dromadaire (*Camelus dromedarius*). *Info. Méd. Vét.* **4**, 314-324.

Khamis, Y., Fouad, K. and Sayed, A. (1973). Comparative studies on tranquilisation and sedation of *Camelus dromedarius*. *Vet. Med. Rev.* **4**, 336-345.

Khan, A. A. (1971). *Sexual behaviour of the male camel (Camelus dromedarius) and some studies on semen.* M.S. Thesis. Bikaner University of Udaipur.

Khan A. A. and Kohli, I. S. (1972). A study on sexual behaviour of male camel (*Camelus dromedarius*). *Indian Vet. J.* **49**, 1007-1012.

Khan, A. A. and Kohli, I. S. (1973). A note on collection of semen from camel with the help of an artificial vagina. *Indian J. Anim. Sci.* **43**, 454-455.

Khan, A. A. and Kohli, I. S. (1973). A note on biometrics of the camel spermatozoa (*Camelus dromedarius*). *Indian J. Anim. Sci.* **43**, 792-793.

Khan, A. A. and Kohli, I. S. (1973). A note on the sexual behaviour of male camel (*Camelus dromedarius*). *Indian J. Anim. Sci.* **43**, 1092-1094.

Khan, A. A. and Kohli, I. S. (1973). A note on variations in blood serum cholesterol in the camel (*Camelus dromedarius*). *Indian J. Anim. Sci.* **43**, 1094-1095.

Khan, A. A. and Kohli, I. S. (1977). A note on some haematological studies on male camel (*Camelus dromedarius*) before and during rut. *Indian J. Anim. Sci.* **48**, 325-326.

Khan, M. K. U. and Appanna, T. C. (1965). Evaluation of biological value of camel milk protein. *J. Nutr. Diet.*, India. **2**, 109-112.

Khan, M. K. U. and Appanna, T. C. (1967). Carotene and vitamin A in camel milk. *J. Nutr. Diet.*, India. **4**, 17-20.

Khatami, K. (1970). *A new promising approach to the solution of the meat and protein problem in the arid and semi-arid countries of the world.* Min. Agriculture: Teheran (mimeo).

Khatami, K. (1970). *Camel Meat.* Min. Agriculture: Teheran.

Khavesson, Y. I. (1950). Les chameaux d'espère *Paracamelus paracamelus alexejori* sp. nov. du Pliocene d'Odessa. *C. R. Acad, Sci,* Moscow. **NS70**, 917-920.

Khaveson, Y. I. (1954). Tertiary camels of the eastern hemisphere (Genus *Paracamelus*). *Proc. Palaeo. Inst. Acad. Sci.* USSR. **47**, 101-162.

Kherasov, S. G. (1961). *Camel's milk as human food* (in Russian). Sborn vses. Konf. po Molochn Delu posvyashch, 100-Letiyn so Dnya Rozhd. Prof. A. A. Kalanatara, Erevan 1960.

Kherasov, S. G. (1961). Composition, properties and nutritive value of camel milk (in Russian). *Vopr. Pitan.* **20**, 69-72.

Kherasov, S. G. (1976). Some biological characters of camels as dairy animals (in Russian). *Trudy Orenburg Sel'-khz Inst.* **30**, 3-9.

Kibasou, M. and Donchenko, A. S. (1976). Experimental determination of economic losses in camels due to tuberculosis (in Russian). *Vest. Sel'-khz Nauk Kazakh.* **12**, 5-8.

King, L. W. (1915). *Bronze Reliefs from the Gates of Shalmaneser.* British Museum: London.

Kingdon, J. (1979). *East African Mammals. Vol. III Part B Large Mammals.* Academic Press: London.

Klein, J. M., Simonkovich, E., Alonso, J. M. and Baranton, G. (1975). Observations ecologiques dans une zone enzootique de peste en Mauritanie. 2. Les puces de rongeurs (Insecta, Siphonaptera). *Cah. Ent. Med. Parasit.*, ORSTOM. **13**, 29-39.

Kligler, I. J. and Weitzmann, I. (1924). Experimental study of Trypanosomiasis in Palestine. *Ann. Trop. Med. Parasit.* **18**, 437.

Kligler, I. J. and Weitzmann, I. (1926). Susceptibility and resistance to Trypanosome infections. *Ann. Trop. Med. Parasit.* **20**, 147.

Knapp, E. (1934). *The tongue, pharynx and larynx of the camel and dromedary.* Dissertation. Med. Fac. University of Munster.

Knoess, K. (1976). *Assignment report on animal production in the Middle Awash Valley.* FAO: Rome.

Knoess, K. H. (1977). The camel as a meat and milk animal. *World Animal Review* **22**, 39-44.

Knoess, K. H. (1977). Le chameau producteur de viande et de lait *Rev. Mond. Zootech.* **22**, 39-44.

Knoess, K. H. (1979). Improvement of camel production (range and livestock development in the Gefara plains, Libya). *FAO Consultant's Report.* UTFN/LIB/010.

Knoess, K. H. (1980). Milk production of the dromedary. In *Workshop on Camels,* Khartoum, Sudan, 18-20 Dec. 1979. Intnl. Foundation for Science: Stockholm, Sweden. 201-214.

Knowles, R. H. (1924). The formol-gel test as applied to camels affected with *Trypanosoma sudanense*. *J. Comp. Path. Therap.* **37**, 37-44.

Knowles, R. H. (1924). *Ann. Rep. Vet. Dept. Sudan Govt.*

Knowles, R. H. (1925). *Ann. Rep. Vet. Dept. Sudan Govt.*

Knowles, R. H. (1925). Treatment of camels affected with *T. sudanense* with 'Bayer 205' and further observations on the formol-gel test. *J. Comp. Path. Therap.* **38**, 42-48.

198

Knowles, R. H. (1927). Trypanosomiasis of camels in the Anglo-Egyptian Sudan: Diagnosis, Chemotherapy, Immunity. *J. Comp. Path. Therap.* **40**, 59-71; 118-143.

Knowles, R. H. (1929). Susceptibility of camels to *Trypanosoma pecandi*. *Royal Army Vet. Corps.* **1**, 42-43.

Koch, D. (1974). Pupiparous Diptera from mammals in the north-eastern Mediterranean area (Ins.: Diptera) (in German). *Senck. Biol.* **55**, 87-104.

Kohli, R. N. (1963). Cellular micrometry of camel's blood. *Indian. Vet. J.* **40**, 134.

Kohli, R. N. and Bhatt, P. L. (1961). A study on the normal specific gravity of blood serum and plasma of the camel. *Indian Vet. J.* **36**, 494-497.

Kolabskii, N. A. and Pashkin, P. I. (1974). Coccidiosis in camels (in Russian). In *Coccidiosis in Farm Animals*. Leningrad, USSR.

Kolpakov, V. N. (1935). On the cross-breeding of camels (in German). *Berlin Tierarztl. Wschr.* **51**, 617-622.

Kon, S. K. (1972). *Milk and Milk Products in Human Nutrition*. FAO Nutrition Studies. **No. 27**. FAO: Rome.

Konuk, T. (1970). The microscopic appearance of camel and llama erythrocytes, *Vet. Fac., Derg University*, Ankara. **17**, 518-522.

Korkonienko-Koneva, Z. P. and Orakhov (1958). Prophylaxie de quelques maladies parasitaires du chameau dans la RSS de Turkmen. *Bull. Off. Int. Epiz.* **49**, 297-312.

Korten, H. (1884). The Syrian Camel (in German). *Das Heilige Land.* **28**, 61-64.

Kospakov, Z. K. (1975). Antibacterial properties of camel milk (in Russian). *Trudy Vses Nauk Inst. Vet. Sanit.* **51**, 37-40.

Kospakov, Z. K. (1976). Cell content in the milk of Bactrian camels depending on stage of lactation and condition of udder. *Prob. Vet. Sanit.* **55**, 21-25.

Kospakov, Z. K. (1976). Phage typing pathogenic staphylococci isolated from milk and environment of camel breeding farms (in Russian). *Prob. Vet. Sanit.* **55**, 32-35.

Koulischer, L., Tijskens, J. and Mortelmans, J. (1971). Mammalian cytogenetics. IV. The chromosomes of two male camelidae: *Camelus bactrianus* and *Lama vicugna*. *Acta Zool. Paht.*, Antwerp. **52**, 89-92.

Koveshnikov, V. S. (1975). *Camel breeding in the USSR* (in Russian). 31-34. Shevchenko, USSR.

Kowalevsky, M. J. M. (1912). Le chameau et ses maladies d'après les observations d'auteurs russes. *J. Méd. Vét. Zootech.*, Lyon **15**, 462-466; 540-549; 600-613.

Kozojed, V., Blazek, K. and Amin, A. (1976). Incidence of toxoplasmosis in domestic animals in Afghanistan. *Folia Parasit.* **23**, 273-275.

Kraft, H. (1957). Behaviour of mother and young camels (in German). *Saugetierk.*, Mitteil. **5(4)**, 174-175.

Kraft, H. (1957). Studies of the blood composition of the Camelidae (in German). *Berlin. Munchen Tierarztl. Wschr.* **70**, 371.

Kreis, H. A. (1938). A contribution to the knowledge of Nematode parasites. VI. Nematode parasites in the Zoological Gardens in Basel (in German). *Zentralbl. Bakt.* **141**, 279-303.

Krishnamurthy, D. and Tyagi, R. (1977). Characteristics of synovial fluid and blood sera of cattle, buffaloes and camels in health and when affected with upward fixation of patella. *Indian Vet. J.* **54**, 995-1004.

Krishnamurthy, D. and Tyagi, R. P. S. (1978). Viscosity of normal bovine and camel synovial fluid. *Indian Vet. J.* **55**, 986-988.

Krishnamurthy, D., Tyagi, R. P. S. and Sharma, D. N. (1979). Absence of the medial patella ligament in camels. *Indian Vet. J.* **56**, 243-245.

Krupenko, S. S. (1972). Camel pox caused by vaccinia virus (in Russian). *Vet.*, Moscow. **6**, 61-62.

Krupenko, S. S., Bailarov, A. and Annaduryev, O. (1973). Lactotherapy (non-specific protein therapy) for camel pox (in Russian). *Vet.*, Moscow. **7**, 51-52.

Kudabaev, K. A., Cherepanova, V. P. and Ponomarev, P. P.(1972). Amino acid composition of the milk of Kazakh Bactrian camels (in Russian). *Vest. Sel'-khz. Stev. Nauk. Alma-Ata.* **15**, 69-73.

Kugenev, P. V. and Medvedeva, M. N. (1960). Composition of camel's milk (in Russian). *Vopr. Pitan.* **19**, 75-76.

Kulaeva, V. (1964). The production of the bactrian camel (in Russian). *Konnevod. Konnyi Sport.* **34**, 9-10.

Kuliev, K. (1959). The utilization of camels' milk (in Russian). *Mol. Promyslenn.* **20(2)**, 28.

Kuliev, K. A. (1959). The mineral content of camels' milk (in Russian). *Kdravookhr.* Turkmen **6**, 27-29.

Kulshreshtha, R. C., Arora, R. G. and Kalra, D. S. (1974). Seroprevalence of Q-fever in camels, buffaloes and pigs. *Indian J. Med. Res.* **62**, 1314-1316.

Kulshreshtha, R. C., Arora, R. G. and Kalra, D. S. (1975). Brucellosis in camels and horses. *Indian J. Anim. Sci.* **45**, 637-675.

Kumar, M., Ghosh, P. K. and Banerjee, S. (1961). Biochemical studies on Indian camel (*Camelus dromedarius*). 1. Blood proteins and lipids. *J. Sci. Indust. Res.* **20C**, 236-238.

Kumar, M. and Banerjee, S. (1962). Biochemical studies on Indian camel (*Camelus dromedarius*). 3. Plasma insulin-like activity and glucose tolerance. *J. Sci. Indust. Res.* **21C**, 291-292.

Kumar, R., Singh, G., Manchar, M. and Nigam, J. M. (1977). Bilateral fracture of mandible in camel. *Indian Vet. J.* **54**, 477-478.

Kumar, V. R., Singh, G. and Dalt, S. C. (1979). Treatment of unilateral fracture of mandible by bone-plating in camels. *Indian Vet. J.* **56**, 58-59.

Kunichkin, G. I. (1975). The camel nostril fly and its control (in Russian). *Vet., Moscow.* No. 9, 77-79.

Kunichkin, G. I. and Eskaliev, T. E. (1975). Control of camel trypanosomiasis (in Russian). *Vet., Moscow.* No. 2, 72-79.

Kural, S. (1948). The anatomy and function of the pelvis and thigh of the camel. *T.C. Yuk Zir-Enst.*, Ankara. **156**, 4-113.

Kushner, H. F. (1941). On the physiological nature of hybrid vigour in animals (in Russian). *C.R. (Dokl) Acad. Sci. USSR.* **NS 19**, 185-188.

Kushner, H. F. and Kitaeva, O. N. (1938). Variation in blood composition of the Bactrian camel, the dromedary and their hybrids with reference to hybrid vigour (in Russian). *Izvest. Akad. Nauk SSR*, *Ord. mat-est., Ser. biol.* 903-916.

Kuthe, G. (1977). Physiological and nutritional requirements of foraging livestock in arid climatic region. *Anim. Res. Develop.* **3**, 112-119.

Kutzner, E. and Hinaidi, H. K. (1968). Contribution to the helminth fauna of Egypt 1. *Cysticercus cameli* Nomani, 1920 (in German). *Zentralbl. Vet. Med.* **15B**, 899-910.

Kuznecov, V. A., Tretjjakov, V. N., Doncenko, V., Ardeeva, K. F., Loza, V. V. and Sinicyna, M. P. (1970). The yield of meat and meat products from the Turkmen one-humped camel (in Russian). *Trudy Turkmen Sel.-khz. Inst.* **15**, 123-125.

Kuznecov, V. A. and Tretjjakov, V. N. (1970). Carcass classification in the Turkmen single-humped camel (in Russian). *Trudy Turkmen Sel.-khz. Inst.* **15**, 130-133.

Lahille, F. (1914). Note on the accidental presence in Buenos Aires of a camel parasite (in Spanish). *Bol. Min. Ag. Buenos Aires.* **17**, 289-293.

Lakhotia, R. L., Bhargava, A. K. and Merrotra, P. N. (1964). Normal ranges for some blood constituents of the Indian camel. *Vet. Rec.* **76**, 121-122.

Lakoza, I. I. (1938). Interspecific hybridization of dromedaries and Bactrians (in Russian). *Bull. Acad. Sci. URSS, Cl. Sci. Math. Nat. (Ser. Biol.)* **4**, 885-902.

Lakoza, I. I. (1938). Further data on camel hybrids (preliminary communication) (in Russian). *Konevodstov.* **1938(2)**, 57-59.

Lakoza, I. I. (ed) (1938). *Camel breeding in the USSR* (in Russian). Seljhozgiz: Moscow.

Lakoza, I. I. (1953). *Camel breeding* (in Russian). Seljhozgiz: Moscow.

Lakoza, I. I. (1962). A valuable source for production of meat, milk and wool (in Russian). *Konevodstvo.* **12**, 2-5.

Lakoza, I. I. and Rumjancev, N. V. (1934). *Camel breeding* (in Russian). Seljhozgiv: Moscow.

199

Lal, B. J., Bhatt, P. L. and Kohli, R. N. (1962). Quantitative biochemical studies on camel's blood. I. Sugar and chloride content. *Indian Vet. J.* **39**, 64-66.

Langman, V. A., Maloiy, G. M. O., Schmidt-Nielsen, K. and Schroter, R.C. (1978). Respiratory water and heat loss in camels subjected to dehydration. *J. Physiol.* **278**, 35.

Langridge, W. P. (1974). *Tsetse and Trypanosomiasis survey of Borana-Sidamo. Part I. Neghelli and Dawa River.* Min. Ag.: Addis Ababa.

Lankisch, P. G., Schroeter, R., Lege, L. and Vogt, W. (1973). Reduced glutathione and glutathione reductase - a comparative study of erythrocytes from various species. *Comp. Biochem. Physiol.* **2**, 639-641.

Laoust, E. (1920). *Mots et choses berbères.* Augustin Challamel: Paris.

Larbauî, D., Allyulya, R., Osiiskaya, L. V., Osiiskii, I. Yu. and Benel'muffok, M. (1980). Hydatidosis in Algiers (in Russian). *Med. Parazit. Parazit. Bolez.* **49**, 21-23.

Larrat, R. (1936). *Conférénce consultative de l'élevage: élevage du dromadaire.* Gouvernement-Général AOF: Dakar.

Larrat, R. (1937). Elevage du dromadaire. *Rec. Méd. Vét. Exot.* **10**, 201.

Lavocat, R. (1958). Classification des Ongules d'après leur origine et leur évolution. *Mammalia.* **22**, 28-40.

Leach, T..M. (1961). Observations on the treatment of *T. evansi* infection in camels. *J. Comp. Path.* **71**, 109-117.

Lebailly, J. (1958). Le nomadisme au Sahara français. Migrations pastorales et courants caravaniers. *Rev. Corps Vét. Armée.* **3**, 145-151.

Leckie, V. C. (1925). Some notes on surra in the camel, its treatment and prevention. *British Vet. J.* **81**, 351, 404.

Lee, D. G. and Schmidt-Nielsen, K. (1962). The skin, sweat glands and hair follicles of the camel (*Camelus dromadarius*). *Anat. Res.* **143**, 71-77.

Leeds, A. and Vayda, A. (eds) (1965). *Man, Culture and Animals.* American Assoc. for the Advancement of Science: Washington.

Leese, A. S. (1908). *Camel Tuberculosis.* Ann. Rep. Officer Investigating Camel Diseases, India.

Leese, A. S. (1909). Two diseases of young camels. *J. Trop. Vet. Sci.* **4**, 1-7.

Leese, A. S. (1909). Note on tapeworms in Punjab camels. *J. Trop. Vet. Sci.* **4**, 305-306.

Leese, A. S. (1910). Acid-fast bacilli in a camel's lung with lesions resembling those of tuberculosis. *J. Comp. Path. Therap.* **23**, 358-359.

Leese, A. S. (1911). Bilharziosis in the camel. *J. Trop. Vet. Sci.* **6**.

Leese, A. S. (1911). Indian camel filiarisis. *J. Trop. Vet. Sci.* **6**, 263-264.

Leese, A. S. (1918). *"Tips" on camels for veterinary surgeons on active service.* Baillière & Tindall: London.

Leese, A. S. (1927). *A treatise on the one-humped camel in health and disease.* Haines & Sons: Stamford, England.

Leese, A. S. (1942). Castor seed poisoning or 'Coldstruck Paralysis' in the camel. *Vet. Rec.* **54**, 246.

Lefèbvre, E. (1907). Le chameau en Egypte. *Act. XIV Congr. Int. Orientalistes, Alger.* 2(*Sect. 7*). 24-62.

Lefèbvre des Noëttes, R. (1924). *La force motrice animale ä travers les âges.* Berger-Levrault: Paris.

Legge, C. M. (1936). The Arabian and the Bactrian Camel. *J. Manchester Georgr. Soc.* **46**, 21-48.

Legrain, L. (1930). *Terra-cottas from Nippur.* University of Pennsylvania Press: Philadelphia.

Lehmann, O. (1891). Das Kamel. *Zeitschr. Wissenschaft, Geog.,* Weimar. **8**, 3-51.

Leitch, I. (1940). *The feeding of camels.* Imp. Bureau of Animal Nutr. Tech. Comm. No. 13.

Lennep, E. W. van (1957). The glands of the digestive system of the one-humped camel. *Acta Morph. Neerlando-Scandinavica.* **1**, 283-292.

Leonard, A. G. (1894). *The Camel: Its uses and Management.* Longmans Green: London.

Lenox-Conyngham and H. M. Burden (1904). *Camels. Their Management and Diseases.* Baillière, Tindall & Cox: London.

Lépiskaar, J. (1979). Man and domesticated animals (in Swedish). *Svensk Veterinärtidning.* **31**, 503-518.

Leriche, A. (1953). Coutumes maures relatives à l'élevage. *Bull. IFAN.* **15**, 1316-1320.

Leriche, P. D. and Sewell, M. M. H. (1978). Identification of *Echinococcus granulosus* strains by enzyme electrophoresis. *Res. Vet. Sci.* **25**, 247-248.

Leroux, Ch. (1960). *Aspects de la régulation thermique des animaux du désert. Observations personelles chez le dromadaire.* Thèse DMV. ENV: Lyon No. 27.

Le Roux, P. L. (1929). Two species of *Haemonchus* Cobl. 1898, parasitizing the camel in the Cape Province. *15th Ann. Rep. Div. Vet. Serv. Union of South Africa.* pp. 439-463.

Lesbre, F.-K. (1903). Recherches anatomiques sur les camélidés. *Arch. Mus. Hist. Nat. Lyon.* **8**, 1-196.

Lesbre, F. X. (1930). *Précis d'exterieur du cheval et des principaux mammifères domestiques.* Vigot Frères: Paris.

Lesley, L. B. (1929). The purchase and importation of camels by the United States Government. *Southwestern Hist. Quart.* **23**, 18-33.

Lesley, L. B. (1929). *Uncle Sam's Camels.* Harvard University Press: Cambridge, Massachusetts.

Letts, G. A. (1964). Feral animals in the Northern Territory. *Australian Vet. J.* **40**, 84.

Leue, G. (1971). A review: First camel race in Europe in 1969 at Cologne Horse Race Track from the veterinary-physiological, genetic and biomechanical point of view (in German). *Deutsche Tierärztl. Wschr.* **78**, 500-503.

Leupold, J. (1967). 3rd Cong. Deutsche Tropenmed. Gesells. Urban & Schwarzonber: Munich.

Leupold, J. (1968). Le chameau, important animal domestique des pays subtropicaux. *Cah. bleus vét.* **15**, 1-6.

Levant, (1934). Rapport sur le fonctionnement du Laboratoire de Recherches du Service Vétérinaire des Troupes du Levant pendant l'annee 1933. *Rev. Vét. Milit.* **18**, 127-142.

Levêque, H. (1956-66). Carence d'origine tellurique chez les dromadaires du Sud tunisien. *Bull. Soc. Sci. Nat., Tunis.* **9/10**, 49-57.

Levêque, H. (1957). Contribution à l'étude d'une maladie appelée "Kraff" chez les chameaux du Sud tunisien. *Rev. Corps Vét. Armée.* **12**, 115-120.

Lévi-Provençal, E. (1950-53). *Histoire de l'Espagne musulmane.* Adrien Maisonneuve: Paris.

Lewis, I. M. (1955). *Peoples of the Horn of Africa.* I.A.I.: London.

Lewis, I. M. (1961). *A Pastoral Democracy.* Oxford University Press: London.

Lewis, I. M. and Andrzejewski, B. W. (1964). *Somali Poetry: An Introduction.* Clarendon Press: Oxford.

Lewis, J. G. (1978). Game domestication for animal production in Kenya: shade behaviour and factors affecting the herding of eland, oryx, buffalo and zebu cattle. *J. Agric. Sci.,* Cambridge. **90**, 587-595.

Lewis, J. H. (1976). Comparative hematology - studies on Camelidae. *Comp. Biochem. Physiol.* **55A**, 367-371.

Lewis, T. R. (1882). *Proc. Asiatic Soc. Bengal.*

Lewis, T. R. (1882). Nematoid hematozoon from a camel. *J. Royal Microscop. Soc.* **2**, 509.

Ley, W. (1951). *Dragons in Amber.* London.

Lhote, H. (1953). Le cheval et le chameau dans les peintures et gravures rupestres du Sahara. *Bull. IFAN.* **15**, 1212-1225.

Lhote, H. (1959). Nouvelle contribution à l'étude des gravures et peintures rupestres du Sahara central; la station de Tit (Ahaggar). *J. Soc. Africanistes.* **29**, 147-192.

Li, C. H., Danho, W. O., Chung, D. and Ruo, A. J. (1975). Isolation, characterization and amino acid sequence of melanotropins from camel pituitary gland. *Biochemistry.* **14**, 947-952.

Li, C. H., Yamashiro, D. and Lemaire, S. (1975). Total synthesis of camel beta-melanotropin by the solid phase method. *Biochemistry.* **14**, 953-956.

Li, C. H. and Chung, D. (1976). Relationship and possible function of the nasal sacs and glands of the one-humped camel *Camelus dromedarius*. Isolation and structure of an untriakontapeptide with opiate activity from camel pituitary glands. *Proc. Nat. Acad. Sci. USA.* **73**, 1145–1148.

Lin, D. K., Bhown, A. S. and Chernoff, A. I. (1976). Studies on camel hemoglobin. 1. Physico-chemical properties and some structural aspects of camel hemoglobin (*Camelus dromedarius*). *Biochim. Biophys. Acta.* **434**, 110–117.

Lingard, A. (1905). *Report on the preparation of rinderpest serum.* Calcutta.

Lingard, A. (1905). *Camel tuberculosis.* Ann. Rep. Imp. Bacteriologist, India.

Little, A., McKenzie, A. J., Morris R. J. H., Roberts, J. and Evans, J. V. (1970). Blood electrolytes in the Australian camel. *Australian J. Exp. Biol. Med. Sci.* **48**, 17–24.

Littlewood, (1888). *Camel tuberculosis.* Egyptian Official Gazette.

Livne, A. and Kuiper, P. J. C. (1973). Unique properties of the camel erythrocyte membrane. *Biochim. Biophys. Acta.* **318**, 41–49.

Lobanov, V. N. (1959). Pathology of experimental plague in camels (in Russian). *Arkh. Pat.* **21(7)**, 37–43.

Lobanov, V. N. (1967). *La peste chez les chameaux.* Seminaire Interrég. OMS Lutte contre la peste: Moscow.

Lodha, K. R. (1964). Some observations on *Microthoracius cameli* (Linnaeus) infestation in camels in Rajasthan, India. *Ceylon Vet. J.* **12**, 18–20.

Lodha, K. R. (1966). Studies on sarcoptic mange in camels (*Camelus dromedarius*). *Vet. Rec.* **79**, 41–43.

Lodha, K. R. (1966). Getting rid of camel mange. *Indian Fmg.* **1966**, 33–34.

Lodha, K. R., Raisinghani, P. M. and Karwaord, R. S. (1977). Chemotherapeutic trials of some anthelmintics against helminth parasites in camels. *Indian J. Anim. Sci.* **47**, 677–682.

Lodha, K. R. and Johnson, S. (1978). First report of *Nematodirella dromedarii* (Nematoda: Trichostrongyloidea) from the Indian camel *Camelus dromedarius*, with remarks on the genus *Nematodirella* Yorke and Maplestone, 1926. *Abs. Asian Cong. Parasit., 23–26 Feb. 1978, Bombay:* Bombay, India. pp. 219–220.

Lodha, K. R. and Raisinghani, P. M. (1979). Report of *Nematodirella dromedarii* (Nematoda: Trichostrongyloidea) from the Indian camel, *Camelus dromedarius*, with remarks on the genus *Nematodirella* Yorke and Maplestone, 1926. *Indian J. Anim. Sci.* **49**, 817–822.

Lodha, K. R. and Raisinghani, P. M. (1980). Report of echinococcosis in Indian camel (*Camelus dromedarius*) including its histopathology. *3rd. Nat Cong. Parasit., Haryana 3 (supp): 101,* Agric. Univ., Hissar, 24–26 Apr. 1980.

Lombardini, L. (1879). *Research on the camel* (in Italian). Tipografia T. Nistri e Ca: Pisa.

Lombardini, C. (1879). On the camels, especially those kept at the Royal dairy at San Rossore (in Italian). *Ann. Univ. Toscane,* Pisa.

Loo, C. T. (1929). Observations on ellipsoid erythrocytes in the blood of *Camelus dromedarius. Chinese J. Physiol.* **3**, 325–334.

Loomis, F. B. (1928). Poëbrotherium. *American J. Sci.* **16(92)**, 137–142.

Loomis, F. B. (1936). The skeleton of a new fossil camel from Wyoming. *Univ. Wyoming Publ.* **2(5–7)**, 59–64.

Luckenbill, D. D. (1926). *Ancient Records of Assyria and Babylonia.* Univ. Chicago Press: Chicago.

Luckens, A. G., Boid, R., Rae, P., Mahmoud, M. M., El Malik, K. H. and Gray, A. R. (1979). Serodiagnosis of infection with *Trypanosoma evansi* in the Sudan. *Trop. Anim. Hlth Prod.* **41**, 1–12.

Lundholm, B. (1976). Domestic animals in arid ecosystems. *Ecol. Bull.,* Stockholm **24**, 29–43.

Lus, J. J. (1938). Distant hybridization of animals - present status and future prospects (in Russian). *Izvest. Akad. Nauk SSSR, Otd. mat-est., Ser. biol.* 775–852.

Lyytinen, J. R. M. (1979). *Helminth infections and diseases of Camelides.* M. Sc. Thesis. Edinburgh.

McCarthy, P. H. (1980). The importation of the one-humped camel (*Camelus dromedarius*) into Australian during 1840–1841. *Australian Vet. J.* **56**, 547–551.

McClelland, N. (1924). *J. Soc. Chem. Indust.* **43**, 164.

Macewan-Jenkinson, D. (1972). Evaporative temperature regulation in domestic animals. *Symp. Zool. Soc.,* London. **31**, 345–356.

Macfarlane, W. V. (1968). Comparative functions of ruminants in hot environments. IN: Hafez, E. S. E. (ed), *Adaptation of Domestic Animals.* Lea & Febiger: Philadelphia Ch. 19: 264–276.

Macfarlane, W. V. (1977). Survival in an arid land. The desert mouse and the camel. *Australian Nat. Hist.* **19**, 18–23.

Macfarlane, W. V., Morris, R. J. H. and Howard, B. (1962). Water metabolism of merino sheep and camels. *Australian J. Sci.* **25**, 112ff.

Macfarlane, W. V., Morris, R. J. H. and Howard, B. (1963). Turnover and distribution of water in desert sheep, cattle and kangaroos. *Nature,* London. **197**, 270–271.

Macfarlane, W. V. and Siebert, B. D. (1967). Hydration and dehydration of desert camels. *Australian J. Exp. Biol. Med. Sci.* **45**, 29ff.

Macfarlane, W. V., Kinne, R., Walmsley, C. M., Siebert, B. D. and Peter, D. (1967). Vasopressins and the increase of water and electrolyte excretion by sheep, cattle and camels. *Nature,* London. **214**, 979–981.

Macfarlane, W. V., Howard, B., Haines, H., Kennedy, P. J. and Sharpe, C. M. (1971). Hierarchy of water and energy turnover of desert mammals. *Nature,* London. **234**, 483–484.

Macfarlane, W. V. and Howard, B. (1972). Comparative water and energy economy of wild and domestic mammals. *Symp. Zool. Soc., London.* **31**, 261–296.

Macfarlane, W. V., Howard, B., Maloiy, G. M. O. and Hopcraft, D. (1972). Tritiated water in field studies of ruminant metabolism in Africa. IN: *Isotope studies on the physiology of domestic animals.* International Atomic Energy Agency: Vienna. pp. 83–94.

Macfarlane, W. V. and Howard, B. (1973). Ruminant water metabolism in arid areas. IN: Wilson, A. D. (ed) *Studies of the Australian Arid Zone II. Animal Production.* Proc. Symp. Rangeland Res. Unit, Alice Springs. pp. 7–22.

MacGuckin de Slane, W. (ed) (1847). *Histoire des Berbères.* Imprimerie du Gouvernement: Alger.

Mackenna, M. C. (1966). Synopsis of Whitneyan and Arikarcean Camelid. *American Mus. Novitates.* **2253**, 1–11.

Mackenzie, P. Z. and Simpson, R. M. (1973). Diseases of Camels. IN: *The African Veterinary Handbook (5th Edition).* Pitman Publishing.

McKnight, T. L. (1969). *The Camel in Australia.* Melbourne University Press: Melbourne.

MacMichael, H. A. (1913). *Brands used by the chief camel-owning tribes of Kordofan.* Cambridge.

Macvenn, D. V. and Vanniasingham, J. (1970). *Trypanosoma evansi* and *Echinococcus granulosus* in a camel (*Camelus dromedarius*) at Zoo Negara. *S. East Asia J. Trop. Med. Publ. Hlth.* **1**, 292–293.

Magzoub, M. and Kasim, A. A. (1978). The prevalence of fascioliasis in Saudi Arabia. *Trop. Anim. Hlth Prod.* **10**, 205–206.

Mahaman, O. (1979). *Contribution à l'étude du dromadaire et de sa pathologie infectieuse. Etat des connaissances. Enquêtes non experimentales dans trois départements de la République du Niger.* Thèse DMV; ESIMEV: Dakar, Sénégal No. 14.

Mahamud Hagi, Locatelli, A. and Marchioni, G. (1979). Osmotic resistance of erythrocyte in the dromedary (in Italian). *Arch. Vet. Ital.* **30**, 125–127.

Mahmoud, A. H. and Abdel-Latif, K. (1958). Treatment of camel trypanosomiasis with suramin, antimosan and their combinations. *Vet. Med. J.,* Giza. **4**, 109–122.

Mahmoud, M. M. and Gray, A. R. (1980). Trypanosomiasis due to *Trypanosoma evansi* (Steel, 1885) Balbiani, 1888. A review of recent research. *Trop. Anim. Hlth Prod.* **12**, 35–49.

Mahnel, H. (1974). Laboratory differentiation of orthopox viruses (in German). *Zentralbl. Vet. Med.* **21B**, 242–258.

Mahnel, H. and Bartenbach, G. (1973). Classification of camel pox virus (in German). *Zentralbl. Vet. Med.* **20B**, 572-576.

Majeed, M. A., Hur, G., Rahman, Z. and Ahmed, A. (1980). Influence du sexe et de la saison sur 10 valeurs hématologiques du dromadaire adulte nomade.

Malbrant, R. (1931). La production animale du Tchad. *Rec. Méd. Vét. Exot.* **4**, 218-236.

Malek, E. (1959). Helminth parasites of the camel (*Camelus dromedarius*) in the Sudan. *J. Parasit.* 45 Supp. **73**, 38-39.

Malek, E. (1959). Check list of helminth parasites in Sudan. *Indian Vet. J.* **36**, 284-285.

Malik, P. D. (1967). Salmonella serotypes from camel in India. *J. Res., Ludhiana.* **4**, 123-126.

Maloiy, G. M. O. (1971). Renal salt and water excretion in the one-humped camel. *Int. Cong. Physiol. Sci.* **25**, 365.

Maloiy, G. M. O. (1972). Renal salt and water excretion in the camel (*Camelus dromedarius*). *Symp. Zool. Soc. London.* **31**, 243-259.

Maloiy, G. M. O. (1972). Comparative studies on digestion and fermentation rate in the free-stomach of the one-humped camel and the zebu steer. *Res. Vet. Sci.* **13**, 476-481.

Maloiy, G. M. O. (ed) (1972). *Comparative physiology of desert animals.* Academic Press: London.

Maloiy, G. M. O. (1973). Water metabolism of East African ruminants in arid and semi-arid regions. *Zeitsch. Tierz. Zuch.* **90**, 219-228.

Maloiy, G. M. O. (1975). Water and salt metabolism in the camel. IN: Johnson, H. D. (ed) *Progress in Animal Biometerology.* Ch. 3B.

Maloiy, G. M. O., Taylor, C. R. and Clemens, E. T. (1978). A comparison of gastrointestinal water content and osmolality in East African herbivores during hydration and dehydration. *J. Agric. Sci.*, Cambridge. **91**, 249-252.

Maloiy, G. M. O. and Clemens, E. T. (1980). Colonic and secretion of electrolytes as seen in five species of East African herbivorous mammals. *Comp. Biochem. Physiol.* **67**, 21-25.

Maloiy, G. M. O. and Clemens, E. T. (1980). Gastrointestinal osmolability, electrolyte and organic acid composition in five species of East African herbivorous mammals. *J. Anim. Sci.* **51**, 966-974.

Marazzani. (1905). The camel (in Italian). *Boll. Agric. Comm., Eritrea.* **3**.

Marchi, E. (1929). *Studies on pastoralism in the colony of Eritrea* (in Italian). Ist. Agric. Colon. Ital., Firenze.

Marennikova, S. S., Shenkman, L. S., Shelukhina, E. M. and Maltseva, N. N. (1974). Isolation of camel pox virus and investigation of its properties. *Acta Virol.* **18**, 423-428.

Mares, R. G. (1954). Animal husbandry, animal industry and animal disease in the Somaliland Protectorate. *British Vet. J.* **110**, 411-423; 470-481.

Mariam, S. H. (1976). Tsetse, trypanosomiasis investigation and control in Ethiopia 1975-1976. *Services Vet., Addis Ababa.* 155-160.

Marly, C. (1961). Le chameau et la civilisation. *Naturalia.* **97**, 28-35.

Maronpot, R. R. and Botros, B. A. M. (1972). Toxoplasma serological survey in man and domestic animals in Egypt. *J. Egyptian Publ. Hlth Assoc.* **47**, 58-67.

Maronpot, R. R. and Barsoum, I. S. (1972). Leptospiral microscopic agglutinating antibodies in sera of man and domestic animals in Egypt. *American J. Trop. Med. Hyg.* **21**, 467-472.

Marsh, G. P. (1885). *The camel.* 9th Ann. Rep. Board Regents Smithsonian Institution. Beverly Tucker: Washington.

Marsh, G. P. (1856). *The camel: His organisation, habits and uses considered with reference to his introduction into the United States.* Gold & Lincoln: Boston.

Marshall, J. (1931). *Mohenjo Daro and the Indus Civilization.* London.

Martin, H. (1939). Les tribus du Sahel mauritanien et du Rio de Oro (Oulad Bou Sba). *Bull. IFAN.* **1**, 587-629.

Martynchenko, V. A. (1968). Clinical picture of plague in camels infected by means of ectoparasite carriers (in Russian). In Kovalenko, Y. R. (ed) *Maloizuchennye Zabolevaniya sel'-khz.* pp. 191-196.

Martynenko, N. I., Yagodinskaya, S. G., Akhundov, A. A., Charyev, K. and Khummedov, O. (1977). Contents of trace elements (Cu, Mn, Mo) in cultured chal and camel's milk and their clinical significance (in Russian). *Zdrav. Turkmen.* No. 3, 20-22.

Masefield, G. B. (1970) *A Handbook of Tropical Agriculture.* Oxford University Press: London.

Masia, R. (1953). *Les maladies microbiennes du dromadaire et leur importance en Afrique du Nord.* Thèse DMV; ENV: Alfort. No 28.

Maskar, Ü. (1949). Specificity of camel anti-serum (in German). *Istanbul Univ. Tip Fak. Meen.* **12**, 239-245.

Maskar, Ü. (1957). The diaphragm bone of the camel (in German). *Acta Anat.* **30**, 461-471.

Maskar, Ü. (1961). Islands of cartilage in the oesphagus of a dromedary foetus (in German). *Acta Anat.* **44**, 206-209.

Mason, F. E. (1906). Filariae in the blood of camels in Egypt. *J. Comp. Path. Therap.* **19**, 118-120.

Mason, F. E. (1910). Sarcocysts in the camel in Egypt. *J. Comp. Path. Therap.* **23**, 168-176.

Mason, F. E. (1911). Note on the camel trypanosomiasis of Egypt and results of first series of experimental drug treatment. *J. Comp. Path. Therap.* **24**, 47-59.

Mason, F. E. (1911). A further note on filariae in the blood of camels in Egypt. *J. Comp. Path. Therap.* **24**, 329-339.

Mason, F. E. (1912). *J. Comp. Path. Therap.* **25**, 93-109.

Mason, F. E. (1912). Some observations on tuberculosis in camels in Egypt. *J. Comp. Path. Therap.* **25**, 109-111.

Mason, F. E. (1912). Dept. Public Hlth (Vet. Sect.): Cairo.

Mason, F. E. (1917). Tuberculosis in camels. *Agric. J.*, Egypt. **7**, 1-11.

Mason, F. E. (1917). Tuberculosis in camels. *J. Comp. Path. Therap.* **30**, 80-84.

Mason, F. E. (1918). Tuberculosis in the camel. *J. Comp. Path. Therap.* **31**, 100-102.

Mason, F. E. (1919). Pseudo-actinomycosis or streptothricosis in the camel. *J. Comp. Path. Therap.* **32**, 34-42.

Mason, F. E. (1920). Pseudo-actinomycosis or streptothricosis in the camel. *Agric. J., Egypt.* **9**, 7-13.

Mason, F. E. (1920). Mortality in camels caused by ingestion of sand. *Agric. J., Egypt.* **9**, 4-6.

Mason, I. L. (1951). *A World Dictionary of Breeds, Types and Varieties of Livestock.* Commonwealth Agricultural Bureaux: Farnham Royal, UK.

Mason, I. L. (1967). How a geneticist views the domestication of animals (in Italian). *Agricoltura*, Roma. **1967**(11).

Mason, I. L. (1979). *Inventory of special herds and flocks of breeds of farm animals (ass, banteng, buffalo, cattle, goat, horse, pig, sheep) including conservation of rare breeds, feral populations, domestic animals in zoos and experimental and selection strains.* FAO: Rome.

Mason, I. L. (1980). Origin, history and distribution of domestic camels. IN: *Workshop on Camels*, Khartoum, Sudan, 18-20 Dec. 1979. Intnl. Foundation for Science: Stockholm, Sweden. pp. 21-23.

Mason, I. L. and Maule, J. P. (1960). *The Indigenous Livestock of Eastern and Southern Africa.* Commonwealth Bureau of Animal Breeding and Genetics: CAB: Farnham Royal, UK. Tech. Comm. No. 14.

Matharu, B. S. (1966). Camel care. *Indian Fmg.* **16**, 19-22.

Mathieu, (1905). Quelques observations sur l'élevage du méhari chez les Chaanba Monadhi (El Goléa). *Bull. Soc. Géogr., Alger.* 353-367.

Mathur, C. S. (1960). Nutrition in relation to satyriasis in camels. *Indian Vet. J.* **37**, 199-201.

Mathur, C. S. (1966). Phog - Fodder for camels. *Indian Fmg.* **16**, 41.

Mathur, C. S. and Purohit, G. R. (1979). Nutritive value of Bekariya (*Indigofera cordifolia*) for camel (*Camelus dromedarius*). *Ann. Arid Zone.* **18**, 269-271.

Mathur, G. N. and Mathur, C. S. (1979). Studies on NPN utilization in camel in Rajasthan desert. Effect of feeding varying levels of urea on feed consumption and water intake in camels (*Camelus dromedarius*).

Trans. Indian Soc. Desert Tech-4: no 1. Univ. Cent. Desert Stud. 105-109.

Matlock, W. C. and Cockrun, E. L. (1974). *A framework for evaluating long-term strategies for the development of the Sahel-Sudan Region.* Center for Policy Alternatives M.I.T. Cambridge, Massachusetts.

Matthew, W. D. and MacDonald, J. R. (1960). Two new species of *Oxydactylus* from the middle Miocene Ruseaud formation in western South Dakota. *American Mus. Novitates.* **2003.**

Matthews, J. M. (1947). *Textile Fibers* (5th Edition). John Wiley & Sons: New York.

Maupas, E. and Seurat, G. (1912). Sur un nématode de l'intestin grêle du dromadaire. *C. R. Séances Soc. Biol.* **73,** 628-632.

Maurice, Y., Provost, A. and Borredon, C. (1967). Présence d'anticorps antibovipestiques chez le dromadaire du Tchad. *Rev. Elev. Méd. Vét. Pays Trop.* **20,** 537-542.

Maurice, Y., Bares, J. F. and Baille (Mme). (1967). Enquête sérologique sur les rickettsioses chez le dromadaire au Tchad. *Rev. Elev. Méd. Vét. Pays Trop.* **20,** 543-550.

Maurice, Y. and Gidel, R. (1968). Incidence of Q fever in Central Africa. *Bull. Soc. Path. Exot.* **61,** 731-736.

Maurice, Y., Quéval, R. and Bares, J. F. (1968). Enquête sur l'infection à virus parainfluenza-3 chez le dromadaire tchadien. *Rev. Elev. Méd. Vét. Pays Trop.* **21,** 443-449.

Maxwell-Darling, R. C. (1938). Notes on the food of camels on the Red Sea coast and in Northern Kordofan. *Sudan Notes Rec.* **21,** 189-195.

Maxwell-Hyslop. K. R. (1955). Note on a Shaft-hole Axe-pick from Khurab, Mesopotamia. *Iraq*, London. **17(2),** 161.

Mayr, A., Mahnel, H. and Munz, E. (1972). Classification and differentiation of pox viruses (in German). *Zentralbl. Vet. Med.* **19B,** 69-88.

Mayr, E. (1970). *Populations, Species and Evolution.* Harvard University Press: Cambridge, Massachusetts.

Mazillier, (1908). Les Rezzous marocains. *Rev. Troupes Colon.* **8(78).**

Meade, G. E. (1942). The gazelle camel, *Stenomylus. Texas Tech. Coll., Lubbock, Res. Publ.* **No. 5,** 1-8.

Mechari, A. (1977). *Etude epidémiologique et prophylactique de l'echinococcose hydatidose dans l'Est algérien.* These DMV: University of Constantine.

Mehta, V. S., Prakash, A. and Singh, M. (1962). Gestation period in camels. *Indian Vet. J.* **39,** 387-389.

Meissner, W. (1913). *Contribution to the study of the dromedary with special consideration of its breeding and employment in South-west Africa.* (in German). Berlin.

Melamid, A. (1965). Political boundaries and nomadic grazing. *Geogr. Rev.* **55,** 287-290.

Menon, P. B. (1957). The incidence of surra and tabanid flies in Rajasthan. *Indian J. Vet. Sci.* **27,** 1-16.

Merlian, C. P., Sikes, J. D., Read, B. W., Boever, W. J. and Konox, D. (1979). Comparative characteristics of spermatozoa and semen from a bactrian camel, dromedary camel and llama. *J. Zoo Anim. Med.* **10,** 22-25.

Merriam, J. C. (1913). The skull and dentition of a camel from the Pleistocene of Rancho La Brea. *Univ. Calif. Press. Bull. Dept. Geol.*: Berkeley. **7(14),** 305-323.

Metcalfe, J., Parer, J. T., Rur, M., El Yassin, D., Outi, J., Bartels, H., Riegel, K. and Kleihauer, E. (1968). Cardiodynamics of the dromedary camel (*Camelus dromedarius*) during phenocyclidine analgesia. *American J. Vet. Res.* **20,** 2063-2066.

Meyerstein, N., Mazor, D., Etzion, C. and Yagil, R. (1978). Permeability of erythrocytes to glycerol and its acylated derivatives in the camel and dog. *Comp. Biochem. Physiol.* **61A,** 261-265.

Michael, S. A. and Saleh, S. M. (1977). The slide agglutination test for the diagnosis of filariasis in camels. *Trop. Anim. Hlth Prod.* **9,** 241-244.

Michael, S. A., Refaii, A. H. el and Morsy, T. A. (1977). Incidence of toxoplasma antibodies among camels in Egypt. *J. Egyptian Soc. Parasit.* **7,** 129-132.

Michael, S. A., Refaii, A. H. el and Huggins, A. J. (1980). Evaluation of oxfendazole against natural infections of gastrointestinal nematodes and cestodes in Egyptian camels. *British Vet. J.* **136,** 84-87.

Michalowski, K. (1962). *Palmyre: Fouilles polonaises.* Panstwowe Wydawbictwo Naukowe, Warsaw.

Michel, E. (1905). Le chameau du Sahara soudanais. *Bull. Soc. Geogr., Alger.* **1905,** 368-385.

Mikesell, M. K. (1955). Notes on the dispersal of the dromedary. *Southwestern J. Anthrop.* **11,** 231-245.

Miller, W. C. and West, G. P. *Black's Veterinary Dictionary.* A. & C. Black: London.

Milovanov, A. F., Zernovov, I. V. and Nikitin, V. P. (1958). The possibility of obtaining butter from camel's milk (in Russian). *Izvest. Akad. Nauk Turkmen SSR.* **1958(5),** 94-97.

Mimram, R. (1962). Les glandes occipitales du dromadaire. *Cah. Fac. Sci., Rabat. Serie Biol. Anim.* **No. 1,** 1-62.

Ministère de la Guerre (1902). Instruction du 25 aout 1902 sur les cosvois de chameaux en Algérie. *Bull. Official Min. Guerre* No 100-9.

Miramon de la Roquette, (1913). Transport des malades a dos de chameaux dans les regions sahariennes. *Paris Med.*

Mirchamsy, H., Bahrami, B., Amighi, M. and Shayf, A. (1971). Development of a camel kidney strain and its use in virology. *Arch. Inst. Razi.* **23,** 15-18.

Mirchamsy, H. and Ahourai, P. (1971). Comparative adaptation of some pox viruses in two cell systems. *Arch. Inst. Razi.* **23,** 93-105.

Mirghani, T. (1971). Fatty acid composition of liver triglycerides of the camel. *Comp. Biochem. Physiol.* **58,** 211-214.

Mirghani, T. (1977). Fatty acid composition of liver triglycerides of camel. *Wld. Rev. Anim. Prod.* **13(1),** 57-59.

Mirza, M. Y. and Al Rawas, A. Y. *Coccidia* (Protozoa: Eimeridae) from camels (*Camelus dromedarius*) in Iraq. *Bull. Biol. Res. Cent. (Baghdad).* **7,** 24-31.

Mirzayans, A. and Halim, R. (1980). Parasitic infections of *Camelus dromedarius* from Iran. *Bull. Soc. Path. Exot.* **73,** 442-445.

Mitzmain, M. F. *Trop. Vet. Bull.* **1,** 47.

Mobarak, A. M. and Elwishy, A. B. (1971). Uterus of the one-humped camel (*Camelus dromedarius*) with reference to rectal palpation. *Indian J. Anim. Sci.* **41,** 846-855.

Mobarak, A. M., Elwishy, A. B. and Samira, M. F. (1972). The penis and prepuce of the one-humped camel (*Camelus dromedarius*). *Zentralbl. Vet. Med.* **19A,** 787-795.

Mobarak, A. M. and Fouad, S. M. (1977). A study on Lig. nuchae of the one-humped camel (*Camelus dromedarius*). *Anat. Histol. Embryologia.* **6,** 188-190.

Mobedi, I., Madadi, H. and Arfaa, F. (1970). Camel (*Camelus dromedarius*) as intermediate host of *Echinocoocus granulosus* in Iran. *J. Parasit.* **56,** 1251.

Moch, R. W., Cornelius, J. B., Boulos, A., Botros, M., Barsoum, I. S. and Mahmoud, A. H. (1974). Serological detection of echinococcal infection in camels by the indirect haemagglutination (IHA) and latex agglutination (LA) tests. *J. Egyptian Publ. Hlth Assoc.* **49,** 146-155.

Mohammed, N. A. (1978). *Anatomical, histomorphological and histochemical studies on the liver of the camel.* Baghdad.

Moldagaliev, T. (1971). The physiology of parturition in the dromedary (in Russian). *Vest. sel'-khz. Nauk Alma-Ata.* **14,** 106-108; 118.

Moldagaliev, T. (1975). The effect of foetal size and pelvic measurements on parturition in different species of camel (in Russian). *Temat. Sb. Nauk Trudy Alma-Ata Semipalat Zoovet. Inst.* **36,** 81-83.

Moll, (1903). *Infanterie montée à chameau: notes sur l'organisation d'une compagnie montée à chameau dans 1er et 3e territoires militaires de l'Afrique occidentale.* H. Charles Lavanzelle: Paris.

Möller, G. (1906). Excavations of the German Oriental Society on the prehistoric graveyards near Abusir-el-Meleq in the summir of 1905 (in German). *Mitt. Deutsch. Orient Ges.: Berlin.* No. 30.

Moniem, K. A. (1968). *Some histological and histochemical studies of the placenta of camel (Camelus dromedarius)*. M.V.Sc. Dissertation, Khartoum University.

Monod, (1893). Le dromadaire de guerre. *Bull. Soc. Cent. Méd. Vét.* **11**, 79-85.

Monod, Th. (ed) (1938). *Contributions à l'étude du Sahara occidentale*. Librarie Larose.

Monod, Th. (1939). Dromadaire "arabe" et dromadaire "africaine". *Bull. Serv. Vet. Epizoot, AOF.* **11**, 39-41.

Monod, Th, (1947). *Méharées, explorations au vrai Sahara*. Je sers: Paris.

Monod, Th. (1947). Sur quelques gravures rupestres de la région d'Aozou (Tibesti). *Riv. Sci. Preist., Firenze*. **2**, 30-47.

Monod, Th. (1951). Peintures rupestres du Zemmour français. *Bull. IFAN.* **13**, 200.

Monod, Th. (1952). Pour une analyse géographique du harnachement méhariste. *Bull. Liais. Sahar.* **9**, 3-4.

Monod, Th. (1955) Consommation d'eau au Sahara. *Bull. Liais. Sahar.* **20**, 34-39.

Monod, Th. (1955). Longs trajets chameliers. *Bull. Liais. Sahar.* **20**, 39-42.

Monod, Th. (1955). Une promenade au Sahara, Oudame-Araouan: 900 km sans eau. *Cah. Ch. de Foucald.* **38**, 157-172.

Monod, Th. (1967). Notes sur le harnachemet chamelier. *Bull. IFAN.* **29B**, 234-306.

Monod, Th. (ed) *Les Societés Pastorales en Afrique Tropicale*. Oxford University Press for the International African Institute: London.

Montagu, I. (1965). Communication on the current survival in Mongolia of the wild horse (*Equus przewalskii*), wild camel (*Camelus bactrianus ferus*) and the wild ass (*Equus hemionus*). *Proc. Zool. Soc. Lond.* **144**, 425-428.

Monteil, V. (1952). *Essai sur le chameau au Sahara occidental*. Centre IFAN: St. Louis du Sénégal.

Monteil, V. (1959). L'evolution et la sedentarisation des nomades IFAN: St. Louis du Sénégal.

Monteil, V. (1959). L'évolution et al sedentarisation des nomades sahariens. *Rev. Int. Soc. Sci.* **11**, 599-612.

Montet, P. (1929). *Byblos et l'Egypte*. P. Geuthner: Paris.

Monteverde, G. (1935). Camel cysts (in Italian). *Rass. Econ. Colon*. **23**, 490-504; 605-619.

Monteverde, G. (1936). Cutaneous cysts in camels (in Italian). *Clin. Vet., Milano*. **59**, 532-543; 602-609.

Monteverde, G. (1937). Anaplasmosis in camels in Cirenaica (in Italian). *Clin. Vet., Milano*. **60**, 73-76.

Moorhouse, G. (1974). *The Fearful Void*. Hodder & Stoughton: London.

Morcos, Z. (1931). Remarks on Naganol treatment (Bayer 205): Trypanosomiasis in camels. *Vet. Rec.* **11**, 162.

Morel, P. C. (1952). Les helminthes des animaux domestiques de l'Afrique occidentale. *Rev. Elev. Méd. Vét. Pays Trop.* **12**, 153-174.

Morel, P. C. (1959). Enquête sur les helminthes parasites des animaux domestiques en République islamique de Mauritanie. Rapport Lab. Elev. Dakar, Sénégal.

Morel, P. C. (1976). *Etude sur les tiques d'Ethiopie (Acariens, Ixodidés)*. IEMVT: Maisons Alford.

Morgan, W. T. W. (ed) (1972). *East Africa, its people and resources*. Oxford University Press: London.

Morton, W. R. M. (1961). Observations on the full term foetal membrane of three members of the Camelidae (*Camelus dromedarius, Camelus bactrianus* and *Lama glama*).

Mostafa, M. S., El-Hagri, M. A., El-Gindy, E. M. and El-Khaligi, G. E. M. (1975). Some morphological features on the prenatal growth of the brain of the one-humped camel (*Camelus dromedarius*). *J. Egyptian Vet. Med. Assoc.* **35**, 45-79.

Mostafa, M. S., El-Gindy, E. M., El-Hagri, M. A. and El-Khaligi, G. E. M. (1976). The ventricular system of the brain of the one-humped camel (*Camelus dromedarius*). *J. Egyptian Vet. Med. Assoc.* **36**, 19-27.

Mostafa, M. S., El-Gindy, E. M., El-Hagri, M. A. and El-Khaligi, G. E. M. (1976). Some postnatal morphological features of the hindbrain (*rhombocephalon*) of the one-humped camel (*Camelus dromedarius*). *J. Egyptian Vet. Med. Assoc.* **36**, 29-44.

Moty, I. A., Mulla, A. el and Zaafer, S. A. (1968). Copper, iron and zinc in the serum of Egyptian farm animals. *Sudan Agric. J.* **3**, 146-151.

Moustafa, A. M. B., Moustafa, I. H. and Soliman, M. K. (1965). Histochemical studies of glycogen depositions in normal camel livers and those infected with *E. granulosus* cysts. *J. Vet. Sci., UAR*. **2**, 83-91.

Moustafa, M. S. el Din, Berg, R. and Taher, el S. (1968). Prenatal growth of some organs in the camel (*Camelus dromedarius*). Part III. Relations of kidney and adrenal weights to body weight and between left and right kidney. *Zentralbl. Vet. Med.* **15A**, 148-155.

Moustafa, M. S. el Din, Berg, R. and Taher, el S. (1969). Prenatal growth of some organs in the camel (*Camelus dromedarius*). Relation between body weight and brain, thymus, stomach and oesophagus. *Zentralbl. Vet. Med.* **16A**, 536-542.

Mozgovoi, A. A., Kornienko, J. P. and Shakhnatova, V. I. (1969). *Ascaris skrjabini* sp. Ascaridata, a parasite of the camel (in Russian). *Parazitologiya*. **3**, 174-175.

Mukasa-Mugerwa, E. (1979). *The role of the camel in Africa* (A literature review). International Livestock Centre for Africa: Addis Ababa (mimeo).

Müller, F. and Wedl, M. (1852). Contribution to the anatomy of the two-humped camel (in German). *Denkschr. Akad. Wiss. Wien, math.-naturwiss. Kl.* **3**, 269.

Müller, R. R. (1933). Contribution to the knowledge of the parasites of the abomasum of the camel (in German). *S. B. Ges. Naturf., Berlin*. **4/7**, 266-271.

Munier, P. (1974). Elevage et palmeraies au Sahara algerien. *Fruits*. **29**, 763-765.

Murray, G. W. (1952). Early camels in Egypt. *Bull. Inst. Fouad Ier Désert*. **2**, 105-106.

Musa, B. E. (1969). *A study of some aspects of reproduction in the female camel*. M. V. Sc. Dissertation, Khartoum University.

Musa, B. E. (1977). A new epidermal membrane associated with the foetus of the camel. *Anat. Histol. Embryol.* **6**, 355-358.

Musa, B. E. (1979). The development, presentation, position and posture of the foetus in the camel (*Camelus dromedarius*). *Sudan J. Vet. Sci. Anim. Husb.* **20**, 39-42.

Musa, B. E. (1979). Studies on the ovary of the camel (*Camelus dromedarius*). *Sudan J. Vet. Sci. Anim. Husb.* **20**, 51-64.

Musa, B. E. (1980). Reproductive patterns in the female camel. IN: *Workshop on camels*, Khartoum, Sudan, 18-20 Dec. 1979. Intnl. Foundation function Science: Stockholm, Sweden.

Musa, B. E. and Abusineina, M. E. (1976). Development of the conception in the camel (*Camelus dromedarius*). *Acta Vet., Yugoslavia*. **26**, 17-24.

Musa, B. E. and Abusineina, M. E. (1976). Some observations on reproduction in the female camel (*Camelus dromedarius*). *Acta Vet., Yugoslavia*. **26**, 63-67.

Musa, B. E. and Abusineina, M. E. (1976). Studies on the allantoic and amniotic fluids of the camel (*Camelus dromedarius*). *Acta Vet., Yugoslavia*. **26**,

Musa, B. E. and Abusineina, M. E. (1978). Clinical pregnancy diagnosis in the camel and a comparison with bovine pregnancy. *Vet. Rec.* **102**, 7-10.

Musa, B. E. and Abusineina, M. E. (1978). The oestrous cycle of the camel (*Camelus dromedarius*). *Vet. Rec.* **103**, 556-557.

Mushkambarova, M. G. and Dobrynin, M. I. (1972). On *Physocephalus sexalatus dromedarii* in Turkmenia. *Izvest. Akad. Nauk Turkmen SSR.* **1972(4)**, 62-67.

Musil, A. (1928). *The manners and customs of the Rwala bedouins*. New York.

Mustafa, A. A. and Awad el Karim, M. H. (1971). A preliminary survey for the detection of Brucella antibodies in camel sera. *Sudan J. Vet. Sci. Anim. Husb.* **12**, 5–8.

Nadim, M. A. and Soliman, M. K. (1967). The prognostic value of the blood picture in animals affected with trypanosomiasis (El dabab). *Indian Vet. J.* **44**, 566–571.

Nagaty, H. F. (1942). On some parasites collected in Egypt from food mammals. *J. Egyptian Med. Assoc.* **25**, 110–111.

Nagaty, H. F. (1947). *Vet. Rec.* **59**, 145–147.

Nagaty, H. F. (1947). *Dipetalonema evansi* (Lewis, 1882) and its microfilaria from *Camelus dromedarius*. *Parasitology.* **38**, 86–92.

Nagaty, H. F., Fahmy, M. A. M. and Hegab, S. M. (1947). New records of some parasites from Egyptian food mammals. *J. Royal Egyptian Med. Assoc.* **28**, 217–218.

Nagaty, H. F., Hegab, S. M. and Fahmy, M. A. M. (1974). On the identity of *Avetellina woodlandi* and *A. nagatyi* with further records of some parasites from Egyptian food mammals. *J. Royal Egyptian Med. Assoc.* **23**, 401–403.

Nair, K. P. D. (1968). Efficacy of methyridine 2 (2-methoxyethyl) pyridine in the treatment of trichuriasis in camel (*Camelus dromedarius*). *Indian Vet. J.* **45**, 252–255.

Nalbandov, A. V. (1958). *Reproductive Physiology*. W. H. Freeman & Co.: London.

Nanda, P. N. (1957). *Camels and their management*. Indian Council Agric. Res. Review Series: New Delhi N°16.

Naquib, G. (1950). The camel in ancient Egypt. *British Vet. J.* **106**, 76–81.

Nash, W. L. (1902). An Egyptian representation of the camel. *Proc. Soc. Bibl. Archaeol.* **24**, 309.

Nasr, H. (1959). Digestion in the Arabian camel. I. Salivary digestion. *Vet. Med. J., Giza.* **6**, 203–208.

Nasr, H., El Amrousi, S., Soliman, M. K. and Youssef, L. B. (1966). The synovial fluid of the tibio-tarsal joint of healthy camels. *Vet. Med. J., Giza.* **11**, 131–137.

Nasr, S., Elbahy, G. and Moursy, A. W. (1965). Studies on camel meat. I. The effect of age and sex on the components of camel meat. *J. Arab Vet. Med Assoc.* **25**, 253–258.

Nassar, S. M., Mansour, S. A. and Lotfi, L. A. (1977). Influence of sex on the normal blood picture of adult Egyptian camel (*Camelus dromedarius*). *Assiut Vet. Med. J.* **4**(7), 43–50.

Nassar, S. M. and Mansour, S. A. (1977). Intestinal mucosal digestion in *Camelus dromedarius*. I. Estimation of amylase, lipase and alkaline phosphatase in mucosal homogenate. *Assiut Vet. Med. J.* **4**(8), 43–53.

Nasseh, G. A. and Khadivi, B. (1975). Epidemiological and clinical aspects of echinococcosis in East Iran. *J. Trop. Med. Hyg.* **78**, 120–122.

Nattan-Larrier, L. and Noyer, B. (1931). Trypanosome du dromadiare et trypanosome du cheval au Maroc. *Bull. Soc. Path. Exot.* **24**, 112–122.

Nattan-Larrier, L. and Noyer, B. (1932). Le trypanosome du Débab aegyptien. *Bull. Soc. Path. Exot.* **25**, 563–569.

Nawar, S. M. A. and El-Khaligi, G. E. M. (1975). Morphological, micromorphological and histochemical studies on the parotid salivary glands of the one-humped camel (*Camelus dromedarius*). *Gegenbaurs Morph. Jahrb.* **121**, 430–449.

Nawar, S. M. A., El-Gaafary, M. A. H., El-Shafey, S. M. and Ali, A. E. A. (1975). Micromorphological studies of the arterial supply of the testis and epididymis of the dromedary camel. *Assiut Vet. Med. J.* **2**, 67–73.

Nawar, S. M. A. and El-Khaligi, G. E. M. (1977). Morphological and histochemical studies of the mandibular salivary glands of the one-humped camel (*Camelus dromedarius*). *Anat. Anz.* **142**, 346–362.

Nawar, S. M. A., Abul-Fadle, W. S. and Mahmoud, S. A. (1978). Studies on the ovarian activity of the dromedary (*Camelus dromedarius*). *Zeitschr. Mikroskop. Anat. Forsch.* **192**, 385–408.

Nawito, M. F. (1973). Uterine infections of the camel. *Egyptian J. Vet. Sci.* **10**, 17–22.

Nawito, M. F., Shalash, M. R., Hoppe, R. and Rakha, A. M. (1967). Reproduction in the female camel. *Bull. Anim. Sci. Res. Inst.* (Cairo) No **2**.

Nayak, R. K. (1977). Scanning electron microscopy of the camel uterine tube (oviduct). *American J. Vet. Res.* **38**, 1049–1054.

Nayak, R. K. (1977). Scanning electron microscopy of the aorta of the camel (Mammalia, Camelidae). *J. Univ. Kuwait (Sci.)* **4**, 75–80.

Nayak, R. K. and Zein, A. (1977). Electron microscopy of the camel oviductal epithelium during early pregnancy. *Proc. Electr. Microscop. Soc.* **35**, 660–661.

Needham, J. and Wang Ling (1965). *Science and Civilisation in China*. Cambridge University Press: Cambridge.

Nehring, A. (1901). A fossil head (*Camelus knoblochi*) from Sarepta on the Volga (in German). *Sitz. Ber. Gesell. Naturf. Freunde, Berlin, Jahrg.* No **5**, 137–144.

Nehring, A. (1901). Fossil camels in Rumania and the Pleistocene layers of central Europe (in German). *Globus.* **79**, 264–267.

Neuman, M. (1974). *Parabronema skrjabini* (Rassovskaya 1924) in sheep, cattle and camels in Israel. *Refuah Vet.* **31**, 75–77; 131–134.

Neuman, M. and Witenburg, G. (1976). Some data on the morphology of *Marshallagia marshali* (Ransom, 1907) Orloff 1933 and *Camelostrongylus mentulatus* (Railliet & Henry, 1909) Orloff 1933 from sheep and camels in Israel. *Refuah Vet.* **33**, 83–86.

Neuville, M. H. (1931). De certaines particularités dentaires des Camelidés. *Bull. Mus. Hist. Nat., Paris.* **Series 2 Vol. 3**, 77–81.

Neuville, R. (1951). Le Paléolithique et le Mésolithique du Désert de Judée. *Mem. Arch. Inst. Paléont. Hun.* **24**, 1–270.

Newbold, D. and Shaw, W. B. K. (1928). An expedition in the south Libyan desert. *Sudan Notes Rec.* **11**, 103–194.

Newman, D. M. R. (1973). *The camel — its potential as a provider of protein in Arid Australia*. Proc. III Wld. Conf. Anim. Prod., Melbourne, Australia Sydney University Press: Sydney, Australia.

Niak, A. (1975). The pathogenicity of blood parasites in ruminants in Iran. *Bull. Off. Int. Epiz.* **81**, 813–816.

Nicholson, R. A. (1956). *A literary History of the Arabs*. Cambridge University Press: Cambridge.

Nicolaisen, J. (1963). *Ecology and culture of the pastoral Tuareg*. National Museum: Copenhagen.

Nicolas, F. (1950). *Tamesna: Les Toullemmeden de l'Est ou Touareg "Kel Dinnik"*. Imprimerie Nationale: Paris.

Nigam, J. M., Gupta, R. C., Khar, S. K. and Shetty, B. (1977). Torsion of uterus in a camel. *Haryana Vet.* **16**, 33–36.

Nomani, A. A. (1920). A new armed hydatid in the camel. *Agric. J., Egypt.* **10**, 69.

Noster, M. B. (1973). Histological structure of the mammary glands of the one-humped camels (*Camelus dromedarius*). *Indian J. Anim. Sci.* **43**, 639–641.

Novikov, I. I. (1939). The chromosomes in the spermatogenesis of the dromedary, the Bactrian camel and their F_1 hybrids (in Russian). *Trudy Inst. Genet. (Moscow).* **13**, 285–296.

Novoa, C. (1970). Reproduction in Camelidae: A review. *J. Reprod. Fert.* **22**, 3–20.

Noyan, A. (1970). The microscopic appearance of camel and llama erythrocytes. *Ankara Vet. Fak. Derg.* **17**, 518–522.

O. C. C. (1938). Presentation of the dromedary (in Italian). *Natura.* **11**, 19–23.

Oemichen, F-O. (1949). *On the degeneration of the heart muscle in a young camel* (in German). Inaugural Dissertation: Hanover.

Oguz, T. and Wiesenhütter, E. (1965). Endoparasites of *Camelus dromedarius* in Syria (in German). *Munchen Tierärztl. Wschr.* **78**, 431–433.

Ohri, S. P. and Joshi, B. K. (1961). Composition of milk of camel. *Indian Vet. J.* **38**, 514–516.

Ohri, S. P. and Joshi, B. K. (1961). Composition of colostrum of camel. *Indian Vet. J.* **38**, 604 - 607.

Okoh, A. E. J. (1979). A survey of brucellosis in camels in Kano, Nigeria. *Trop. Anim. Hlth Prod.* **11**, 213 - 214.

Olitzki, L. (1942). Comparative studies on *Salmonella* strains isolated in Palestine from camels and a human being. *J. Hyg., Cambridge.* **42**, 547 - 548.

Olitzki, L. and Ellenbogen, V. (1940). A *Salmonella* strain isolated from camels in Palestine. *J. Comp. Path. Therap.* **53**, 75 - 79.

Olitzki, L. and Ellenbogen, V. (1947). A *Salmonella* strain isolated from camels in Palestine. *J. Comp. Path. Therap.* **57**, 47 - 51.

Olmstead, R. T. (1948). *History of the Persian Empire*. Chicago.

Ono, Y. (1943). Haemorrhagic enteritis in camels (in German). *Japanese J. Vet. Sci.* **5**, 113 - 114.

Ono, Y. and Ikeda, S. (1941). Sarcoptic mange in camels (in Japanese). *Japanese J. Vet. Sci.* **3**, 33 - 42.

Oppenheim, M. von (1931). *Tell Halaf. A new culture in oldest Mesopotamia*. London.

Oppenheim, M. von (1955). *Tell Halaf*. Walter de Gruyter: Berlin.

Orekov, M. D. (1952). *Acanthocheilonema evansi* infestation of camels in Turkmenia (in Russian). *Vet. Moscow.* **29**, 28 - 30.

Orekhov, M. D. and Ped'ko, G. M. (1952). Enzootic encephalomyelitis in camels (in Russian). *Vet. Moscow.* **29**, 27 - 29.

Orlov, F. M. (ed) (1974). *Little known contagious diseases of animals (in Russian)*. Izdatel'stvo Kolos: Moscow.

Orlov, J. A. (1927). On fossil Camelidae remains of the region of Akmolinsk in Western Siberia (in German). *Ann. Mus. Zool. Acad. USSR.* **28**, 496 - 538.

Orlov, J. A. (1930). On fossil Camelidae remains of the region of Semipalatinak in Western Siberia (in German). *Ann. Soc. Palaeont. Russie, Leningrad.* **8**, 99 - 116.

Orlov, J. A. (1933). Fossil camels of the old world (in German). *Trudy Lab. Genet., Acad. Nauk Leningrad.* **1**, 211 - 237.

Ortiz, A. and Mukasa-Mugerwa, E. (1979). *The camel. A review of some aspects of the physiology, productivity and diseases of the dromedary*. International Livestock Centre for Africa: Addis Ababa

Osman, A. M. and El-Azab, E. A. (1974). Gonadal and epididymal sperm reserves in the camel. *J. Rep. Fert.* **38**, 425 - 430.

Osman, D. I., Moniem, K. A. and Tingari, M. D. (1976). Studies on the testis of the camel (*Camelus dromedarius*). III. Histochemical observations. *Histochem. J.* **8**, 579 - 590.

Osman, D. I., Tingari, M. D. and Moniem, K. A. (1979). Vascular supply of the testis of the camel (*Camelus dromedarius*). *Acta Anat.* **104**, 16 - 22.

Osman, D. I., Moniem, K. A. and Tingari, M. D. (1979). Histological observations on the testis of the camel with special emphasis on spermatogenesis. *Acta Anat.* **104**, 164 - 171.

Ostrovidov, P. I. (1954). Development of resistance to brucellosis in camels (in Russian). *Trudy Inst. Vet. Akad. Nauk Kazakh. SSR, Alma-Ata.* **6**, 51 - 56.

Ostrovidov, P. I. (1954). Experiments on rearing healthy camels from dams infected with brucellosis (in Russian). *Trudy Inst. Akad. Nauk Kazakh. SSR, Alma-Ata.* **6**, 62 - 68.

Ottogali, G. and Resmini, P. (1976). Milk production in Somalia: physico-chemical characteristics of cattle and camel milk (in Italian). *Indust. Latte.* **12**, 3 - 10.

Ozerskaya, V. N. (1953). Experimental application of phenothiazine in nematodiasis of the digestive tract of camels (in Russian). *Trudy Vseso. Inst. Gelmint. Imen Akad. Skrjabina.* **5**, 165 - 166.

Pal, M. (1976). Allergic rhinitis in a camel. *Uttar Pradesh Vet. J.* **4**, 161 - 163.

Pal'gov, A. A. (1954). Physico-morphological changes in the blood of camels with brucellosis (in Russian). *Trudy Inst. Vet. Akad. Nauk Kazakh. SSR, Alma-Ata.* **6**, 30 - 36.

Pal'gov, A. A. (1954). Streptococcal abortion in camels (in Russian). *Trudy Inst. Vet. Akad. Nauk Kazakh. SSR, Alma-Ata.* **6**, 234 - 240.

Pal'gov, A. A. and Zhalobovski, I. Z. (1954). Diagnosis of brucellosis in camels and methods of eliminating infection from camel herds (in Russian). *Trudy Inst. Vet. Akad. Nauk Kazakh. SSR; Alma-Ata.* **6**, 43 - 50.

Paling, R. W., Macowan, K. J. and Karstad, L. (1978). The prevalence of antibody to contagious caprine pleuropneumonia (*Mycoplasma* strain F 38) in some wild herbivores and camels in Kenya. *J. Wildl. Dis.* **14**, 305 - 308.

Paling, R. W., Jessett, D. M. and Heath, B. R. (1979). The occurrence of infectious diseases in mixed farming of domesticated wild herbivores and domestic herbivores including camels in Kenya. I. Viral Diseases: a serological survey with special reference to foot and mouth disease. *J. Wildl. Dis.* **15**, 351 - 358.

Palmer, A. C. (1980). Ataxia and spinal cord degeneration in llama, wildebeeste and camel. *Vet. Rec.* **107**, 10 - 13.

Paltrimeri, S., Caccarelli, A. and Menascre, I. (1939). Transmission experimentale du surra à un dromadaire de la race autochtone de Somalie. *Boll. Soc. Eustach.* **3**, 107.

Pampiglione, S. (1965). Hydatidosis of camels in Algeria (in Italian). *Parasitologia.* **7**, 27 - 29.

Pampiglione, S. (1966). Hydatidosis in Algerian dromedaries (in Italian). *Proc. 1st. Int. Congr. Parasit., Roma 1964.* **2**, 766 - 767.

Panasenko, A. G. and Luvsan, B. (1971). Age changes in live weight of Mongolian camels (in Russian). *Vest. Sel'-khoz. Nauk.* **14**, 59 - 62.

Pande, B. P., Rai, P. and Bhatia, B. B. (1962). On two new records of a Trichostrongylid and a Heliomostatid nematode hitherto unknown from *Camelus dromedarius* L. in India with remarks on the genus *Impalaia* Monnig. *Indian J. Vet. Sci.* **32**, 27 - 32.

Pant, R. and Chandra, P. (1980). Composition of cow and camel milk proteins and industrial casein. *Mildwissenschaft.* **35**, 91.

Paperna, I. and Giladi, M. (1974). Morphological variability, host range and distribution of ticks of the *Rhipicephalus sanguineus* complex in Israel. *Ann. Parasit. Hum. Comp.* **49**, 357 - 367.

Paris, E. (1953). Recherches sur l'origine des marque de tribus. *Bull. IFAN.* **15**, 1619 - 1632.

Parker, O. F. and Burkitt, M. C. (1932). Rock engravings from Onib, Wadi Allaki, Nubia. *Man, London.* **32**, 249 - 250.

Pastner, S. (1971). Camels, sheep and nomad social organisation: a comment on Rubel's model. *Man, London.* **NS 6**, 285 - 288.

Pathak, R. C. and Bansal, S. R. (1969). Soluble antigen of *Trypanosoma evansi* in blood serum of infected animals. *Curr. Sci.* **38**, 568 - 569.

Patrushev, V. I. (1938). Inheritance of biochemical characters in animals in connection with growth. III. On some indices of the blood composition of the hybrids between Bactrian camels and dromedaries in connection with heterosis (in Russian). *C. R. (Dokl) Acad. Sci. USSR.* **NS 19**, 285 - 290.

Patrushev, V. I. (1938). Variation in the blood composition of animal hybrids. I. On some indices of the bloods of hybrids of the Bactrian camel and the dromedary and their bearing on heterosis (in Russian). *Izvest. Akad. Nauk SSSR, Otd. mat-est., Ser. biol.* **1938**(4), 917ff.

Paul, A. (1954). *A History of the Beja Tribes of the Sudan*. Cambridge University Press: Cambridge.

Pavaux, C. (1965). Contribution à l'étude de la topographie viscérale des camelidés. *Rev. Méd. Vét.* **66**, 409 - 418.

Peck, E. F. (1938). The relationship of salt starvation to contagious necrosis and lameness in camels. *Vet. Rec.* **50**, 409 - 410.

Peck, E. F. (1938). Notes relating to the camel. *Vet. Rec.* **50**, 1052 - 1054.

Peck, E. F. (1939). Salt intake in relation to cutaneous necrosis and arthritis of one-humped camels (*Camelus dromedarius*, L.) in British Somaliland. *Vet. Rec.* **51**, 1355 - 1360.

Peck, E. F. (1940). Ulcerative stomatitis of camels. *Vet. Rec.* **52**, 602 - 603.

Peck, E. F. (1942). Castor speed poisoning in a camel. A note on gastric lavage. *Vet. Rec.* **54**, 184.

Peck, E. F. (1943). The use of antimosan against *Trypanosoma evansi* infection in the one-humped camel. *Vet. Rec.* **55**, 110 - 111.

Pegram, R. G. and Scott, J. M. (1976). The prevalence and diagnosis of *Trypanosoma evansi* infection in camels in Southern Ethiopia. *Trop. Anim. Hlth Prod.* **8**, 20-27.

Pellegrini, D. (1942-45). Natural and experimental *Trypanosoma cazalboni vivax* infection in camels (in Italian). *Racc. Stud. Pat. Vet. Somali.* **1**, 12-32.

Pellegrini, D. (1942-45). Spontaneous tuberculosis in camels in Somaliland. Experimental diagnosis (in Italian). *Racc. Stud. Pat. Vet. Somali.* **1**, 33-41.

Pellegrini, D. (1942-45). Cysticercosis in the camel (in Italian). *Racc. Stud. Pat. Vet. Somali.* **1**, 42-48.

Pellegrini, D. (1942-45). *Cysticercus dromedarius* in cattle (in Italian). *Racc. Stud. Pat. Vet. Somali.* **1**, 49-52.

Pellegrini, D. (1947). *Cysticercus dromedarii*, a new species in camels, and related cysticercosi (in Italian). *Boll. Soc. Ital. Med. Ig. Trop., Eritrea.* **7**, 317-324.

Pellegrini, D. (1947). *Cysticercus dromedarii* in cattle (in Italian). *Boll. Soc. Ital. Med. Ig. Trop., Eritrea.* **7**, 550-553.

Pellegrini, D. (1947). *Cysticercus dromedarii*, Pelligrini 1945, (the larval stage of *Taenia hyaenae* Baer 1947 (in Italian). *Boll. Soc. Ital. Med. Ig. Trop., Eritrea.* **7**, 554-565.

Pellegrini, D. (1947). *Cysticercus dromedarii* in the mesenteric lymph nodes in cattle (in Italian). *Boll. Soc. Ital. Med. Ig. Trop., Eritrea.* **7**, 566-572.

Pellegrini, D. (1948). *Trypanosoma simiae* (Bruce) infection in camels. *E. Afr. Agric. J.* **13**, 207-209.

Pellegrini, D. (1950). *Cysticercus dromedarii* of camels and cattle (Pelligrini, 1945) and the corresponding *Taenia hyaenae* in hyaenas (Baer, 1927) (in Italian). *Bull. Off. Int. Epiz.* **33**, 21-27.

Pellegrini, D. (1950). *Trypanosoma vivax* infection in the camel (in Italian). *Clin. Vet., Milano.* **73**, 65-76.

Pellegrini, D. and Bonelli, G. (1951). *Profilassi.* **24**, 78-85.

Perk, K. (1962). Seasonal change in the glandule bulbo-urethralis of the camel. *Bull. Res. Council Israel.* **10**, 37-49.

Perk, K. (1963). The camel's erythrocyte. *Nature, London.* **200**, 272-273.

Perk K. and Loble, (1961). A study of serum protein and lipoprotein of the camel and their relation to its resistance to heat and thirst. *Refuah. Vet.* **18**, 119-121.

Perk, K., Frei, Y. F. and Herz, A. (1964). Osmotic fragility of red blood cells of young and mature domestic and laboratory animals. *American J. Vet. Res.* **25**, 1241ff.

Perreau, P. (1973). *Maladies Tropicales du Bétail.* P U F: Paris.

Perreau, P. and Maurice, Y. (1968). Epizootologie de la pasteurellose des chameaux au Tchad. Enquête sérologique. *Rev. Elev. Méd. Vét. Pays Trop.* **21**, 451-456.

Perret, R. (1936). Recherches archeologiques et ethnographiques au Tassili des Ajjers (Sahara central). Les gravures rupestres de l'oued Djaret, la population et les ruines d'Ihérir. *J. Soc. Africanistes.* **6**, 41-64.

Peshin, P. K., Nigram, J. M., Singh, S. C. and Robinson, B. A. (1980). Evaluation of Xylazine in camels. *J. American Vet. Med. Assoc.* **177**, 875-878.

Pester, N. (1960). Comment le chameau résout-il le problème de la deshydratation cellulaire? Remarques de physiologie comparée. *Presse Méd.* **68**, 847-848.

Peters, E. L. (1967). Some structural aspects of the feud among the camel-herding bedouin of Cyrenaica. *Africa.* **37**, 261-282.

Petit, M. (1928). Les ganglions lymphatiques du chameau. *Rev. Vét. J. Méd. Vét. Zootech.* **80**, 547-553.

Petrie, J. (1927). Note on the urea content of camel urine (in German). *Zeitschr. Physiol. Chem.* **166**, 125-127.

Petrie, J. (1928). Excretion of camels. *J. Biol. Chem.* **78**, 409-411.

Petrie, W. M. F. (1903). *Abydos Part III.* Mem. Egyptian Expl. Found., London.

Petrie, W. M. F. (1907). Gizeh and Rifeh. *British Sch. Archeol., Egypt.* **13th Year.**

Petris, M. A. (1956). Caesarean operation in camels. *Vet. Rec.* **68**, 367-368.

Petrovskii, V. V. (1974). Next task - eradication of trypanosomiasis (in Russian). *Vet., Moscow.* **5**, 68-70.

Petrovskii, V. V. and Khamiev, S. Kh. (1974). Resistance to naganin (suramin) of strains of trypanosomes (isolated from camels) (in Russian). *Vet., Moscow.* **4**, 83-84.

Petrovskii, V. V. and Khamiev, S. Kh. (1977). Therapeutic efficacy of Azidin (diminazene) against trypanosomiasis in camels (in Russian). *Bull. Vses. Inst. Eksp. Vet.* **31**, 50-52.

Petter, F. (1956). La fin d'une longue erreur scientifique: Comment le chameau resiste à la soif. *La Nature.* No 3255, 263-265.

Petunin, F. A. (1958). Camel pox (in Russian). *Sborn. Inst. Vet. Res. Turkmenistan.* **1958**, 351.

Petzsch, H. (1951). On the scientific value of the hybridisation of vertebrates in the Zoological Gardens and crosses of yak and Scottish Highland cattle in Dresden Zoo (in German). *Zool. Gart. (Lpz).* **18**, 183-196.

Phakadze, G. M. (1932). Histological structure of the testis of hybrids of the Bactrian camel and the dromedary (in Russian). *Trudy Lab. Genet. (Leningrad).* **9**, 243-249.

Piessio, E. (1912). *Il Camello.* Hoepli Edizione: Milano.

Pigoury, L. and Bernard, M. (1938). La trypanosome du dromadaire en Syrie. *Rec. Méd. Vét. Exot.* **11**, 57-71.

Pilliet, A. (1885). Structure de la portion gaufrée de l'estomac du chameau. *Bull. Soc. Zool. France.* **10**, 40-41.

Piot Bey, J. B. (1889). *Le Chameau.* Rev. Egypte.

Piot Bey, J. B. (1890). *El Debab ou Maladie de la Mouche.* Imprimerie Nationale: Le Caire.

Pirani, H. (1939). Strongylosis among the animals of the Italian Empire with special attention to that of horses and with emphasis on symptomatology (in Italian). *Clin. Vet., Milano.* **62**, 447-484.

Placidi, L. and Santucci, J. (1956). Agglutination comparée des hématies de la poule, du chameau et des equides par les virus de la maladie de Newcastle et de la peste aviaire. *Ann. Inst. Pasteur.* **90**, 528-529.

Planol X. de (1964). Recherche sur la géographie de l'Iran. *Mém. Doc.* **9**, 3-78.

Plantereux, E. (1923). La formole gélification dans la trypanosomiase des dromadaires. *C. R. Séances Soc. Biol.* **88**, 1189-1190.

Plantereux, E. (1924). Au sujet de la formol-gélification chez les dromadaires et les bovides. *Arch. Inst. Pasteur, Alger.* **2**, 163.

Pocock, R. I. (1910). On the specialised cutaneous glands of ruminants. *Proc. Zool. Soc. London.* **1910**, 840-986.

Podberezkin, Ja. (1951). Experience of the work of a better camel-breeding farm (in Russian). *Konevodstvo.* **10**, 42-43.

Pohl, A. (1950). Das Kamel in Mesopotamien (in German). *Orientalia.* NS19, 251-253.

Pohl, A. (1952). Camel nomads in Mesopotamia (in German). *Orientalia.* NS21, 373.

Pohl, A. (1954). On the training of camels (in German). *Orientalia.* NS23, 448.

Polyakov, V. F. and Sabanshiev, M. S. (1977). Comparison of blood protein fractions and serological reactions in trypanosomiasis of camels (in Russian). *Bull. Vses. Inst. Eksp. Vet.* **31**, 54-56.

Pomel, A. (1893). Camelins et Cervidés. *Paléont. Mon. Carte Géol. Alger.* **2**, 1-52.

Pomel, A. (1893). Monographie des Camélins. *Bull. Serv. Géol., Alger.*

Poncet, A. (1938). Spirochète des dromadaires. *Bull. Soc. Path. Exot.* **31**, 478-479.

Ponder, J., Yeager, F. and Charipper, H. A. (1928). Haematology of the Camelidae. *Sci. Contrib. New York Zool. Soc.* **11**, 1-7.

Pope, A. U. (1938). *A survey of Persian Art.* Oxford University Press: London.

Porte, L. (1815). *The camel in Tuscany* (in Italian). Pisa.

Postiglione, E. (1935). The veterinary service and the most serious infectious diseases of livestock in our colony of East Africa (in Italian) *Clin. Vet., Milano*. **58**, 640-690.

Pottier, R. (1951). Cheptel saharien: le chameau. *Encyclop. Col. Marit.* **1(7)**, 59-61.

Pousty, I. (1977). Anatomical and histological study of the pituitary gland in the dromedary (Iranian breeds). *J. Vet. Fac. Univ. Teheran*. **33**, 9-21.

Pousty, I. (1977). Anatomical and histological study of the thyroid gland in the dromedary (Iranian breeds). *J. Vet. Fac. Univ. Teheran*. **33**, 41-52.

Prasad, H. (1960). Studies on the coccidia of some mammals of the Bovidae, Cervidae and Camelidae. *Z. Parasiterk*. **20**, 390-400.

Prashad, B. The animal remains from Harappa. *Mem. Archaeol. Survey India: Delhi*. No 51.

Prakash, A. (1962). Normal parturition in camels. *Indian Vet. J.* **39**, 551-553.

Pratt, D. J. and Gwynne, M. D. (1977). *Rangeland Management and Ecology in East Africa*. Hodder & Stoughton: London.

Pricolo, A. (1913). Larves de filaires dans le sang des chameaux tunisiens et de l'Erythrée. *Zentralbl. Bakt. Parasit*. **67**, 478-479.

Pricolo, A. (1913). Sur une filaire hématique du chameau. *Zentralbl. Bakt. Parasit*. **71**, 199-200.

Pricolo, A. (1913). Strongle capillaire du chameau. *Zentralbl. Bakt. Parasit*. **71**, 201-202.

Pricolo, A. and Ferraro, G. (1920). Camel trypanosomiasis (in Italian). *Clin. Vet., Milano*.

Pringle, R. (1955). Foot and mouth disease in camels (from the Vet. J., September 1880). *British Vet. J.* **111**, 416.

Provenzale, F. (1913). The origins of the domestic species and races in Somalia. (in Italian) *Nuovo Ercolani*. **5**, 65.

Provenzale, F. (1913). Livestock rearing in our Somalia (in Italian). *Nuovo Ercolani*. **5**, 109; 190; 203; 382.

Provenzale, F. (1914). *Livestock rearing in our Somalia* (in Italian). Governo della Somalia Italiana. Tip. Naz. G. Bertero & Co.: Roma.

Provost, A., Maurice, Y. and Borredon, C. (1968). Note sur la peste bovine expérimentale du dromadaire. *Rev. Elev. Méd. Vét. Pays Trop.* **21**, 293-296.

Provost, A., Haas, P. and Dembelle, M. (1975). Premiers cas au Tchad de botulisme animal (type C): Intoxication de dromadaires par l'eau d'un puits. *Rev. Elev. Méd. Vét. Pays Trop*. **28**, 9-11.

Przezdziecki, (1942). *Notes préliminaires concernant l'alimentation des chameaux dans la zone nomade du parcours de la compagnie saharienne*. Mimeo.

Przibran, H. (1910). *Experimental-Zoologie. III. Ch. 4 Hybridisation* (in German). Franz Deutticke: Leipzig and Vienna.

Puigaudeau, O. du and Serrous, M. (1935). Nomadisation en Mauritanie. *La Géographie, Paris*. **63**, 192-214.

Pulling, J. A. (1973). Camels and camel hair. *Wool Rec. Text. Wld.* **123(3310)**, 6-7.

Purchase, M. S. (1943). Some experiments in the making of butter, ghee and cheese from camels' milk *E. Afr. Agric. J.* **9**, 39-41.

Purohit, M. S. (1957). A diaphragm bone in the camel (in German). *Deutsche Tierarztl. Wschr*. **64**, 487.

Purohit, M. S. and Lodha, K. R. (1958). Haemonchosis in a camel. *Indian Vet. J.* **35**, 219-221.

Purohit, M. S. and Singh, B. (1958). The poll glands in camel. *British Vet. J.* **35**, 296-298.

Purohit, M. S. and Rathor, S. (1962). Stomach of the camel in comparison to that of the ox. *Indian Vet. J.* **39**, 604-608.

Purushotham, N. P. and Mahendar, M. (1963). A note on the comparative study of the blood picture in domestic animals. *Indian Vet. J.* **40**, 553.

Quéval, R., Graber, M. and Brunet (Mme) (1967). Etude de la protidémie et des constantes hématologiques des camélidés en fonction des helminthes dont ils sont porteurs. *Rev. Elev. Méd. Vét. Pays Trop.* **20**, 437-449.

Rabagliati, D. S. (1920). Tetanus in the camel. *J. Comp. Path. Therap.* **33**, 10-12.

Rabagliati, D. S. (1923). Poly-Arthritis in camels. *J. Comp. Path. Therap.* **36**, 90-96.

Rabagliati D. S. (1923). The examintion of the camel for soundness with indications as to its age. *Vet. J.* **79**, 1-31.

Rabagliati, D. S. (1924). *The Dentition of the Camel*. Government Press: Cairo.

Race, G. J. and Wu, H. M. (1964). Corticoids in the three zones of the camel (*Camelus dromedarius*) adrenal cortex. *Gen. Comp. Endocrinol.* **4**, 199-209.

Rackham, H. (translator) (1969). *Pliny: Natural History*. Harvard University Press: Cambridge, Massachusetts.

Radclyffe, C. E. (1938). Movements of camels. *Field, London*. **172(4483)**, 1306.

Radmanesh, H. (1974). Choledochoduodenal junction in the dromedary. *Acta Anat.* **90**, 507-513.

Rafyi, A. and Maghami, G. (1953). *Bull. Soc. Path. Exot.* **46**, 676-680.

Rafyi, A. and Maghami, G. (1954). Sur la présence de Q fever en Iran. *Bull. Soc. Path. Exot.* **47**, 766-768.

Rafyi, A. and Maghami, G. (1959). Sur la fréquence de la leptospirose en Iran. *Bull. Soc. Path. Exot.* **52**, 592-596.

Rahi, A. H. S., Sheikh, H. and Morgan, G. (1980). Histology of the camel eye. *Acta Anat.* **106**, 345-350.

Railliet, M. A. (1896). Sur quelques parasites du dromadaire. *C. R. Séances Soc. Biol.* **2**, 489-492.

Railliet, M. A. (1896). Sur les variations morphologiques des strongles de l'appareil digestif et sur un nouveau strongle du dromadaire. *C. R. Séances Soc. Biol.* **3**, 540.

Raisinghani, P. M., Bhatia, J. S., Dwaraknath, P. K. and Lodha, K. R. (1980). Plasma monoamine oxidase (MAO) levels in trypanosomiasis in camel. *Indian Vet. J.* **57**, 780-782.

Raisinghani, P. M., Bhatia, U. K., Vyas, P. L. Arya and Lodha, K. R. (1980). Pathology of experimental surra in camels. *Indian J. Anim. Sci.* **50**, 966-969.

Rak, H. and Anwar, M. (1974). Some diptera larvae causing myiasis in Iran. *Entomol. Monthly Mag.* **110**, 79-80.

Rakhimzhanov, G. R. (1971). Semen collection from the two-humped camel (in Russian). *Vest. Sel'-khoz. Nauk. Alma-Ata.* **14**, 100-102; 119.

Ralston, G. B. (1975). Proteins of the camel erythrocyte membrane. *Biochem. Biophys. Acta.* **401**, 83-94.

Ram, C., Khanna, N. D., Sinha, D. P. and Prabhu, S. S. (1964). Studies on camel blood antigenic factors detected through cattle blood-group reagents. *Indian J. Vet. Sci.* **34**, 239-241.

Ram, S., Singh, B. and Dhanda, O. P. (1977). A note on genetic studies on gestation length, birth weight and intra-uterine development index in Indian camel (*Camelus dromedarius*) and factors affecting them. *Indian Vet. J.* **54**, 953-955.

Ram, S. M. T., Dutt, S. C., Behl, S. M. and Malhotra, D. V. (1980). Comparative efficacy of some acaricides in the control of sarcoptic mange in camels. *J. Res. Haryana Agric. Univ.* **10**, 298-302.

Ramachandranlyer, P. K., Ramachandran, S. and Joshi, T. P. (1968). An outbreak of haemorrhagic gastro-enteritis in camels (*Camelus dromedarius*). *Ann. Parasit. Hum. Comp.* **43**, 5-14.

Ramadan, F. M. and Sadek, I. M. (1971). Parameters of salmonellosis in Egypt. *J. Egyptian Vet. Med. Assoc.* **31**, 193-218.

Ramadan, R. O. and Elhassan, A. M. (1980). Fibrous exulis in a one-humped camel (*Camelus dromedarius*) (in German). *Zentralbl. Vet. Med.* **27A**, 675-677.

Ramon, G. and Lemetayer, E. (1934). Sur l'immunité antitétanique naturellement acquise chez quelques espèces de ruminants. *C. R. Séances Soc. Biol.* **116**, 275-277.

Ramyar, H. and Hessami, M. (1972). Isolation, cultivation and characterisation of camel pox virus (in German). *Zentralbl. Vet. Med.* **19B**, 182-189.

Ramyar, H. and Hessami, M. (1972). Isolation, cultivation and characterisation of camel pox virus. *Arch. Inst. Razi.* 24, 13 - 21.

Rao, M. B., Gupta, R. C. and Dastur, N. N. (1970). Camel's milk and milk products. *Indian J. Dairy Sci.* 23, 71 - 78.

Rathjens, C. (1953-55). Sabaeica. *Mitteil, Mus. Volkerkunde Hamburg.* 24, 11 - 19.

Rathor, S. S. and Chouhan, D. S. (1971). Dorsal fixation of the patella in camel. *Indian Vet. J.* 48, 531 - 532.

Rathore, M. S. and Lodha, K. R. (1973). Observations on sacroptic mange in camels (*Camelus dromedarius*) in Rajasthan. I. Incidence and intensity. *Indian Vet. J.* 50, 1082 - 1088.

Rathore, M. S. and Lodha, K. R. (1974). Studies on sarcoptic mange in camels (*Camelus dromedarius*). II. Trials with some insecticides. *Indian Vet. J.* 51, 149 - 153.

Ravaglia, F. (1949). Strongylosis (*Anthostrongylus somaliensis* Croveri) in Libyan camels imported into Somaliland (in Italian). *Nuova Vet.* 25, 455 - 460.

Read, B. E. (1925). Chemical constituents of camels' urine. *J. Biol. Chem.* 64, 615 - 617.

Receveur, A. E. F. (1938). Notes sur certaines affections du cheptel des régions nord-est du Tchad. *Rec. Méd. Vét. Exot.* 11, 113 - 118.

Redzhepov, A., Taimatov, R. Sh., Agapovich, Zh. A. and Stepanov, D. F. (1972). Helminth fauna of carnivores and ruminants (in Russian). *Vet., Moscow.* 49, 71 - 72.

Reiss-Gutfreund, R. J. (1955). Isolement de souches de *Rickettsia prowazeki* à partir du sang des animaux domestiques d'Ethiopie et de leurs tiques. *Bull. Soc. Path. Exot.* 48, 602 - 607.

Reiss-Gutfreund, R. J. (1961). Nouveau isolements de *R. prowazeki* à partir d'animaux domestiques et de tiques. *Bull. Soc. Path. Exot.* 54, 284 - 297.

Rennes (1903-05). Nouveau cas de débab chez les dromadaires dans la région de la Zousfana. *Bull. Soc. Cent. Méd. Vét.* Sept. 1903; April 1904; Feb. 1905.

Rezakhani, A. and Szabuniewicz, M. (1977). The electrocardiogram of the camel, *Camelus dromedarius*. *Zentralbl. Vet. Med.* 24A, 277 - 286.

Rhotert, H. (1938). *Transjordanien*. Forschungsirst Kulturmorphol.: Frankfurt.

Ribbeck, R. and Beulig, W. (1977). Vaginal myiasis in a camel (in German). *Monat. Vet. Med.* 32, 354.

Ricard, M. (1953). *Le bossu au pied mou*. Conférence prononcée le 23 December 1951; Editions Ami de Fès: Fez.

Richard, D. (1974). *Notes sur l'élevage camelin en Ethiopie*. Min. Ag.: Addis Ababa.

Richard, D. (1975). *Etude de la pathologie du dromadaire dans la sous-province du Borana (Ethiopie)*. Thèse DMV. ENV: Alfort No 75.

Richard, D. (1976). The diseases of the dromedary (*Camelus dromedarius*) in Ethiopia. *Ethiopian Vet. Bull.* 2, 46 - 67.

Richard, D. (1980). Le dromadaire: de la légende à la production. *Afr. Agric.* 63, 18 - 20.

Richiardi, (1879). *Note on the anatomy of the camel* (in Italian). Pisa.

Rifaat, M. A., Khalil, H. M. and Salem, S. A. (1973). *The use of antigens extracted from camel filaria (Acanthocheilonema evansi) in serologic diagnosis of human filariasis in Egypt*. In: 9th Intnl. Cong. Trop. Med. Malaria, Athens, 14 - 21 Oct. 1973. Vol. II.

Rifaat, M. A., Khalil, H. M., Salem, S. A. and Mohamed, N. H. (1973). The camel filaria (*Dipetalonema evansi*) and the use of its antigens in the diagnosis of filariasis in Egypt. *J. Egyptian Vet. Med. Assoc.* 33, 75 - 83.

Rifaat, M. A., Morsy, T. A., Sadek, M. S. M., Khalid, M. L. M., Azab, M. E. and Safar, E. H. (1978). Prevalence of toxoplasma antibodies in slaughtered animals in Lower Egypt. *J. Egyptian Soc. Parasit.* 8, 339 - 345.

Riggs, E. S. (1945). A rare cameloid from the late Pleistocene sands of South-Western Kansas. *Trans., Kansas Acad Sci.* 48, 101 - 104.

Rihani, A. (1930). *Around the Coasts of Arabia*. Constable: London.

Rinaldi, L. (1933). On a camel trypanosome recognised in Tripolitania (Misurata) (in Italian). *Arch. Ital. Sci. Med. Colon.* 14, 141 - 143.

Rioux, J. A. (1960). *Mission épidémiologique au Nord Tchad*. Arts et Métiers: Paris.

Ripinsky, M. M. (1975). The camel in ancient Arabia. *Antiquity.* 49, 295 - 298.

Ritscher, D., Seidel, H. and Koch, M. (1978). Problems in the artificial rearing of a female dromedary (in German). In: Ippen, R. & Schroder, H. D. (eds). *Proc. 20th Intnl. Symp. Dis. Animals in Zoo Gardens* Akademie Verlag: Berlin, GDR. pp. 89 - 94.

Robertson, J. (1908). *With the Cameliers in Palestine*.

Robichon, C. and Varille, A. (1955). *Eternal Egypt*. Gerald Duckworth: London.

Robinson, A. F. (1936). The camel in antiquity. *Sudan Notes Rec.* 19, 47 - 69.

Robinson, P. (1885). Two camels from the Soudan (El Teb) in the Zoological Gardens. *Graphica.* **18th July, 1885.**

Rodinson, M. (1971). *Mohammed*. Allen Lane, The Penguin Press: London.

Roetti, C. (1940). *Trypanosoma theileri* in Somali camels (in Italian). *Ann. Pat. Trop. Parassit.* 1, 295 - 297.

Rogier, F. (1934). *Contribution à l'étude du système lymphatique du chameau*. Thèse DMV; ENV: Toulon.

Rollinson, D. H. L., Injidi, M. H. and Jenkinson, D. McE. (1972). The distribution of nerves, monoamine oxidase and cholinesterase in the skin of the camel (*Camelus dromedarius*). *Res. Vet. Sci.* 13, 304 - 305.

Romanelli, P. (1930). Life in Tripolitania as shown in pictorial art (in Italian). *Afr. Italiana.* 3, 53 - 75.

Romanovitch, M. I. (1916). *Deraiophoronema cameli* (n.g., n.sp.). *C. R. Séances Soc. Biol.* 79, 745.

Rombol, B. (1942). Enzootic *Bacterium coli* infection in newborn camels (in Italian). *Nuova Vet.* 20, 85 - 93.

Romer, A. S. (1929). A fresh skull of an extinct American camel. *J. Geol.* 37, 261 - 267.

Romer, A. S. and Sutton, A. H. (1928). A "fossil" camel recently living in Utah. *Science.* NS68, 19 - 20.

Rosborough, J. P., Bailey, E. M., Geddes, L. A. and Tacker, W. A. (1974). Experimental anesthetization of a dromedary camel. *Zentralbl. Vet. Med.* 21A, 149 - 156.

Rosenstiehl, D. (1959). *Contribution à l'étude des pâturages camelins dans l'Azaouad*. Thèse DMV. ENV: Alfort. No 63.

Rosenstrauch, A., Bedrak, E. and Friedlander, M. (1979). Androgen synthesis in testicular tissue of the suckling camel (*Camelus dromedarius*). *Israel J. Med. Sci.* 15, 548.

Roslyakov, A. A. (1972). Comparison of the ultrastructure of camel pox virus, the virus of a pox-like disease of camels, and contagious ecthyma virus (in Russian). *Voprosy Virus.* 17, 26 - 30.

Rossetti, G. and Congiu, S. (1955). *Zootechnical and veterinary research on the domestic animals of Somalia*. Ispet. Vet. Ammin. Fid. Ital. della Somalia: Mogadishu.

Rostovtzeff, M. *Caravan Cities*. Clarendon Press: Oxford.

Round, M. C. (1972). The helminth parasites of domesticated animals in Kenya. *J. Helminth.* 36, 375 - 379.

Rousseau, R. (1943). Le chameau au Sénégal. *Bull. IFAN.* 5, 67 - 79.

Roux, J. P. (1959). Le chameau en Asie central. *Cent. Asiatic J.* 5, 35 - 76.

Rozier, J. and Lépissier, H. (1974). La production de viande en Afrique noire francophone. *Rec. Méd. Vét.* 150, 305 - 317.

Rubel, P. G. (1969). Herd composition and social structure: on building models of nomadic pastoral societies. *Man, London.* NS4, 268 - 273.

Rusconi, C. (1931). The dentition of *Palaeolama* in relation to other camelids (in Spanish). *Rev. Med. Vet., Buenos Aires.* 13, 250 - 273.

Russell, A. (1974). *Natural History of Aleppo*. London.

Russell, K. P. (1977). The speciality animal fibres. *Textiles.* 6, 8 - 12.

Rutter, T. E. G. (1967). Diseases of camels: protozoal diseases. *Vet. Bull.* 37, 611 - 618.

209

Rutter, T. E. G. and Mack, R. (1963). Diseases of camels: bacterial and fungal diseases. *Vet. Bull.* **33**, 119-124.

Saad, M. A. G. and Hussein, A. M. (1975). Isolation of *Salmonellae* from camels in the Sudan. *Proc. 7th Ann. Conf. Sudan Vet. Assoc.*

Saad, Z. Y. (1947). Royal excavations at Saqqara and Helwan (1941-45). *Suppl. Ann. Service Archéol. Egypte.* **3**, 1-258.

Sabanshiev, M. (1972). Fluorescent antibody test for *Trypanosoma ninaekohljakimovi* infection in camels (in Russian). *Vet., Moscow.* **5**, 65-66.

Sabanshiev, M. S. (1973). Fluorescent antibody test in *Trypanosoma ninaekohljakimovi* infection (in Russian). *Vet., Moscow.* **6**, 63-64.

Sabban, M. S., Hussein, N., Sadek, B. and El-Dahaby, H. (1968). Q fever in the United Arab Republic. *Bull. Off. Int. Epiz.* **69**, 745-760.

Saber, M. S., Reda, I. M., Tantawi, H. H., Shahaby, M. A., Hamed, O. M. and Gorshiniria, V. (1978). Studies on the cross antigenic relationship between camel pox, buffalo pox, sheep pox and vaccinia virus. *Vet. Med. J., Cairo Univ.* **26**.

Saceghem, R. van (1922). *C. R. Séances Soc. Biol.* **87**, 995-998.

Sadana, J. R., Mahajani, S. K. and Satija, K. C. (1980). Notes on *Papilloma* in a camel. *Indian J. Anim. Sci.* **50**, 793-795.

Sadykov, R. G. (1970). *Cultivation of camel pox virus in chick embryos* (in Russian). Vir. Bol. Sel'-khoz. Zhivetnvkh: Moscow.

Sadykov, V. M. (1967). Unilocular hydatid of camel in Uzbekhistan (in Russian). *Trudy Uzbek Nauk Inst. Vet.* **18**, 283-292.

Saez, H. and Rinjard, J. (1973). *Trichosporon capitatum*, un constituant de la flore fongique du tube digestif de certains suidés. *Ann. Méd. Vét.* **117**, 177-182.

Said, A. H. (1963). Rumenotomy and experimental traumatic reticulitis in the camel. *Vet. Rec.* **75**, 966-969.

Said, A. H. (1964). Some aspects of anaesthesia of the camel. *Vet. Rec.* **76**, 550-554.

Said, A. H. and Youssef, L. B. (1966). Urethrotomy in the camel. *J. Vet. Sci. UAR.* **3**, 15-20.

Said, M. S. (1946). *Mange in Egyptian camels. The morphology, life history and bionomics of Sarcoptis scabiei var. cameli with an outline of the history, pathology and treatment of the disease.* Ph. D. Thesis. University of Cairo.

Said, M. S., Atef, M., El-Refail, A. H., Michael, S. and El-Sadr, H. (1971). Experiments on Asuntol and Bercotox for tick control. *J. Egyptian Vet. Med. Assoc.* **31**, 43-54.

Saidi, S., Casals, J. and Faghih, M. A. (1975). Crimean haemorrhagic fever - Congo (CHF-C) virus antibodies in man, and in domestic and small mammals. *American J. Trop. Med. Hyg.* **24**, 353-357.

Saini, T. D. and Sreemannarayana, O. (1980). Meningitis in camels - a preliminary report. *Indian Vet. J.* **57**, 681-683.

Saint-Hilaire, I. G. (1861). *Acclimatation et domestication des animaux utiles.* Librairie Agricole de la Maison Rustique: Paris.

Sakkal, F. B. (1945). *Le Chameau: Animal de Boucherie.* Thèse DMV; ENV: Alfort. **No 15**.

Salah, S. M. (1975). *Filariasis in camel in Egypt.* M. V. Sc. Dissertation. University of Cairo.

Saleh, M. S., Mobarak, A. M. and Fouad, S. M. (1971). Radiological, anatomical and histological studies of the mammary gland of the one-humped camel (*Camelus dromedarius*) I. The teat (*Papilla mammae*). *Zentralbl. Vet. Med.* **18A**, 347-352.

Salonen, A. (1956). *Hippologica Accadia.* Suomalainen Tiefeakatemia Helsinki.

Saluy, G. (1953). L'économie pastorale saharienne. *Doc. Française.* **1730**, 1-45.

Salzer, E. H. (1969). Battle of the dromedaries. *Kosmos.* **65**, 167-169.

Samartsev, A. A. (1940). Treatment of surra in camels (in Russian). *Vet., Moscow.* **5**, 69-71.

Samartsev, A. A. (1950). Pustular dermatitis in camels (in Russian). *Trudy Inst. Vet. Akad. Nauk Kazak. SSR, Alma-Ata.* **5**, 190-197.

Samartsev, A. A. and Arbuzov, P. N. (1940). Contribution to the study of the susceptibility of the camel to glanders, rinderpest and CBPP (in Russian). *Vet., Moscow.* **4**, 59-63.

Sanaa, M. N., Soud, A. M. and Lotfi, L. A. (1976). Influence of sex on the normal blood picture of adult Egyptian camel (*Camelus dromedarius*). *Assiut Vet. Med. J.* **4**, 43-50.

Sandiford, B. R. (1944). Food poisoning due to *Bacterium typhimurium* (Anaerogenes). *J. Path. Bact.* **56**, 254-255.

Sandiford, B. R., El-Gheriany, M. G., Abu-Ela, M. and Keram, A. M. (1943). Food poisoning outbreak in Egypt associated with *Bacterium aertrycke*. *Lab. Med. Progr.* **4**, 14-18.

Santi, G. (1811). Mémoire sur les chameaux de Pisa. *Ann. Mus. Hist. Nat., Paris.* Volume 17.

Santini, R. (1964). *Etude topographique et histologique de l'hypothalamus du dromadaire.* Diplôma d'Etude supérieure, Rabat.

Sara, L. S. and Chouhan, D. S. (1975). Prolapse of rectum in camel (*Camelus dromedarius*). *Indian Vet. J.* **52**, 652-653.

Sato, S. (1978). *Preliminary report of camel ecology among the Rendille in Northern Kenya.* Primate Research Institute, Kyoto University, Japan.

Satterfield, W. C. and Lester, G. A. (1974). Bilateral epiphyseal avulsion of the olecranon processes in a dromedary camel. *J. Zoo Anim. Med.* **5**, 34-35.

Savi, P. (1828). *On the so-called palate projecting from the mouth of the camel* (in Italian). Memoire scientific e. Tipografia Nistri: Pisa.

Savi, P. (1843). On the involuted foetal placenta of *Camelus dromedarius* (in Italian). *Misc. Med. Chir. Farm., Pisa* (Sess. Zool. Comp. Anat. Sci. Ital., Padua 1842).

Schafer, E. H. (1950). The camel in China down to the Mongol dynasty (in German). *Zeitschr. Chines. Kult. Wissensch.* **2**, 263-290.

Schafer, E. H. (1950). The camel in China down to the Mongol dynasty. *Sinologia.* **2**, 165-194.

Schauenburg, K. (1956). The Camelidae of Ancient Times (in German). *Bonn Jahrb.* **145-6**, 59-94.

Schebitz, H. (1948). Elephantiasis of the sheath and phumosis in a camel (in German). *Mh. Vet.-Med.* **3**, 111-113.

Schejter, A., Grosman, Z. and Sokolovsky, M. (1972). Isolation, properties and partial sequence of the cytochrome of the camel (*Camelus dromedarius*). *Israel J. Chem.* **10**, 37-41.

Schels, H. F. and Mowrouzian, I. (1977). The effects of reversible narcotic immobilisation in the Iranian camel. *Vet. Rec.* **101**, 388.

Schels, H. F. and Mostafawi, D. J. (1978). Ultrasonic pregnancy diagnosis in the camel. *Anim. Repr. Sci.* **1**, 19-23.

Schillhorn van Veen, T. W. (1974). Filariasis in domestic animals in northern Nigeria and its relation to human health. In: Soulsby, E. J. L. (ed) *Parasitic zoonoses. Clinical and Experimental studies.*

Schillhorn van Veen, T. W., Bello, S. I. and Folaranmi, D. O. B. (1976). *Onchocerca armillata* Railliet & Henry 1909, from a new host *Camelus dromedarius*. *Rev. Elev. Méd. Vét. Pays Trop.* **29**, 227-228.

Schmatz, H. D., Krauss, H., Viertel, P., Ismail, A. S. and Hussein, A. A. (1978). Serological curvey of *Rickettsia* and *Chlamydia* antibodies in domestic ruminants in Egypt, Somalia and Jordan (in German). *Acta Trop.* **35**, 101-111.

Schmidt, C. R. (1973). Breeding seasons and notes on some other aspects of reproduction in captive camelides. *Int. Zoo Yearbook.* **13**, 387-390.

Schmidt, and Morsch, (1943). Arab method of slaughtering camels for food (in German). *Zeitschr. Veterinark.* **55**, 199-202.

Schmidt-Nielsen, B., Schmidt-Nielsen, K., Jarnum, S. A. and Houpt, T. R. (1955). Dehydration and rehydration in the camel. *Fed. Proc. Centre Recherches Sahariennes: Beni Abbes, Algeria.* **14**, 132-133.

Schmidt-Nielsen, B., Schmidt-Nielsen, K., Houpt, T. R. and Jarnum, S. A. (1956). Water balance of the camel. *American J. Physiol.* **185**, 185-194.

Schmidt-Nielsen, B., Schmidt-Nielsen, K., Houpt, T. R. and Jarnum, S. A. (1957). Urea excretion in the camel. *American J. Physiol.* **188**, 477-484.

Schmidt-Nielsen, K. (1955). *Rapport préliminaire sur les recherches concernant la physiologie du chameau.* Comité consultatif de recherche sur la zone aride. 9ème session. UNESCO: Paris.

Schmidt-Nielsen, K. (1955). Recherches sur la physiologie du chameau. *Trav. Inst. Rech. Sahar.* **13**, 179-188.

Schmidt-Nielsen, K. (1955). The camel: facts and fables. *UNESCO Courier.* **8-9**, 29-32; 63.

Schmidt-Nielsen, K. (1956). Rapport préliminaire concernant la physiologie du chameau. *Bull. Liais. Sahar.* **7**, 16-28; 29-37; 99-101.

Schmidt-Nielsen, K. (1956). Water storage in the camel. *Proc. 76th Meeting American Physiol. Soc. 1956. Atlantic City, New Jersey.* Part I.

Schmidt-Nielsen, K. (1956). Animals and arid conditions: physiological aspects of productivity and management. In: *The Future of Arid Lands.* American Soc. Adv. Sci.: Washington, D. C. pp. 368-382.

Schmidt-Nielsen, K. (1959). The physiology of the camel. *Sci. Amer.* **200**, 140-142; 144; 146-148; 150-151.

Schmidt-Nielsen, K. (1964). The Camel. In: *Desert Animals: Physiological problems of heat and water.* Clarendon Press: Oxford.

Schmidt-Nielsen, K. and Schmidt-Nielsen, B. (1952). Water metabolism in desert mammals. *Physiol. Rev.* **32**, 135-166.

Schmidt-Nielsen, K., Schmidt-Nielsen, B., Houpt, T R. and Jarnum, S. A. (1955). Body temperature of the camel. *Fed. Proc. Centre Recherches Sahariennes: Beni Abbes, Algeria.* **4**, 133.

Schmidt-Nielsen, K., Schmidt-Nielsen, B., Houpt, T. R. and Jarnum, S. A. (1956). The question of water storage in the stomach of the camel. *Mammalia.* **20**, 1-15.

Schmidt-Nielsen, K., Schmidt-Nielsen, B., Jarnum, S. A. and Houpt, T. R. (1957). Body temperature of the camel and its relation to water economy. *American J. Physiol.* **188**, 103-112.

Schmidt-Nielsen, K., Crawford, E. C., Newsome, A. E. and Rawson, K. S. (1963). The metabolic rate of camels. *Fed. Proc. Centre Recherches Sahariennes: Beni Abbes, Algeria.* **22**, 176.

Schmidt-Nielsen, K. Crawford, E. C., Newsome, A. E., Rawson, K. S. and Hammel, H. T. (1967). Metabolic rate of camels: effect of body temperature and dehydration. *American J. Physiol.* **212**, 341-346.

Schmidt-Nielsen, K., Schroter, R. C. and Schkolnik, A. (1980). Desaturation of the exhaled air in the camel. *J. Physiol.* **305**, 74P-75P.

Schmitt, G. (1913). Le dromadaire en Mauritanie. *Bull. Soc. Zool. Acclim.* **60**, 473-480.

Schwarzlose, F. W. (1886). *About the arms of the ancient Arabs as presented by their poets* (in German). J. C. Hinrichs: Leipzig.

Schweinfurth, G. (1912). Animal pictures and rock signatures at Assuan (in German). *Z. Ethnol.* **4**, 527-658.

Scott, G. R. and MacDonald, J. (1962). Kenya camels and rinderpest. *Bull. Epiz. Dis. Afr.* **10**, 495-497.

Scott, G. R., Coakley, W., Roach, R. W. and Cowdy, N. R. (1963). Rift Valley fever in camels. *J. Path. Bact.* **86**, 229-231.

Scott, J. M. (1973). *An interim report on the bovine and camel situation in the Negelle (Boran) region, Sidamo.* Min. Agric. Vet.: Addis Ababa (mimeo).

Scott, W. B. (1937). *A History of Land Mammals in the Western Hemisphere.* Macmillan Co.: New York.

Scott, W. B. (1940). Artiodactyla. In: Scott, W. B. & Jepson, G. L. Part 4. *The Mammalian Fauna of the White River Oligocene.* Trans. American Phil. Soc. NS78, 363-746.

Sebek, Z. (1974). Results of serologic examination of domestic animals for leptospirosis in the Mongolian People's Republic (in Russian). *Folia Parasit.* **21**, 21-28.

Sebek, Z., Sery, V. and Saboor, A. (1972). Results of the first leptospirological study carried out in Afghanistan. *J. Hyg. Epid. Microbiol. Immun., Prague.* **16**, 314-324.

Seddon, H. R. (1952). Diseases of Domestic Animals. Part 4. *Dept. of Health: Canberra Service Publ. (Div. Vet. Hyg.)* **No 8**.

SEDES (1976). *Inventaire Qualitatif et Quantitatif du cheptel tchadien.* SEDES: Paris.

Sedik, M. F., Roushdy, S., Zidau, M. and Salam, M. A. (1977). Incidence of echinococcosis among slaughtered animals at Cairo abattoir. *Assiut Vet. Med. J.* **4**, 171-178.

Sedov, V. A. (1973). Official communication: measures for the prevention and eradication of camel pox (in Russian). *Vet., Moscow.* **12**, 63-64.

Seguy, M. E. (1933). Mission saharienne Augiéras - Draper. *Bull. Mus. Nat. Hist. Nat., Paris.* **2**, 122.

Sekeles, E., Cohen, R., Yagil, R. and Etzion, Z. (1979). Sweat glands of the bedouin camel. *Refuah Vet.* **36**, 71.

Selim, M. K. and Rahman, M. S. (1972). Enteric nematodes of camels in Egypt. *Egyptian J. Vet. Sci.* **9**, 75-80.

Seran, J. (1951). Miloud ou les mémoires d'un chameau de selle. *Cah. Ch. de Foucald.* **6**, 97-130.

Serebrowskii, A. A. (1935). *Hybridization of Animals* (in Russian). Biomedgiz., Moscow.

Sergent, E. and Sergent, E. (1905). Trypanosomiase des dromadaires de l'Afrique du nord. *Ann. Inst. Pasteur.* **19**, 17-48.

Sergent, E. and Sergent, E. (1905). Sur des embryons de filaires dans le sang du dromadaire. *C. R. Séances Soc. Biol.* **58**, 672-675.

Sergent, E., Sergent, E., Foley, H. and Lhéritier, A. (1918). De la mortalité dans le debab, trypanosomiase du dromadaire. *Bull. Soc. Path. Exot.* **11**, 568-570.

Sergent, E. and Lhéritier, A. (1919). Note sur la température rectale des dromadaires. *C. R. Séances Soc. Biol.* **82**, 172-175.

Sergent, E., Sergent, E. and Lhéritier, A. (1919). Dromadaires immunisés contre le trypanosomiase "Debab". *Bull. Soc. Path. Exot.* **12**, 86-90.

Sergent, E. and Lhéritier, A. (1919). Gale du dromadaire. *Bull. Soc. Path. Exot.* **12**, 94-99.

Sergent, E., Sergent, E. and Donatien, A. (1920). Deuxième note sur l'héridité de l'infection et de l'immunité dans la trypanosomiase des dromadaires. *Bull. Soc. Path. Exot.* **13**, 525-527.

Sergent, E., Sergent, E. and Foley, H. (1921). Essais de traitement du debab, trypanosomiase des dromadaires. I. Afidol, II. Trypanobleu, III. Emétique et Atoxyl. *Ann. Inst. Pasteur.* **35**, 204-211.

Sergent, E. and Donatien, A. (1922). *C. R. Acad. Sci.* **174**, 582-584.

Sergent, E. and Donatien, A. (1924). Debab et nagana chez le dromadaire. *Arch. Inst. Pasteur, Alger.* **2**, 162.

Sergent, E. and Poncet, A. (1939). Spirochete sanguicole du dromadaire, *Spirochaeta dromadis* n. sp. *Arch. Inst. Pasteur, Alger.* **17**, 509-511.

Sergent, E. and Poncet, A. (1942). Etude morphologique du sang des dromadaires sahariens. *Arch. Inst. Pasteur, Alger.* **20**, 204-208.

Seurat, L. G. (1912). Sur la presence en Algerie du *Spiroptera sexalata* Molin chez le dromadaire et chez l'âne. *C. R. Séances Soc. Biol.* **75**, 507-520.

Seurat, L. G. (1913). Sur l'évolution de *Physocephalus sexalatus* Molin. *C. R. Séances Soc. Biol.* **75**, 507-520.

Seurat, L. G. (1916). Sur les gongylonemes du Nord africain (contribution à l'étude de la variation chez les nématodes). *C. R. Séances Soc. Biol.* **79**, 717-742.

Seurat, L. G. (1918). Contribution à l'étude de la faune parasitaire de la Tunisie. *Arch. Inst. Pasteur, Tunis.* **10**, 243-275.

Shagaeva, V. G. and Kurnosov, K. M. (1974). Morphogenesis of the placenta in the Bactrian camel (in Russian). *Zool. Zh.* **53**, 1058-1065.

Shah, S. M. A. and Khan, G. S. (1936). Pneumonia in camels. *Indian Vet. J.* **12**, 206-220.

Shahien, Y. M., Fahmy, M. F. and El-Shafei, S. M. (1974). A histochemical study of the skin of the camel (*Camelus dromedarius*). *Assiut Vet. Met. J.* **1**, 15-23.

Shahien, Y. M. and El Mougy, S. A. (1975). The harderian gland of the one-humped camel (*Camelus dromedarius*). II. Histochemistry. *Assiut Vet. Met. J.* **2**, 49-55.

Shakhov, S. D. (1972). Amnion of the somite embryon of the dromedary (in Russian). *Ark. Anat. Histol. Embriol.* **62**, 96-99.

Shalash, M. R. (1980). Utilization of camel meat and milk in human nourishment. In: *Workshop on Camels*, Khartoum, Sudan 18-20

Dec. 1979. Intnl. Foundation for Science: Stockholm, Sweden. pp. 295–306.

Shalash, M. R. and Nawito, M. (1963). Sterility in female camels. *Deutsche Tierarztl. Wschr.* **70**, 522.

Shalash, M. R. and Nawito, M. (1964). Some reproductive aspects in the female camel. *Proc. 5th Int. Congr. Anim. Reprod. A. I.*, Trento, 6–13 Sept. 1964. Vol. II: 263–273.

Shalash, M. R. and Nawito, M. (1965). Some reproductive aspects in the female camel. *Wld. Rev. Anim. Prod.* **1**, 103–109.

Sharma, C. M. and Vashishta, M. S. (1976). Post parturient bleeding in she-camel. *Livestock Advis.* **1**, 35.

Sharma, D. P., Malik, P. D. and Sapra, K. L. (1973). Age-wise and species-wise haematological studies in farm animals. *Indian J. Anim. Sci.* **43**, 289–295.

Sharma, S. P. and Gautam, O. P. (1974). A note on the prevalence of toxoplasma antibodies among camels and pigs in Hissar. *Indian J. Anim. Sci.* **44**, 214–215.

Sharma, S. S. (1968). *Studies on gestation, birth weight, parturition and involution of uterus in the camel.* M. Sc. Thesis. Coll. Vet. Med., Punjab University, Hissar.

Sharma, S. S. (1972). Involution of uterus and vulva in camels. *Ceylon Vet. J.* **20**, 9–10.

Sharma, S. S. and Vyas, K. K. (1970). Parturition in the camel (*Camelus dromedarius*). *Ceylon Vet. J.* **18**, 7–9.

Sharma, S. S. and Vyas, K. K. (1970). A study of factors affecting the birth weight in Bikaneri camel. *Punjab Vet.* **9**, 8–13.

Sharma, S. S. and Vyas, K. K. (1971). Peculiar antepartum characteristic behaviour in single-humped camel (*Camelus dromedarius*). *Haryana Vet.* **10**, 59–62.

Sharma, S. S., and Vyas, K. K. (1971). Factors affecting gestation length in the Bikaneri camel (*Camelus dromedarius*). *Ceylon Vet. J.* **19**, 67–68.

Sharma, S. S. and Vyas, K. K. (1972). Involution of uterus and vulva in camels. *Ceylon Vet. J.* **20**, 9–10.

Sharma, S. S. and Satija, K. C. (1974). Trials with Promintic in clinical cases of pica in camels. *Indian Vet. J.* **51**, 231–232.

Sharma, V. D., Bhargava, K. K. and Singh, M. (1963). Secondary sex ratio of normal births in Bikaneri camels. *Indian Vet. J.* **40**, 561–563.

Sharma, V. D. and Bhargava, K. K. (1963). The Bikaneri camel. *Indian Vet. J.* **40**, 639–643.

Shary, S., Yagil, R. and Berlyne, G. M. (1978). Hydroxycholecalciferol levels in camel, sheep and goat. *Comp. Biochem. Physiol.* **59**, 139–140.

Shatilov, M. I. (1972). Camel raising: a profitable branch of the animal industry (in Russian). *Zhivotnovodstvo.* **11**, 23–24.

Shehata, R. (1964). Medullary tubes in the ovary of the camel and other mammals. *Vet. Rec.* **76**, 750–753.

Shehata, R. (1978). Comparative study of Gartner's duct in the camel. *Acta Anat.* **100**, 89–97.

Sherkov, S. N., El Rabie, Y. and Kokash, L. (1976). A survey of parasitic blood diseases "tickborne fever" in domestic animals in Jordan. *Egyptian J. Vet. Sci.* **13**, 29–35.

Sherkov, S. N., Leitch, B. and El Rabie, Y. (1976). A survey of *Sarcosporidia* in domestic animals in Jordan. *Etyptian J. Vet. Sci.* **13**, 45–51.

Sherkov, S. N. and El Rabie, Y. (1978). A survey of *Linguatula serrata* (*Pentostomum denticulatum*) in domestic animals in Jordan. *Egyptian J. Vet. Sci.* **15**, 89–97.

Shigidi, M. A. (1973). Aerobic microflora of respiratory tract of camels. *Sudan J. Vet. Sci. Anim. Husb.* **14**, 9–14.

Shigidi, M. A. (1974). Animal leptospirosis in the Sudan. *British Vet. J.* **130**, 528–531.

Shoeb, Z. E. and Osman, F. (1972). Studies on animal fats. I. The component glycerides of Egyptian camel, *Camelus dromedarius*, fat. *Fette Seifen Ans.* **74**, 396–399.

Shtan'ko, V. A. (1965). A disease of camels characterised by purulent lymphadenitis (in Russian). *Trudy 7 Sess. Akad. Nauk Turkmen SSR, Ashkhabad.* **1954**, 388–390.

Shumilina, Z. V. (1953). *A study of dictyocaulus disease in camels* (in Russian). Pap. Helminth. Akad. K. I. Skrjalin 75th Birthday, Moscow Izdat. Akad. Nauk SSR. pp. 793–800.

Shumilov, K. V. (1974). Diagnostic value of agglutination and complement fixation tests for brucellosis in camels (in Russian). *Trudy Vses. Inst. Eks. Vet.* **42**, 279–282.

Siebert, B. D. (1967). *Water turnover of desert cattle and camels.* Ph.D. Thesis. University of Adelaide.

Siebert, B. D. and Macfarlane, W. V. (1971). Water turnover and renal function of dromedaries in the desert. *Physiol. Zool.* **44**, 225–240.

Siebert, B. D. and Macfarlane, W. V. (1975). Dehydration in desert cattle and camels. *Physiol. Zool.* **48**, 36–48.

Silberman, L. (1959). Les nomades du Plateau Somali. *Rev. Int. Sci. Soc.* **11**, 582–598.

Silvey, R. E. (1977). Immobilon and camels (correspondence). *Vet. Rec.* **101**, 470.

Silvey, R. E. (1978). Castration of camels (correspondence). *Vet. Rec.* **102**, 134–135.

Simon, E. (1965). Endocranium, end cranial cast and brain of the dromedary (*Camelus dromedarius*). *Acta Anat.* **60**, 122–151.

Simonetta, B. (1927). On the blood of the camel (in Italian). *Pathologica.* **19**, 116–119.

Simpson, G. G. (1945). The principles of classification and a classification of mammals. *Bull. American Mus. Nat. Hist.* **85**, 1–350.

Simpson, V. R. (1979). Bluetongue antibody in Botswana's domestic and game animals. *Trop. Anim. Hlth Prod.* **11**, 43–49.

Singh, A. and Chhabra, R. C. (1973). Incidence of arthropod pests of domesticated animals and birds. *Indian J. Anim. Sci.* **43**, 393–397.

Singh, H. (1963). *A Handbook of Animal Husbandry for Extension Workers.* Min. Food Agric.: New Delhi.

Singh, H. (1966). Camel Care. *Intensive Agric.* **9**,

Singh, K. V. and Ata, F. A. (1967). Experimental rinderpest in camels – A preliminary report. *Bull. Epiz. Dis. Afr.* **15**, 19–23.

Singh, K. V. and Ata, F. A. (1967). Presence of antibodies against parainfluenza-3 virus in camel and sheep sera. *Vet. Rec.* **81**, 84.

Singh, M. (1958). *Indian Vet. J.* **35**, 296.

Singh, M. P. and Singh, C. M. (1969). Mycotic dermatitis in camels. *Indian Vet. J.* **46**, 854–856.

Singh, R., Rathor, S. S. and Kohli, R. N. (1962). A note on preliminary observations on the use of some general anaesthetics on the camel. *Indian Vet. J.* **39**, 614–616.

Singh, R. P., Washishta, M. S. and Kala, C. (1980). *Diseases of Camels.* Seven Seas: Hyderabad, India.

Singh, U. B. and Bharadwaj, M. B. (1978). Morphological changes in the testes and epididymis of camels (*Camelus dromedarius*). *Acta Anat.* **101**, 275–279.

Singh, U. B. and Bharadwaj, M. B. (1978). Histological and histochemical studies on the testis of camel (*Camelus dromedarius*) during the various seasons and ages. *Acta Anat.* **101**, 280–288.

Singh, U. B. and Bharadwaj, M. B. (1978). Anatomical, histological and histochemical observations and changes in the poll gland of the camel (*Camelus dromedarius*). *Acta Anat.* **102**, 74–83.

Singh, V. and Prakash, A. (1964). Mating behaviour of camel. *Indian Vet. J.* **41**, 475–477.

Sinhgvi, N. M. and Bhargava, A. K. (1971). Complications of wound healing in camels (*Camelus dromedarius*). *J. Remount Vet. Corps. India.* **10**, 37–40.

Sisson, S. and Grossman, J. D. (1953). *The Anatomy of the Domestic Animals.* (4th Ed. 1959; 5th Ed. 1975). W. B. Saunders Co.: London.

Slimane-Taleb, S., Bererhi, A. and Zidane, C. (1968). Aspects morphologiques des noyaux supra-optiques et paraventriculaires de l'hypothalamus du dromadaire (*Camelus dromedarius*). *Bull. Soc. Hist. Nat. Afr. Nord.* **59**, 165–170.

Smith, H. W. and Silvette, H. (1928). Chemical constituents of camels' urine *J. Biol. Chem.* **78**, 409–411.

Sobrero, R. (1960). Domestic animals in Somalia as natural hosts of *Schistosoma bovis* (in Italian). *Riv. Parasit.* **21**, 125–130.

Sobrero, R. and Goffredo, G. (1972). A variety of *Trichostrongylus colubriformis* (Giles, 1892) (in Italian). *Parassitologia* **14**, 193–198.

Soliman, K. N. (1955). Immature stage of filarial (probably *Deraiophoronema evansi* (Lewis 1882) Romanovitch 1916) in camel. *Trans. Royal Soc. Trop. Med. Hyg.* **49**, 29.

Soliman, K. N. (1955). Schistosomes from Egyptian and Sudanese camels. *Trans. Royal Soc. Trop. Med. Hyg.* **49**, 291.

Soliman, K. N. (1956). The occurrence of *Schistosoma bovis* (Sonsino 1876) in the camel (*Camelus dromedarius*) in Egypt. *J. Egyptian Med. Assoc.* **39**, 171–181.

Soliman, K. N. (1956). On a new species of the nematode genus *Impalaia* from the camel (*Camelus dromedarius*) in Egypt. *British Vet. J.* **112**, 507–512.

Soliman, M. K. and Elamrousi, S. (1965). Serum bilirubin levels in Egyptian buffaloes and camels. *Vet. Rec.* **77**, 633.

Soliman, M. K. and Elamrousi, S. (1966). Erythrocyte fragility of healthy fowl, dog, sheep, cattle, buffalo, horse and camel blood. *Vet. Rec.* **78**, 429.

Soliman, M. K. and Shaker, M. (1966). Cytological studies on the blood of adult she-camels. *Indian Vet. J.* **44**, 989–995.

Soliman, M. K. and Elamrousi, S. (1974). Serum icteric index of healthy dogs, sheep, cattle, buffaloes, horses and camels. *Indian Vet. J.* **51**, 679–682.

Soliman, M. K., Youssef, G. W. and Mansour, S. A. (1975). Ascorbic acid content of erythrocytes, plasma, leucocytes and whole blood of healthy camels. *Egyptian J. Vet. Sci.* **12**, 107–110.

Solonitsuin, M. O. (1949). Brucellosis in camels (in Russian). *Vet., Moscow.* **26**, 16–20.

Solonitsuin, M. O. and Pal'gov, A. A. (1950). Brucellosis (in Russian). *Trudy Inst. Vet. Akad. Nauk Kazakh. SSR, Alma-Ata.* **5**, 58–67; 68–74.

Somaliland (Peck, E. F.). (1936). *Ann. Rep. Vet. Agric. Dept.* 1935.

Somaliland (Peck, E. F.). (1953). *Ann. Rep. Vet. Agric. Dept.* 1952.

Soni, B. K. and Aggarwala, A. C. (1958). Studies in the physiology of the camel (*Camelus dromedarius*). I. Cellular blood constituents. *Indian Vet. J.* **35**, 209–214.

Sosnowski, A. (1972). Morphological studies of the blood of Old and New World Camelidae (in Polish). *Med. Wet.* **28**, 292–295.

Sotnikov, M. I. (1973). Camel Plague (in Russian). In: Orlov, F. M. (ed) *Little-known contagious diseases of animals.* pp. 213–222.

Soueid'Ahmed, A. (1965). *La production laitière en Mauritanie.* Thèse DMV; ENV: Toulouse **No 32**.

Souguenet, Le dernier chameau, le premier pneu, la première aile. In: *Mission au Sahara 1915–1918.* Editions Eventail: Paris.

Souteyrand-Boulenger, J. D. (1968). Muscle articulaire de la hanche chez les camélidés. *Rev. Elev. Méd. Vét. Pays Trop.* **21**, 289–292.

Spackman, W. C. (1923). Serum-aldehyde test applied to trypanosomiasis. *British Med. J.*

Spencer, P. (1973). *Nomads in alliance: Symbiosis and growth among the Rendille and Samburu of Kenya.* Oxford.

Spesivtseva, N. A. and Noskov, A. I. (1959). Epizootic lymphangitis in camels (in Russian). *Trudy Vses. Inst. Vet. Saait. Ektoparasit.* **14**, 86.

Spooner, (1832). Notes of the post-mortem examination of a dromedary (*Camelus dromedarius*). *Proc. Comm. Sci. Corres. Zool. Soc. London.* **2**, 126–127.

Sreemannarayana, O., Rao, V. V. R. and Dutt, P. A. K. (1971). Treatment of sarcoptic mange in camels with Sumithion. *Indian Vet. J.* **48**, 433–434.

Srinivasan, V. (1940). Active immunisation of camels against rinderpest with goat blood virus. *Indian Vet. J.* **16**, 159–160.

Srivastava, K. B. and Dwaraknath, P. K. (1971). Ceruloplasmin (copper oxidases) activity in the serum of animals. *Indian J. Anim. Sci.* **41**, 1044–1046.

Stanic, M. N., Arnautovic, I. and Abusineina, M. E. (1968). Some major differences between the course and branching of the facial nerve in the camel and in other animals (horse, ox). *Rep. 12th Cong. Anat., Yugoslavia.*

Stanic, M. N., Arnautovic, I. and Abusineina, M. E. (1970). The course and branches of the facial nerve of the one-humped camel. *J. Anat.* **106**, 341–348.

Stanic, M., Abusineina, M. E. and Arnautovic, I. (1972). A study of induced disfunction of the facial nerve in one-humped camel. *Vet. Rec.* **90**, 442–446.

Stanic, M. N., Imbab, S. E. and Arnautovic, I. (1976). Akinesia of the *orbicularis oculi* muscle in the one-humped camel. *Acta Vet., Yugoslavia.* **26**, 93–98.

Stark, F. (1939). *Seen in the Hadhramaut.* E. P. Dutton: New York.

Steel, J. H. (1890). *A manual of the diseases of the camel.* Indian Veterinary Manuals. III. Laurence Asylum Press: Madras.

Steele, Z. (1946). How the camel came to America. *Fauna Phil.* **8**, 78–79.

Steevenson, G. F. (1938). The application of the Mercuric chloride test in an outbreak of Surra in Waziristan. *J. Royal Army Vet. Corps.* **9**, 83–85.

Stein, A. (1937). *Archaeological Reconnaissances in North-Western India and South-Eastern Iran.* London.

Stein, L. (1967). The Sammar-Gerba: Bedouins in transition from nomadism to sedentarization (in German). *Veröff. Mus. Völk., Leipzig.* H 17.

Stekelis, H. (1951). A new Neolithic industry: the Yarmukian of. Palestine. *Israel Expl. J., Jerusalem.* **1**, 1–19.

Stekelis, H. (1952). *American J. Archaeol.* **56**, 141.

Steklenev, E. P. (1968). *Anatomical-morphological characters and physiological functions of the oviducts in the genera Lama and Camelus.* VIe Congr. Reprod. Insém. Artif., Paris 1968.

Stepankina, M. K. and Tashenov, K. T. (1958). Water metabolism in the camel (in Russian). *Sechenov J. Physiol.* **44**, 991–996.

Stevenson, P. H. (1921). The extrahepatic filiary tract of the camel. *Anat. Rec.* **22**, 85–95.

Steward, J. S. (1950). Notes on some parasites of camels in the Sudan. *Vet. Rec.* **62**, 835–837.

Steward, J. S. (1950). Trichostrongylosis and haemonchosis in the camel: their recognition response to phenothiazine. *Vet. Rec.* **62**, 837–839.

Stocking, H. E. (1944). The camel brigade. *Nat. Hist., New York.* **53**, 396–433.

Stoppoloni, G. and Cardona, L. (1937). Some notes on the camel (in Italian). *Azione Vet. Italia.* **6**, 98–106.

Streeter, D. W. (1927). *Camels.* New York.

Strogov, A. K. (1957). Paratuberculosis in camels (in Russian). *Trudy Vses. Inst. Eksp. Vet.* **20**, 120–131.

Strogov, A. K. (1959). Plague in camels (in Russian). In: *Maloizvestnye zarasnye bolezni Zhivotnykh.* Sel'-khoz.: Moscow. pp. 262–280.

Stünzi, H. (1947). Chronic myocarditis in a young camel (in German). *Schweiz. Z. Path. Bakt.* **10**, 731–732.

Sudan. *Annual Reports of the Vet. Dept..*

Sudan Government (1929). *Annual Report of the Vet. Services.*

Sudan Government (Bennett, S. C. J.) (1929). *Annual Report of the Vet. Research Officer.*

Sudan Government (Bennett, S. C. J.) (1930). *Annual Report of the Vet. Research Officer.*

Sudan Government (Kennedy, W.) (1930). *Annual Report Sudan Vet. Service.*

Sudan Government (Kennedy, W.) (1932). *Annual Report Sudan Vet. Service.*

Sudan Government (Bennett, S. C. J.) (1932). *Annual Repot Sudan Vet. Service.*

Sudan Government (Kennedy, W.) (1933). *Annual Report Sudan Vet. Service.*

Sultanov, M. A., Kabilov, T., Atakhanova, Kh. and Dadaev, S. (1973). On the discovery of the intermediate hosts of the agent of physocephalosis in camels - *Physocephalus sexalatus dromedarii* Muschkambarowa 1967 (in Russian). *Dokl. Akad. Nauk Uzbek. SSR.* 1, 42-43.

Sultanov, M. A., Azimov, D. A., Gekhtin, V. I. and Muminov, P. A. (1975). Helminths of camels (*Camelus dromedarius*) (in Russian). IN: *Helminths of domestic mammals in Uzbekistan*: Uzbekskaya SSR, USSR. pp. 80-81.

Surcouf, J. M. R. (1922-23). Note sur le dromadaire. *Bull. Soc. Hist. Nat. Afr. Nord.* 13,

Sureau, P. and Klein, J. M. (1980). Arbovirus en Iran. *Med. Trop.* 40, 549-554.

Sweden, International Foundation for Science (1980). Workshop on Camels, Khartoum, Sudan, 18-20 Dec. 1979. Stockholm, Sweden.

Sweet, L. (1965). Camel raiding of North Arabian Bedouin: a mechanism of ecological adaptation. *American Anthr.* 67, 1132-1150.

Sweet, L. (1965). Camel Pastoralism in North Arabia and the Minimal Camping Unit. IN: Leeds, A. & Vayda, A. (eds) *Man, culture and animals*: Washington.

Swift, J. J. (1973). Disaster and a Sahelian nomad economy. In: Dalby & Church (eds) *Drought in Africa*.

Swift, J. J. (1979). *The Economics of Traditional Nomadic Pastoralism: The Twareg of the Adrar n Iforas (Mali)*. Ph.D. Thesis, Sussex University.

Swift, J. J. (1979). The development of livestock trading in a nomad pastoral economy: The Somali case. In: *Pastoral Production and Society*, Cambridge University Press: Cambridge. pp. 447-465.

Swinhoe, R. (1861). *Narrative of the North China Campaign of 1860.* Smith, Elder: London.

Szewzyck, (1903). Sur une maladie des dromadaires, le debab, constatée dans la region de la Zousfana. *Bull. Soc. Cent. Méd. Vét.* 10.

Tadros, G. (1964). On *Chabertiella pesteri* gen. et sp. nov. (Cyathostomidae) from a Giraffe and on the validity of *Chabertia rishati* Akhtar 1937. *J. Helminth.* 38, 109-116.

Taha, A. A. M. and Abdalla, A. B. (1980). Light and electron microscopy of the sweat glands of the dromedary camel. *Acta Vet., Brno.* 49, 31-36.

Taha, A. A. M. and Abdalla, A. B. (1980). Structure of the poll glands of the dromedary. *Acta Vet., Beograd.* 30, 247-252.

Taher, el S., Moustafa, M. S. el Din and Berg, R. (1967). Prenatal growth of some organs in the camel (*Camelus dromedarius*). *Zentralbl. Vet. Med.* 14A, 819-824.

Taher, el S. and Berg, R. (1969). Micromorphological studies on the coronary vessels of the camel (*Camelus dromedarius*). *Zentralbl. Vet. Med.* 16A, 52-60.

Taher, el S., El-Gaafary, M. A. and Al-Shaikhly, A. K. (1975). Some studies of the centrum tendineum of the diaphragm of camel (*Camelus dromedarius*). *Anat. Anz.* 138, 192-202.

Taher, el S., Al-Shaikhly, A. K. and Lawand, S. (1975). Morphological and micromorphological studies of the epiphysis cerebri of the dromedary (*Camelus dromedarius* Linne 1758). *Saug. Mitt.* 23, 223-230.

Tall, A. G. (1972). *La production laitière en République du Mali.* Thèse DMV. ENV: Alfort No 11.

Tantaui, Kh., Gorshenina, V. and Rida, I. (1974). Cultivation of camel pox virus in developing chick embryos (in Russian). *Vet. Moscow.* 4, 51.

Tantawi, H. H. (1974). Comparative studies on camel pox, sheep pox and vaccinia virus. *Acta Virol.* 18, 347-351.

Tantawi, H. H., Soban, M. S., Reda, I. M. and Dahaby, H. (1974). Camelpox virus in Egypt. I. Isolation and characteristics. *Bull. Epizoot. Dis. Afr.* 22, 315-319.

Tantawi, H. H. and Soban, M. S. (1975). Histopathological study of tissue reactions in chlorio-allantoic membrane and cell-culture infected with camel-pox and buffalo-pox viruses. *Indian J. Anim. Sci.* 45, 76-80.

Tantawi, H. H., El-Dahaby, H. and Fahmy, L. S. (1978). Comparative

studies on poxvirus strains isolated from camels. *Acta Virol.* 22, 451-457.

Tarantino, G. B. (1928). Can the camel contract smallpox from a man vaccinated against it? (in Italian). *Rinn. Med-Giorn. Ital. Mal. Esot. Trop.* 9, 3-6.

Tarantino, G. B. (1934). The riding camel (recub) of Somalia (in Italian). *Riv. Zool.* 11, 392-398.

Tarantino, G. B. (1937). Exploitation of the Imperial camels (in Italian). *Azione Vet.* pp. 759-760.

Tarizzo, M. L. (1957). Epidemiological notes on the Eastern province of Saudi Arabia. *American J. Trop. Med. Hyg.* 6, 786-803.

Tartour, G. (1966). Ph.D. Thesis. University of London.

Tartour, G. (1969). Studies on the metabolism of copper and iron in the camel. *Sudan J. Vet. Sci. Anim. Husb.* 10, 14-20.

Tartour, G. and Idris, O. F. (1970). Serum iron and serum iron binding capacity in the dromedary (*Camelus dromedarius*). *J. Zool. London.* 161, 351-354.

Tartour, G. and Idris, O. F. (1970). Studies on copper and iron metabolism in the camel foetus. *Acta Vet., Brno.* 39, 397-403.

Tawney, A. E. (1928). A camel pack battery. *J. Royal Artillery.* 54, 228-232.

Tayeb, M. A. F. (1945). *The Anatomy of the Genital Organs of the Camel, Male and Female*, M. V. Sc. Thesis. Fouad University: Cairo.

Tayeb, M. A. F. (1948). Urinary system of the camel. *J. Arab Vet. Med. Assoc.* 113, 568-572.

Tayeb, M. A. F. (1948). Studies on the anatomy of the ovary and corpus luteum of the camel. *British Vet. J.* 104, 179-186.

Tayeb, M. A. F. (1949). L'appareil urinaire du chameau. *Rev. Elev. Méd. Vét. Pays Trop.* 3, 175-180.

Tayeb, M. A. F. (1950). The pharyngeal cavity of the camel. *British Vet. J.* 106, 29-31.

Tayeb, M. A. F. (1950). Les cavités nasales, le larynx, les organes annexes de l'appareil respiratoire du chameau. *Rev. Elev. Méd. Vét. Pays Trop.* 4, 21-24.

Tayeb, M. A. F. (1950). Les muscles de la tête du chameau. *Rev. Elev. Méd. Vét. Pays Trop.* 4, 145-149.

Tayeb, M. A. F. (1950). L'appareil glandulaire de la tête du chameau. *Rev. Elev. Méd. Vét. Pays Trop.* 4, 151-155.

Tayeb, M. A. F. (1950). La cavité buccale du chameau. *Rev. Elev. Méd. Vét. Pays Trop.* 4, 157-160.

Tayeb, M. A. F. (1950). Etude sur l'anatomie de l'ovaire et du corps jaune de la chamelle. *Rev. Elev. Méd. Vét. Pays Trop,* 4, 177-182.

Tayeb, M. A. F. (1951). A study on the blood supply of the camel's head. *British Vet. J.* 107, 147-155.

Tayeb, M. A. F. (1951-52). L'appareil génital mâle du chameau. *Rev. Elev. Méd. Vét. Pays Trop.* 5, 203-212.

Tayeb, M. A. F. (1953). Les organes genitaux de la chamelle. *Rev. Elev. Méd. Vét. Pays Trop.* 6, 17-21.

Tayeb, M. A. F. (1953). Etude sur les nerfs pneumogastrique et spinal du chameau. *Rev. Elev. Méd. Vét. Pays Trop.* 6, 167-168.

Tayeb, M. A. F. (1957). The cranial nerves of the camel. *Vet. Med. J., Giza.* 4, 171-182.

Tayeb, M. A. F. (1962). The eyes of the camel as an animal adapted to live in the desert. *Vet. Med. J., Giza.* 8, 135-151.

Tayeb, M. A. F. (1964). The respiratory system of the camel. *J. Vet. Sci. UAR.* 1, 39-61.

Taylor, C. M., Saha, D. N. and Singh, B. N. (1980). Camel breeding. Its importance and development possibilities. *Livestock Advis.* 5, 21-25.

Taylor, K. M., Hungerford, D. A., Snyder, R. L. and Ulmer, F. A. (1968). Uniformity of karyotypes in the Camelidae. *Cytogenetics.* 7, 7-15.

Taylor, W. P. (1968). The susceptibility of the one-humped camel to infection with rinderpest virus. *Bull. Epiz. Dis. Afr.* 16, 405-410.

Terentjev, S. (1956). Performance tests for the Astrakhan breed of camel (in Russian). *Konevodstvo*. **26**, 27-29.

Terentjev, S. (1963). Camel breeding in Astrakhan province (in Russian). *Zivotnovdstvo*. **25**, 54-56.

Terentjev, S. (1966). Improvement of the Kalmyk breed of camel (in Russian). *Konevod Konnyi Sport*. **36**, 19-20.

Terentjev, S. (1973). Increasing the productivity of the camel (in Russian). *Zivotnovdstvo*. **35**, 32-34.

Terentjev, S. (ed) (1975). *Camel breeding* (in Russian). Verblyudovodstvo: Moscow.

Terre et Eaux (1955). L'abreuvement des troupeaux dans les régions sahariennes. *Terre et Eaux: Gouv. Gen. Algérie*. **25**, 32-35.

Theiler, A. (1905). *Transvaal Agric. J.* **3**, 717-721.

Thesiger, W. (1959). *Arabian Sands*. Longmans: London.

Thomson, J. K. (1978). Castration of camels (correspondence). *Vet. Rec.* **102**, 92.

Tingari, M. D. and Moniem, K. A. (1979). On the regional histology and histochemistry of the epididymis of the camel (*Camelus dromedarius*). *J. Reprod. Fert.* **57**, 11-20.

Toofanian, F. and Aliakbari, S. (1977). Studies on the digestion of carbohydrates in the camel *Camelus dromedarius*. *Trop. Anim. Hlth Prod.* **10**, 75-81.

Toofanian, F. and Aliakbari, S. (1978). Small intestinal cannulation in the camel (*Camelus dromedarius*). *Indian Vet J.* **55**, 722-724.

Torry, W. I. (1971). *Animal husbandry and social organization among the Gabbra with notes on the Rendille tribe*. Range Management Div., Min. Agric: Nairobi (mimeo).

Torry, W. I. (1974). Life in the camel's shadow. *Nat. Hist. Magazine*. May 1974, 60-68.

Toupet, C. (1963). L'evolution de la nomadisation en Mauritanie sahelienne. IN: *Nomades et Nomadisation-Recherche sur la Zone Aride*. UNESCO: Paris.

Tour, G. D. de la (1971). Inheritance of the hump in the camel, dromedary and cow (in German). *Saug. Mitt.* **19**, 193-194.

Trancart, A. (1940). La pâturage en haut Adrar. *Bull. IFAN.* **11**, 285-298.

Tret'yakov, V. N. (1970). Meat characteristics in the Turkmen single-humped camel (in Russian). *Trudy Turkmen Sel'-khoz. Inst.* **15**, 126-129.

Tret'yakov, V. N. (1971). Morphological composition of carcasses of the one-humped camel (in Russian). *Trudy Turkmen Sel'-khoz. Inst.* **16**, 15-18.

Trincao, G. (1951). Le sang des camélidés. *Le Sang.* **4**, 323-325.

Tripier, (1955). Psychologie du nomade en Mauritanie. *Doc. CHEAM.* No 2522, 1-6.

Tripolitania. (1929). *The camel, an indication of an enormous health problem* (in Italian). Div. Vet.: RTC Tripolitania.

Trofimova, R. M. (1959). Regulation nerveuse de la sécrétion salivaire chez le mouton et le chameau (in Russian). *Trudy Zoovet. Inst. Alma-Ata.* **11**, 421-432.

Troncy, P. M. (1968). *Echinococcose-hydatidose dans le bassin tchadien*. Thèse DMV. ENV: Alfort. No 101.

Troncy, P. M. and Oumate, O. (1976). Experimentation au Tchad du Tartrate de Morantel pour le contrôle des nématodes gastrointestinaux du dromadaire (*Camelus dromedarius*). *Rev. Elev. Méd. Vét. Pays Trop.* **29**, 229-232.

Tsaprun, A. A. (1935). Biology of the Camel Bot Fly (*Cephalopsis titillator*) (in Russian). *Trudy Inst. Med. Eksp. Vet.* **11**, 136-151.

Tsedev, N. (1974). Laboratory diagnosis of sarcoptic mange in camels (in Russian). *Vet., Moscow.* **2**, 114-115.

Tserendash, C. and Shumilov, K. V. (1970). Diagnosis of brucellosis in camels (in Russian). *Vet., Moscow.* **1**, 116-117.

Tserenpuntsag, S. (1971). Change in the free amino-acid content in camel meat (in Russian). *Vet., Moscow.* **6**, 114-115.

Tsuigankov, A. A. (1955). Incidence and mode of infection of coccidia in camels (in Russian). *Trudy Zool. Inst. Alma-Ata.* **3**, 140-150.

Tuci, P. (1939). Dromedaries as carriers of Brucella infection (in Italian).

P. V. Soc. Tosc. Sci. Nat. **47**.

Tulenbekov, I. M. (1969). The effect of milking frequency on lactational performance in camels (in Russian). *Sb Ref. Nauk Rab Kazakh. Ped.* **13**, 292-296.

Turkewitsch, B. G. (1936). Bony internal ear of camels. *Zool. Jahrb.* **61**, 107-120.

Turner, J. C., Anderson, H. M. and Gandal, C. P. (1958). Species differences in red blood cell phosphatides separated by column and paper chromatography. *Biochim. Biophys. Acta.* **30**, 130-134.

Tylden, E. D. (1959). The Camel Corps and the Nile Campaign of 1884-85. *J. Soc. Army Hist. Res.* **27**,

Ucko, P. J. and Dimbleby, G. W. (eds). (1969). *The Domestication and Exploitation of Plants*. Gerald Duckworth: London.

Uhden, R. (1927). Contribution to the history of the camel in North Africa (in German). *Petermanns Mitt. Just. Perthes Geogr. Anst.* **75**, 307.

Uilenberg, G. (1959). *Tijdschr. Diergeneesk.* **84**, 610-611.

UNESCO (1963). *Nomades et Nomadisme au Sahara - Recherches sur la Zone Aride*. UNESCO: Paris.

Urazakov, N. U. and Bainazarov, S. (1974). "Tushchibek" - the first clinic in history for the treatment of pulmonary tuberculosis with cultured camels' milk. *Problemy Tuberkuleza*. No. 2, 89-90.

US War Department (1857). *Reports upon the purchase, importation and use of camels and dromedaries, to be employed for military purposes*. US War Dept.: Washington, DC.

Vachetta, G; (1927). *The Somali camel*. (in Italian). Ist. Siero Vacc. Somalo, Merca.

Vallon, M. (1856). Mémoire sur l'histoire naturelle du dromadaire. *Rec. Mém. Obs. Hyg. Méd. Vét. Milit.* **7**, 351-614.

Van der Schaaf, A., Numans, S. R. and Smidt, A. C. de (1964). Nocardiosis in a dromedary. *Tijdschr. Diergeneesk.* **89 (Supp. 1)**, 180-186.

Van Lennep, E. W. (1957). The glands of the digestive system in the one-humped camel. *Camelus dromedarius* L. I. The salivary glands. *Acta Morph. Neerlando-Scandinavica.* **1**, 286-292.

Van Lennep, E. W. (1964). The placenta of the one-humped camel (*Camelus dromedarius*) during the second half of gestation. *Acta Morph. Neerlando-Scandinavica.* **5**, 373-379.

Vashishta, M. S. and Bhardwaj, R. M. (1976). "Girbi" in a camel calf. Condition caused by slipped tendon in the fetlock joint of forelimb. *Livestock Advis.* **10(1)**, 33-34.

Vayse, M. J. (1948). Brucella infection in Morocco. *Bull. Off. Int. Epiz.* **30**, 90-95.

Veisseyre, R. (1966). *Techniques Laitières* (2èmes édition). Maison Rustique: Paris.

Velu, H. and Barotte, J. (1938). La campagne d'Ethiopie et le moteur animé. *Rev. Vét. Milit.* **22**,

Venel and Bouchez, (1910). *Guide de l'officier méhariste au territoire militaire du Niger.* E. Larose: Paris.

Verger, (1938). Accident de regurgitation chez le chameau. *Bull. Ser. Zool. Epizool. AOF.* **1**, 25.

Vialatte, G. (1916). Rapport sur le fonctionnement du laboratoire de microscopie de Béni-Abbès (Sahara oranais) en 1915. *Bull. Soc. Path. Exot.* **9**, 482-483.

Vibe, P. P., Tishchenko, V. V. and Petrov, V. S. (1969). Role of domestic and wild animals in the spread of hydatidosis in southern Kazakhstan (in Russian). IN: *Problemy prirodnoi ochagovosti gel'mintozov cheloveka*. Materialy simpoziuma, posvyashchennogo 30-letiyu ucheniya Akademika E. N. Pavlovskogo Tyumen, USSR.

Vignier, J. P. (1953). *Dromadaires de la région du Batha*. Doc. CHEAM. No 2165.

Vignier, J. P. (1963). *Sur l'élevage du chameau au Tassili des Ajjers*. Thèse DMV. ENV: Lyon. No 36.

Villachon, M. A. (1962). *Aliments et Alimentation du Dromadaire au Tassili-N-Ajjer (Sahara Central)*. Thèse DMV. ENV: Toulouse. No 31.

Vitale, M. A. (1928). *The camel and the camel detachments* (in Italian). Sindicato Italiano Arti Grafiche: Roma.

215

Vogelsang, E. G. (1948). Echinococcus in a dromedary. *Rev. Med. Vet. Parasit., Caracas.* 7, 213-215.

Voinot, L. (1910). *L'artillerie à dos de chameau.* Berger-Leorault: Paris.

Volcani, R. (1952). *Seasonal activity of gonads and thyroids in camels, cattle, sheep and goats.* Thesis. University of Jerusalem.

Volcani, R. (1954). Seasonal variations in spermatogenesis of some farm animals under the climatic conditions of Israel. *Refuah Vet.* 11, 169-174.

Von Bissing, F. W. (1900). Contribution to the history of the camel (in German). *Zeitschr. Agyp. Sprach. Alter-thumsk., Leipzig.* 38, 68-69.

Vosdingh, R. A. and Vanniasingham, J. A. (1969). Balantidiasis in a camel (*Camelus dromedarius*). *J. American Vet. Med. Assoc.* 155, 1077-1079.

Wace, A. J. B. (1932). *Chamber Tombs at Mycenae.* Society of Antiquaries: Oxford.

Wace, A. J. B. (1932). Chamber tombs at Mycenae. *Archaeologia.* 82, 1-242.

Wachi, P. (1900). *Rôle militaire du Chameau en Algérie et en Tunisie.* H. Charles Lavanzelle: Paris.

Waghela, S., Fazil, M. A., Gathuma, J. M. and Kapunga, D. K. (1978). A serological survey of brucellosis in camels in north-eastern province of Kenya. *Trop. Anim. Hlth Prod.* 10, 28-29.

Wahby, A. M., Abdalla, A. and Barakat, M. Z. (1959). N-Bromosuccinimide as an effective insecticide against Acarina. *Zentralbl. Vet. Med.* 6, 825-831.

Wahid, A. (1954). Pak-camels. *Proc. 6th Sci. Cong. Pakistan.*

Walker, E. P. (1975). *Mammals of the World. Vol. II.* (3rd edition revised by J. L. Paradiso). Johns Hopkins University Press: Baltimore.

Wallach, J. D. and Frueh, R. (1968). Pilot study of an organophosphate anthelmintic in camels and primates. *J. American Vet. Med. Assoc.* 153, 798-799.

Walters, H. B. (1934). *The Art of the Greeks.* (3rd Edition). London.

Walton, (1865). *The Camel, its Anatomy, Proportions and Paces.* Day: London.

Walz, R. (1951). A consideration of the problem of the timing of the domestication of Old-World Camelidae (in German). *Zeit. Deutsch. Morgenländ. Ges. Weisbaden.* NS26, 29-51.

Walz, R. (1954). Recent studies on domestication problems of the Old-World Camelidae (in German). *Zeit. Deutsch. Morgenland. Ges.* NS29, 45-87.

Walz, R. (1956). Contribution to the earliest history of Old-World Camelidae with special consideration of the timing of domestication (in German). *Act IVe Cong. Int. Sci. Anthrop. Ethn., Wien 1952.* 3, 190-204.

Watson, R. M. (1972). *Results of aerial livestock surveys of Kaputei division, Samburu district and North-Eastern province.* Statistics Division, Min. Fin. Planning: Nairobi.

Watson, R. M., Tippett, C. I., Rizk, F., Jolly, F., Beckett, J., Scholes, V. and Casbon, F. (1977). *Sudan National Livestock Census and Resource Inventory. Vol. III.* Resource Management & Research Ltd.: Nairobi.

Watt, W. M. (1953). *Muhammed at Mecca.* Clarendon Press: Oxford.

Way, A. G. (translator) (1964). *Caesar: Alexandrian, African and Spanish Wars.* Harvard University Press: Cambridge, Massachusetts.

Webb, S. D. (1972). Locomotor evolution in camels. *Forma et Functio.* 2, 99-111.

Weber, M. and Abel, O. (1928). *The Mammals* (2^e edition) (in German). Jena.

Webster, C. C. and Wilson, P. N. (1966). *Agriculture in the Tropics.* Longman: London.

Wei, D. (1980). Chinese camels and their productivities. IN: *Workshop on Camels,* Khartoum, Sudan, 18-20 Dec. 1979. Intnl. Foundation for Science: Stockholm, Sweden. pp. 55-72.

Welento, J., Jastrzebski, M., Flieger, S. and Lakomy, M. (1979). Structure and topography of the co-ordinating motor centres in the cerebellum (in Polish). *Medycyna Weterynaryjna.* 35, 441-443.

Welling, G. W., Mulder, H. and Beintema, J. J. (1975). The amino-acid sequence of dromedary pancreatic ribonuclease. *Trans. Biochem. Soc.* 147, 505-511.

Welling, G. W., Mulder, H. and Beintema, J. J. (1976). Allelic polymorphism in Arabian camel ribonuclease and the amino-acid sequence of Bactrian camel ribonuclease. *Biochem. Genet.* 14, 309-317.

Wellstead, J. R. (1840). *Travels to the City of the Caliphs Along the Shore of the Persian Gulf and the Mediterranean.* Henry Colburn: London.

White, P. (1914). Buonaparte's Camel Corps. *Cavalry J.* 154-158.

Wiesner, J. (1953). The camel as a domestic animal (in German). *Kosmos.* 49, 549-552.

Williams, J. J. (1930). The diagnosis of cameline surra. *J. Royal Army Vet. Corps.* 1, 240.

Williams, R. E., Hoogstraal, H., Casals, J., Kaiser, M. N. and Moussa, M. I. (1973). Isolation of Wanowrie, Thogoto and Dhori viruses from Hyalomma ticks infesting camels in Egypt. *J. Med. Ent.* 10, 143-146.

Williams, V. J. (1963). Rumen function in the camel. *Nature,* London. 197, 1221.

Williamson, G. and Payne, W. J. A. (1978). *An Introduction to Animal Husbandry in the Tropics* (Third Edition). Longman: London.

Wilson, R. T. (1976). Some quantitative data on the Tigre salt trade from the early 19th century to the present day. *Ann. Ist. Univ. Orient. Napoli.* 36, 157-164.

Wilson, R. T. (1978). Studies on the livestock of Southern Darfur, V. Notes on camels. *Sudan Trop. Anim. Hlth Prod.* 10, 19-25.

Wilson, R. T. (1978). Studies on the livestock of Southern Darfur, VI. Notes on equines. *Sudan Trop. Anim. Hlth Prod.* 10, 183-189.

Wilson, R. T. (1978). The 'gizu': Winter grazing in the south Libyan desert. *J. Arid Envir.* 1, 325-342.

Winkler, H. A. (1938). Rock drawings of southern Upper Egypt. *Egypt Expl. Soc., London.*

Winkler, H. A. (1939). Rock drawings of southern Upper Egypt, I, II. *Egypt. Expl. Soc., London.*

Wiseman, D. J. (1959). Ration lists from Alalakh VII. *J. Cuneiform. Stud.* 8, 29.

Wohleb, M. J. (1958). Les chameaux de la Baar. *Bull. Liais. Sahar.* 9, 254-258.

Wolff, H. (1884). *Les Régiments de Dromadaires.* Challanul Ainé: Paris.

Wool Record (1979). Speciality and rare fibres. *Wool Record.* 136(3416), 41-67.

Wortman, J. W. (1898). The extinct Camelidae of North America and some associated forms. *Bull. American Mus. Nat. Hist.* 10, 93-162.

Wundersee, W. J. and Tschernet, W. (1976). On the treatment of *Dictyocaulus filaria* infection in pack animals with Mebenvet-Granulat 10 (in German). IN: Ippen, R. & Schroder, H. D. (eds) *Erkrankungen des Zootiere* (Diseases of Zoo Animals) Proc. XVIII Int. Symp. 16-20 June 1976, Innsbruck, Akadamie Verlag: Berlin, GDR.

Yagil, R. (1976). Renal functions of the camel with glucose loading. *Refuah Vet.* 33, 166.

Yagil, R. (1976). Role of aldosterone in the dehydrated camel. *Israel J. Med. Sci.* 13, 1138.

Yagil, R., Sod-Moriah, U. A. and Meyerstein, N. (1974). Dehydration and camel blood. I. Red blood cell survival in the one-humped camel *Camelus dromedarius. American J. Physiol.* 226, 298-300.

Yagil, R., Sod-Moriah, U. A. and Meyerstein, N. (1974). Dehydration and camel blood. 2. Shape, size and concentration of red blood cells. *American J. Physiol.* 226, 301-304.

Yagil, R., Sod-Moriah, U. A. and Meyerstein, N. (1974). Dehydration and camel blood. 3. Osmotic fragility, specific gravity and osmolability. *American J. Physiol.* 226, 305-308.

Yagil, R., Etzion, Z. and Berlyne, G. M. (1975). Acid-base parameters in the dehydrated camel. *Tijdschr. Diergeneesk.* 100, 1105-1108.

Yagil, R. and Berlyne, G. M. (1976). Sodium and potassium metabolism in the dehydrated and rehydrated camel. *J. Appl. Physiol.* 41, 457-461.

Yagil, R., Sod-Moriah, U. A. and Meyerstein, N. (1976). Effect of ambient temperature on red blood cells in the dehydrated camel. *Israel J. Med. Sci.* 12, 878-880.

Yagil, R., Etzion, Z. and Berlyne, G. M. (1976). Effect of dehydration on the urea-nitrogen metabolism in the camel. *Israel J. Med. Sci.* 12, 1514.

Yagil, R. and Berlyne, G. M. (1977). Renal handling of creatinine in various stages of hydration in the camel. *Comp. Biochem. Physiol.* 56A, 15-18.

Yagil, R. and Berlyne, G. M. (1977). Glucose loading and dehydration in the camel. *J. Appl. Physiol.* 42, 690-693.

Yagil, R., Etzion, Z. and Ganani, J. (1978). Camel thyroid metabolism: effect of season and dehydration. *J. Appl. Physiol.: Resp., Envir., Exerc., Physiol.* 45, 540-544.

Yagil, R. and Etzion, Z. (1978). Dehydration tolerance in the bedouin camel. *Refuah Vet.* 35, 24-25.

Yagil, R. and Etzion, Z. (1979). The role of antidiuretic hormone and aldosterone in the dehydrated and rehydrated camel. *Comp. Biochem. Physiol.* 63A, 275-278.

Yagil, R. and Etzion, Z. (1979). Seasonal changes in hormones and behaviour in the male camel. *Refuah Vet.* 36, 70.

Yagil, R. and Etzion, Z. (1980). Hormonal and behavioural patterns in the male camel (*Camelus dromedarius*). *J. Reprod. Fert.* 58, 61-65.

Yagil, R. and Etzion, Z. (1980). Effect of drought conditions on the quality of camel milk. *J. Dairy Res.* 47, 159-166.

Yagil, R. and Etzion, Z. (1980). Milk yield of camels (*Camelus dromedarius*) in drought areas. *Comp. Biochem. Physiol.* 67A, 207-209.

Yakimoff, W. L. (1916). Microfilaires des animaux au Turkestan russe. *Bull. Soc. Path. Exot.* 9, 219-228.

Yakimoff, W. L. (1921). A propos de l'identification du trypanosome des chameaux du Turkestan russe. *Bull. Soc. Path. Exot.* 14, 138-140.

Yakimoff, W. L. and Schokhor, N. J. (1914). Recherche sur les maladies tropicales humaines et animales au Turkestan. Les trypanosomiases des chameaux et des ânes au Turkestan. *Bull. Soc. Path. Exot.* 7, 187.

Yakimoff, W. L. and Wassilewsky, W. J. (1916). Le traitement de la trypanosomiase des chameaux du Turkestan russe. *Bull. Soc. Path. Exot.* 9, 230.

Yakimoff, W. L., Schokhor, N. S., Koselkine, P. M. and Paroisky, P. S. (1917). Maladies animales du Turkestan russe à parasites endoglobulaires. *Bull. Soc. Path. Exot.* 10, 302-311.

Yakimoff, W. L. and Amanschuloff, C. A. (1927). An experiment on the prophylactic use of Naganol (Bayer 205) in camel trypanosomiasis (in Russian). *Russian J. Trop. Med.* 5, 48.

Yakimoff, W. L. and Amanschuloff, C. A. (1927). An experiment on the prophylactic use of Naganol (Bayer 205) in camel trypanosomiasis (in German). *Arch. Schiffs. Trop. Hyg.* 31, 536-541.

Yakimoff, W. L. and Matschoulsky, S. N. (1939). On a new *Coccidium* from camels, *Eimeria dromedarii* n.sp. *J. R. Microscop. Sci.* 59, 26-29.

Yakovlev, L. A. (1945). The eating of wool by camels as a result of salt deficiency (in Russian). *Vet. Moscow.* 4-5, 41.

Yan, T. (1956). The Camel (in Chinese). *Shen-usyue Tunbao.* 6, 12-15.

Yasarol, S. (1960). L'hydatidose echinococcose en Turquie. *Bull. Off. Int. Epiz.* 54, 492-501.

Yasin, S. A. and Abdul Wahid (1957). Pakistan camels - a preliminary survey. *Agric. Pakistan.* 8, 289-295.

Yasin, S. A. and Abdussalam, M. (1958). *Bull. Off. Int. Epiz.* 49, 473-480.

Yeivin, S. (1952). Archaeological News, Israel. *American J. Archaeol.* 56, 141.

Young, G. F. (1913). *The Medici.* E. P. Dutton: New York.

Youssef, A. H. (1976). Orchidectomy in camel filariasis. *J. Egyptian Vet. Med. Assoc.* 35, 147-157.

Zaganelli, M. and Benvenuti, C. (1975). Variations in the dimensions of the uterus of the dromedary (in Italian). *Atti Soc. Ital. Sci. Vet.* 29, 238-240.

Zaki, H. (1967). Salmonellosis in UAR. *Bull. Off. Int. Epiz.* 68, 257-260.

Zaki, O. A. (1956). The incidence of salmonella infections in camels. *J. Egyptian Pub. Hlth Assoc.* 31, 75-79.

Zaki, R. (1948). Brucella infection among ewes, camels and pigs in Egypt. *J. Comp. Path.* 58, 145-159.

Zanderkin, A. I. (1951). Results and prospects of the work on livestock breed formation in Kazakhstan (in Russian). *Sovetsk. Zootech.* 6, 58-61.

Zannini, P. (1927). *The diaphragm bone of the camel* (in Italian). Soc. Tipografia Modenese: Modena.

Zannini, P. (1929). The inter-related bone structure studied by Muller in the camel and various other mammals (in Italian). *Est. Atenco Parmense.* 1.

Zannini, P. (1931). The iris of the camel (in Italian). *Atti Mem. Royal Acad. Sci. Lett.*

Zarins, J. (1978). The camel in ancient Arabia: a further note. *Antiquity.* 52, 44-46.

Zedtwitz, F. X. (1931). Small purchases, donations and rare progeny in the Berlin Zoo (in German). *Zool. Gart.* 4, 227-235.

Zein el Abdin, Y., Hamza, S. W., Abdel Rahman, M. S. and Abdel Wahab, M. (1975). Comparative studies on some serum contituents and some serum enzyme activities of normal and nematode infested camels. *Egyptian J. Vet. Sci.* 12, 31-43.

Zeuner, F. E. (1955). The identity of the camel on the Khurab Pick. *Iraq, London.* 17, 162-163.

Zeuner, F. E. (1963). *A History of Domesticated Animals.* Hutchinson: London.

Ziegler, C. (1962). *The Terracottas from Warka* (in German). Gebruder Mann: Berlin.

Zöhrer, L. G. A. (1953). Les populations du Sahara antérieures à l'apparition du chameau. *Bull. Soc. Neuchâtel Geogr.* 51, 3-133.

Zöhrer, L. G. A. (1965). The study of the nomads of Somalia. *Arch. Volk.* 19, 129-165.

Zuckerman, S. (1953). The breeding seasons of mammals in captivity. *Proc. Zool. Soc. London.* 122, 827.

Index

222